D0065138

United States National Museum

Bulletin 212

CHECKLIST
OF THE MILLIPEDS
OF NORTH AMERICA

By RALPH V. CHAMBERLIN

Department of Zoology

University of Utah

RICHARD L. HOFFMAN

Department of Biology

Virginia Polytechnic Institute

SMITHSONIAN INSTITUTION ● WASHINGTON, D. C. ● 1958

Publications of the United States National Museum

The scientific publications of the National Museum include two series known, respectively, as *Proceedings* and *Bulletin*.

The *Proceedings* series, begun in 1878, is intended primarily as a medium for the publication of original papers based on the collections of the National Museum, that set forth newly acquired facts in biology, anthropology, and geology, with descriptions of new forms and revisions of limited groups. Copies of each paper, in pamphlet form, are distributed as published to libraries and scientific organizations and to specialists and others interested in the different subjects. The dates at which these separate papers are published are recorded in the table of contents of each of the volumes.

The series of *Bulletins*, the first of which was issued in 1875, contains separate publications comprising monographs of large zoological groups and other general systematic treatises (occasionally in several volumes), faunal works, reports of expeditions, catalogs of type specimens, special collections, and other material of similar nature. The majority of the volumes are octavo in size, but a quarto size has been adopted in a few instances. In the *Bulletin* series appear volumes under the heading *Contributions from the United States National Herbarium*, in octavo form, published by the National Museum since 1902, which contain papers relating to the botanical collections of the Museum.

The present work forms No. 212 of the *Bulletin* series.

REMINGTON KELLOGG,
Director, United States National Museum.

UNITED STATES
GOVERNMENT PRINTING OFFICE
WASHINGTON : 1958

For sale by the Superintendent of Documents, U. S. Government Printing Office
Washington 25, D. C. - Price $1 (paper)

Contents

III

Contents

iii

Introduction

So many additions to our knowledge of the millipeds of North America and so many changes in their classification have been made since the issue of Charles H. Bollman's "Catalogue of the Known Myriopods of North America North of Mexico" [1] that an up-to-date checklist has long been a desideratum. The present annotated list has been prepared to meet this need. Bollman's catalogue recognized 114 species under 29 genera (subsequently adding 5 more species). The present list accounts for approximately six times as many, recording some 749 species and subspecies, and 200 genera from the same area.

The work thus far on our milliped fauna has been mainly descriptive, but the time now seems ripe for synthesis and evaluation of the information at hand. It is hoped that this compilation will stimulate and facilitate the work of other students, for much remains to be done, both to fill in the gaps in our knowledge and to clarify the taxonomy, distributions, and ecological relationships of this relatively neglected group of arthropods.

It is not the purpose of a checklist such as this to revise groups or to initiate changes. In general, we record genera, species, and other groups as they have been published, indicating however, those names that we judge to be synonyms and giving in all cases pertinent bibliographic references. For each species we have sought to give the type locality as accurately as possible, the location of the type specimen, and the distribution as far as is presently known. The latter usually can be stated in general terms only, because of the dearth of records (a shortcoming that must be remedied by future workers). Particularly is this true of the western forms, the majority of which are "known from the type locality only." Our statements of distribution are based primarily upon localities for specimens examined by us, and by literature references which we consider reliable.

We cite in our references not only the original description, but also literature giving an illustration or other such information regarded as important, and also the place in which the binomial here adopted was first used. Where synonyms are indicated, the type locality for each form placed in synonymy is given, where possible, following the literature reference.

The several instances of departure from established arrangement are based upon unpublished studies by one or both of the authors and are indicated by footnote commentary.

---

[1] Published posthumously in his "Myriapoda of North America," U. S. Nat. Mus. Bull. 46, pp. 117–130, 1893.

The area covered by this checklist takes in all of North America north of México, and we include, in addition to native American forms, most of the introduced European and subtropical millipeds, the majority of which have become well established in our region.

In the following essay we have discussed reasons for the adoption of the present system of ordinal names. It might be added at this point that little uniformity between family and order has obtained with respect to group-name endings. In accord with what seems to be general practice in a great many animal groups, we have adopted the ending "-idea" for suborder and "-oidea" for superfamily.

Studies of the phylogeny of diplopods have not yet been made which would permit a "natural" arrangement of the groups. Although our sequence of orders is that used by several workers, it cannot be said to show progressive specialization or any other form of evolutionary pattern. We have adopted the expedient of listing families, genera, and species alphabetically, and this method certainly has its advantages in terms of convenience to the user. We venture the optimistic hope that the next listing of this sort will be able to boast at least a preliminary arrangement of families according to their natural relationships!

Ordinal nomenclature

In the matter of nomenclature of the diplopods, there persists considerable confusion, particularly with reference to the groups above the rank of family, largely because the International Rules of Zoological Nomenclature provide no standard for fixing the validity of names at that level. In this respect few branches of systematic zoology have suffered more vicissitudes. It seems desirable, therefore, to summarize here something of the history of the changes in classification as they have arisen, and of several systems in use by different authors and students of the Diplopoda or to be encountered in the literature.

Linnaeus in 1758 ("Systema Naturae," ed. 10) under his "Insecta Aptera," placed the only two genera of myriapods recognized by him, namely *Julus* and *Scolopendra* (and, curiously enough, referred the forms now called *Polyxenus* to the latter). From the time when, in 1802–1805, Latreille ("Histoire Naturelle . . . des Crustacés et des Insectes") set up his "legion" Myriapoda with its two orders Chilognatha and Syngnatha, and Leach in 1814 elevated the Myriapoda to the rank of a separate class coordinate with Crustacea, Arachnida, and Insecta, there has continued the expansion and development of a system more and more adequately representing the Chilopoda and Diplopoda and their relationships.

With Brandt (1833–1841), Gervais (1837–1847), Newport (1844), Wood (1864–67), and Saussure (1872), the classification was much elaborated. Brandt in 1833 proposed for the Chilognatha three subdivisions based on the degree of coalescence of the visible elements of a segment, naming them Pentazonia, Trizonia, and Monozonia. The first of these has maintained its position as correct down to the present, although the name has not been in general use.

In 1840 Brandt divided his order Myriapoda into two subdivisions: the Gnathogena—for the Chilopoda and most of the Diplopoda, and the Sugentia—corresponding precisely to the diplopod group now commonly termed the Colobognatha. Gervais in 1837 made but two divisions of the Chilognatha, the Oniscoidea and the Juloidea. In 1847 he replaced the term Chilognatha with the name Diplopoda of Blainville, and dropped his original primary subdivisions, recognizing the following families: Polyxenidae, Glomeridae, Julidae, and Polyzoniidae. The English zoologist Newport (1844, "List of the . . . Myriapoda in . . . British Museum") followed Brandt as to the divisions Pentazonia and Monozonia, but introduced a division Bizonia to embrace the Brandtian Trizonia and Sugentia. C. L. Koch (1847) ignored the primary divisions above the level of family, describing under the Chilognatha numerous new species and genera in the families Polyxenidae, Glomeridae, Sphaeriotheridae, Julidae, Blaniulidae, Chordeumidae, Polydesmidae, and Polyzoniidae.

C. S. Rafinesque, the first American worker to describe our native millipeds, in 1820 named four new genera and species in his "Annals of Nature;" in 1821 Thomas Say noted ten species as occurring in the United States, and scattered accounts of others were added by Brandt, Koch, Gervais, and Saussure; but the real foundation for the study of North American diplopods was laid by Horatio C. Wood in a series of papers appearing from 1861 to 1867, the most important of these being the "Myriopoda of North America" (1865), in which he described the forms known at that time to occur in this country. The total recognized by Wood comprised 18 genera and 92 species, of which 10 genera (including subgenera) and 41 species are diplopods, the remaining are chilopods. In his general arrangement of diplopods, Wood adopted as suborders the Pentazonia and Sugentia set up by Brandt, but introduced as a third suborder the Strongylia, under which he placed the millipeds arranged by Brandt under Trizonia and Monozonia. His classification was as follows:

Order Chilognatha
Suborder Pentazonia
Families:
Glomeridae
Sphaeriotheridae
Suborder Strongylia
Families:
Polyxenidae
Polydesmidae
Julidae
Lysiopetalidae
Suborder Sugentia
Families:
Polyzoniidae
Siphonophoridae

In 1872 Saussure and Humbert in their "Études sur les Myriapodes" (*in* "Mission Scientifique au Mexique") while dealing primarily with the Mexican fauna, gave a complete list of the species known at that time from the entire North American continent. In this work they recognized, without naming, three suborders of Chilognatha of which their "I" corresponds to the Pentazonia, "II" to the Polyxenidae, and "III" to the remaining families.

Very influential and important to all subsequent work upon the diplopods was that of Latzel in 1884, "Die Myriapoden der Österreichisch-Ungarischen Monarchie." His diagnoses and descriptions set a high standard for accuracy and clarity. These he founded more extensively than had previously been done on important anatomical characters, emphasizing especially the value of the copulatory appendages in diagnosis. In this classic work Latzel used the term Diplopoda, as has been done subsequently by all others, to designate the entire group of millipeds, which he divided into three suborders: the Pselaphognatha for the Polyxenidae, the Colobognatha for Brandt's Sugentia, and the Chilognatha for the remainder.

Pocock in 1887 first elevated the Chilopoda and Diplopoda to the rank of separate classes. He divided the Diplopoda into the two subclasses Pselaphognatha and Chilognatha, and the latter into two orders, the Oniscomorpha and Helminthomorpha (including the two suborders Polydesmoidea and Juloidea). In America, Bollman, in his paper "Classification of the Myriapoda" (U. S. Nat. Mus. Bull. 46, pp. 153–162, 1893), accepted Pocock's classification down to the suborders, but reduced the Diplopoda to the rank of a subclass and the Chilognatha to a superorder, and erected a separate superorder, Podochila, for the Pselaphognatha. His complete system may be summarized as follows:

Subclass Diplopoda
Superorder Podochila
Order Pselaphognatha
Family Polyxenidae
Superorder Chilognatha
Order Colobognatha
Family Polyzoniinae
Subfamilies:
Siphonophorinae
Polyzoniinae
Andrognathinae
Platydesminae
Order Helminthomorpha
Suborder Iuluidea
Superfamily Juloidae
Family Julidae
Subfamilies:
Spirobolinae
Spirostreptinae
Cambalinae
Parajulinae

Nemasominae
Julinae
Family Craspedosomidae
Subfamilies:
Craspedosominae
Campodinae
Chordeuminae
Striariinae
Superfamily Callipodoidae
Family Callipodidae
Suborder Polydesmoidea
Family Polydesmidae
Subfamilies:
Polydesminae
Sphaeriodesminae
Order Oniscomorpha
Family Glomeridae
Subfamilies:
Sphaerotherinae
Glomerinae
Oligaspinae

In 1894 Pocock ("Diplopoda," *in* Weber, "Zoologische Ergebnisse einer Reise in Niederländisch Ost-Indien," vol. 3) modified his earlier system by adding an order Limacomorpha and by recognizing five suborders under the Helminthomorpha in place of his former two, these being the Callipodoidea, Colobognatha, Chordeumoidea, Juloidea, and Polydesmoidea.

O. F. Cook, in 1895, dropping the Helminthomorpha of Pocock, gave the Colobognatha a rank on a level with that of the Oniscomorpha and Limacomorpha. He placed the Stemmiulidae in a distinct order Monocheta and likewise gave the Spirobolidae subordinal rank under a new order Anocheta. To the Spirostreptidae he likewise gave subordinal rank under a new order Diplocheta, under which he also at first placed the Juloidea and Cambaloidea. Under still another new order, Merocheta, he originally placed the Lysiopetaloidea, Craspedosomoidea, and Polydesmoidea. Later in the same year, however, he contracted the Diplocheta by removing from it the Juloidea as a new order Zygocheta, and also restricted the Merocheta by the transfer of the Lysiopetaloidea and Craspedosomoidea to another new order, the Coelocheta. His revised system of the Chilognatha, as far as the suborders he thus recognized, was as follows:

Subclass Chilognatha
Order Oniscomorpha
Suborder Glomeroidea
Suborder Zephronoidea
Order Limacomorpha
Suborder Glomeridesmoidea
Order Colobognatha
Suborder Polyzonoidea
Suborder Platydesmoidea
Suborder Siphonocryptoidea

> *Order* Monocheta
> > *Suborder* Stemmiuloidea
> *Order* Coelocheta
> > *Suborder* Lysiopetaloidea
> > *Suborder* Striarioidea
> > *Suborder* Chordeumatoidea
> *Order* Merocheta
> > *Suborder* Polydesmoidea
> *Order* Zygocheta
> > *Suborder* Juloidea
> *Order* Diplocheta
> > *Suborder* Cambaloidea
> > *Suborder* Spirostreptoidea
> *Order* Anocheta
> > *Suborder* Spiroboloidea

In 1897 Silvestri, in a paper entitled "Systema Diplopodum," gave an outline of a system in which he recognized, under the Chilognatha, the superorders Opisthandria and Proterandria proposed by Verhoeff in 1894. Under the Proterandria he set up as new an order Olognatha, under which he recognized Cook's orders as suborders, thus:

> *Order* Olognatha
> > *Suborder* Monocheta
> > > *Tribe* Stemmatiuloidea
> > > *Tribe* Xyloiuloidea
> > *Suborder* Coelocheta
> > > *Tribe* Lysiopetaloidea
> > > *Tribe* Striarioidea
> > > *Tribe* Chordeumoidea
> > *Suborder* Merocheta
> > > *Tribe* Polydesmoidea
> > > *Tribe* Spirostreptoidea
> > *Suborder* Anocheta
> > > *Tribe* Spiroboloidea

Among European workers on the Diplopoda since the beginning of the present century, Attems, Brölemann, Silvestri, and Verhoeff have been most active in extending the knowledge of the group. Of these investigators, Verhoeff has been particularly active in proposing new divisions and names too numerous to be discussed here in detail; the major divisions and terms of the system at which he lately arrived (1926, *in* Bronn, "Die Klassen und Ordnungen des Tier-Reichs . . . ," Band 5) are as follows:

> *Subclass* Pselaphognatha
> > *Order* Schizocephala
> *Subclass* Chilognatha
> > *Superorder* Opisthandria
> > > *Order* Limacomorpha
> > > *Order* Armadillomorpha [2]

---

[2] Armadillomorpha was proposed as a substitute for Oniscomorpha, which Verhoeff felt was unsuitable in its implication of a resemblance of the diplopods to oniscoid isopods. Apparently he felt no misgivings in preferring to compare them to the mammalian armadillo!

> Superorder Proterandria
>> Order Proterospermophora
>>> Suborder Polydesmoidea
>> Order Nematophora
>>> Suborder Striaroidea
>>> Suborder Ascospermophora
>>> Suborder Lysiopetaloidea
>>> Suborder Stemmatoiuloidea
>> Order Opisthospermophora
>>> Suborder Symphyognatha
>>> Suborder Chorizognatha

The preceding review of nomenclatorial changes and diversity should help to emphasize how unfortunate it has been that the International Rules make no provision for regulating names above the level of family. It has long seemed to some workers that confusion would be avoided and simplicity and stability secured by extending the "type genus" concept above the rank of family to affect the names of orders and intermediate groups. Such an extension of the idea, and a proper regard for priority in all cases, would have prevented such unnecessary duplications as the following: in Verhoeff's scheme, his order Schizocephala is antedated by Podochila of Bollman (1893), by Ancyrotricha Cook (1895), and Penicillata Latreille (1829); his superorder Opisthandria corresponds precisely to Pentazonia of Brandt (1833); his order Proterospermophora, as amended, to the revised Merocheta of Cook, and this, in turn, to the earlier Polydesmoidea of Pocock; and his Symphyognatha (1911–14) is identical with the Zygocheta of Cook and also with the Juloidea and with the Julidae as used by Meinert and others.

The senior author, having long been convinced of the desirability of having some regular method for establishing ordinal names and of eliminating duplications due to personal points of view or idiosyncracies, made use of the type concept, mentioned above, in which the ordinal name is based upon the oldest or best known of the included families. Since most of the orders were originally treated as families by early workers, application of this principle has been much easier for diplopods than it would be for insects or mammals.

The arrangement and terminology which we have adopted, and which we hope will meet with general approval, are given below. Of the twelve orders recognized, all but the Glomeridesmida are represented in our fauna by native species. It will be seen that for the second superorder under the Chilognatha we retain the name Helminthomorpha, of which the Olognatha of Silvestri (1897) and Eugnatha of Attems (1899) are exact synonyms.

> Class Diplopoda
>> Subclass Pselaphognatha
>>> Order Polyxenida
>> Subclass Chilognatha
>>> Superorder Pentazonia
>>>> Order Glomerida
>>>> Order Glomeridesmida

Superorder Helminthomorpha
  Order Polydesmida
    Suborder Polydesmidea
    Suborder Strongylosomidea
  Order Chordeumida
    Suborder Chordeumidea
    Suborder Lysiopetalidea
    Suborder Striariidea
  Order Stemmiulida
  Order Julida
    Suborder Julidea
    Suborder Paraiulidea
  Order Spirobolida
  Order Spirostreptida
  Order Cambalida
Superorder Colobognatha
  Order Polyzoniida
  Order Platydesmida

Checklist of the Millipeds of North America

Class DIPLOPODA

Diplopoda Gervais, 1844, Ann. Sci. Nat., ser. 3, vol. 2, p. 51.—Latzel, 1884, Myr. Öst.-Ung. Monarch., vol. 2, p. 40.—Verhoeff, 1926, *in* Bronn, Klass. und Ordn. des Tier-Reichs, Band 5, Abt. 2, Lief. 1, p. 4.

KEY TO THE SUBCLASSES OF DIPLOPODA

1. Body soft, the exoskeleton not calcified, bearing clusters of peculiar setae, some of which are branched or laterally armed; head with trichobothria; males without gonopods . . . . PSELAPHOGNATHA (p. 9)
Body hard, the exoskeleton more or less calcified, setae, when present, simple and not clustered; head without trichobothria; males with characteristic gonopods.
CHILOGNATHA (p. 11)

Subclass PSELAPHOGNATHA

Pselaphognatha Latzel, 1884, Myr. Öst.-Ung. Monarch., vol. 2, p. 64.
Podochila Bollman, 1893, U. S. Nat. Mus. Bull. 46, p. 153.

Order POLYXENIDA

Penicillata Latreille, 1829, *in* Cuvier, Le règne animal, vol. 4, p. 326.
Polyxenidae Gray, 1842, *in* Todd, Cyclop. Anat. and Physiol., vol. 3, p. 546.
Ancyrotricha Cook, 1895, Ann. New York Acad. Sci., vol. 9, p. 1.
Schizocephala Verhoeff, 1926, *in* Bronn, Klass. und Ordn. des Tier-Reichs, Band 5, Abt. 2, Lief. 1, p. 26.

Family POLYXENIDAE Gray

Polyxenidae Gray, 1842, *in* Todd, Cyclop. Anat. and Physiol., vol. 3, p. 546.

Genus POLYXENUS Latreille

Pollyxenus Latreille, 1802, Histoire naturelle . . . des crustacés et des insectes, vol. 3, p. 45.
Polyxenus Goldfuss, 1820, Handbuch der Zoologie, vol. 1, p. 199.—Latzel, 1884, Myr. Öst.-Ung. Monarch., vol. 2, p. 71.
GENEROTYPE: *Scolopendra lagura* Linnaeus, by monotypy.
RANGE: Nearly cosmopolitan.
SPECIES: About a dozen; seven occur in our area.

Polyxenus anacopensis Pierce

Polyxenus anacopensis Pierce, 1940, Bull. Southern California Acad. Sci.,
vol. 39, p. 164, figs. 3, 6, 9, 15–18.
Type: Los Angeles Museum.
Type Locality: Middle Anacapa Island, Santa Barbara County, California.
Range: Known only from type locality.

Polyxenus bartschi Chamberlin

Polyxenus bartschi Chamberlin, 1922, Ent. News, vol. 33, p. 165.
Type: Mus. Comp. Zool.
Type Locality: Tortugas Key, Monroe County, Florida.
Range: Known only from type locality.

Polyxenus fasciculatus fasciculatus Say

Polyxenus fasciculatus Say, 1821, Journ. Acad. Nat. Sci. Philadelphia,
vol. 2, p. 108.—Wood, 1865, Trans. Amer. Philos. Soc., vol. 13, p.
228.—Pierce, 1940, Bull. Southern California Acad. Sci., vol. 39, No.
2, p. 163.
Type: None known to exist.
Type Locality: "Southern States."
Range: Eastern, southeastern, and midwestern United States, from Long
Island to Texas. Absent or very scarce in the Appalachian region.

Polyxenus fasciculatus victoriensis Pierce

Polyxenus fasciculatus victoriensis Pierce, 1940, Bull. Southern California
Acad. Sci., vol. 39, No. 2, p. 163.
Type: Los Angeles Museum.
Type Locality: Victoria, Victoria County, Texas.
Range: Known only from type locality.

Polyxenus lagurus (Linnaeus)

Scolopendra lagura Linnaeus, 1758, Systema naturae, ed. 10, p. 637.
Pollyxenus lagurus Latreille, 1804, Histoire naturelle . . . des crustacés
et des insectes, vol. 7, p. 82.
Polyxenus lagurus Latzel, 1884, Myr. Öst.-Ung. Monarch., vol. 2, p. 74,
figs. 22–39.—Schubart, 1934, *in* Dahl, Die Tierwelt Deutschlands,
Teil 28, p. 20, figs. 4–6.
Type: Not known to exist.
Type Locality: Probably vicinity of Uppsala, Sweden.
Range: Throughout Europe, from Scandanavia to the Balkans, Italy,
North Africa, Spain, and the Azores. In America known definitely only
from Nova Scotia, but it is quite likely that at least part of the records for
P. fasciculatus pertain to the present species, which is not infrequently inter-
cepted at quarantine in cargoes from Europe.

Polyxenus pugetensis Kincaid

Polyxenus pugetensis Kincaid, 1898, Ent. News, vol. 9, p. 192.

TYPE: Location unknown.

TYPE LOCALITY: Western Washington.

RANGE: Washington and British Columbia.

Polyxenus tuberculatus Pierce

Polyxenus tuberculatus Pierce, 1940, Bull. Southern California Acad. Sci., vol. 39, No. 2, p. 166.

TYPE: Los Angeles Museum.

TYPE LOCALITY: Sabinal, Uvalde County, Texas.

RANGE: Known only from type locality.

Subclass CHILOGNATHA

Chilognatha Latreille, 1802, Histoire naturelle . . . des crustacés et des insectes, vol. 3, p. 44 (in part).

Chilognatha Latzel, 1884, Myr. Öst.-Ung. Monarch., vol. 2, p. 354 (as suborder).

KEY TO SUPERORDERS OF CHILOGNATHA

1. Gonopods of male at caudal end of body, modified from last two pairs of legs; legs of 7th segment not modified; tracheae dichotomously branched.

   PENTAZONIA (p. 11)

   Gonopods of male modified from legs of the 7th segment; tracheae not branched as above 2

2. First legs of 7th segment of male not modified; eight pairs of legs in front of the gonopods; head small, mandibles usually much reduced; labrum without teeth.

   COLOBOGNATHA (p. 181)

   First legs of 7th segment of male always modified into gonopods; seven pairs of legs in front of gonopods; head not reduced, mouthparts of normal size; labrum usually with three teeth . . . . HELMINTHOMORPHA (p. 13)

Superorder PENTAZONIA

Pentazonia Brandt, 1833, Bull. Soc. Nat. Moscou, vol. 6, p. 194.—Attems, 1914, Arch. Naturg., Abt. A., vol. 80, p. 135.—Brölemann, 1935, Myr. Diplop., Chilognathes I, *in* Faune de France, No. 29, p. 88.

Oniscomorpha Pocock, 1887, Ann. Mag. Nat. Hist., ser. 5, vol. 20, p. 291.—Bollman, 1893, U. S. Nat. Mus. Bull. 46, p. 161.—Cook, 1895, Ann. New York Acad. Sci., vol. 9, p. 2.—Attems, 1899, Denkschr. Akad. Wiss., Wien, vol. 67, p. 226.

Opisthandria Verhoeff, 1894, Verh. Zool.-Bot. Ges. Wien, vol. 44, p. 17.—Attems, 1926, *in* Kükenthal-Krumbach, Handbuch der Zoologie, vol. 4, p. 114.

KEY TO ORDERS OF PENTAZONIA

1. Body composed of 14 to 16 segments, covered with 11 to 13 tergites; body contractile
into a ball . . . . GLOMERIDA (p. 12)
Body composed of 22 segments, more elongate and not contractile into a ball
GLOMERIDESMIDA [3]

Order GLOMERIDA

Glomeridia Brandt, 1833, Bull. Soc. Nat. Moscou, vol. 6, p. 194.—Attems,
1914, Arch. Naturg., Abt. A., vol. 80, p. 135.
Glomeridae Leach, 1815, Trans. Linn. Soc. London, p. 376.—Latzel, 1884,
Myr. Öst.-Ung. Monarch., vol. 2, p. 81.—Bollman, 1893, U. S. Nat.
Mus. Bull. 46, p. 161.
Oniscomorpha Pocock, 1887, Ann. Mag. Nat. Hist., ser. 5, vol. 20, p. 291.
Glomeroidea Cook, 1895, Ann. New York Acad. Sci., vol. 9, p. 2.
Plesiocerata Verhoeff, 1910, Die Diplopoden Deutschlands, p. 21.

Family GLOMERIDAE Leach

Glomeridae Leach, 1815, Trans. Linn. Soc. London, p. 376.—Latzel, 1884,
Myr. Öst.-Ung. Monarch., vol. 2, p. 81.—Cook, 1895, Ann. New
York Acad. Sci., vol. 9, p. 2.
Glomerididae Cook, 1896, Brandtia, No. 10, p. 45.

Genus ONOMERIS Cook

Onomeris Cook, 1896, Brandtia, No. 10, p. 43.—Loomis, 1943, Bull. Mus.
Comp. Zool., vol. 92, No. 7, p. 373.
GENEROTYPE: Onomeris underwoodi Cook, by original designation.
RANGE: Central Alabama and the mountains of western North Carolina
and north Georgia.
SPECIES: Two.

Onomeris australora Hoffman

Onomeris australora Hoffman, 1950, Journ. Elisha Mitchell Sci. Soc.,
vol. 66, p. 13, figs. 1, 2.
TYPE: U. S. Nat. Mus. (No. 1872).
TYPE LOCALITY: Reed Creek Falls on Glade Mountain, near Satolah, Rabun
County, Georgia.
RANGE: Southern Blue Ridge above 3,000 feet in Rabun County, Georgia,
and Macon County, North Carolina.

Onomeris underwoodi Cook

Onomeris underwoodi Cook, 1896, Brandtia, No. 10, p. 43.
TYPE: U. S. Nat. Mus.

---

[3] Not represented in America north of Mexico; species occur in Central America
and the Greater Antilles.

TYPE LOCALITY: Auburn, Lee County, Alabama.
RANGE: Known only from the type locality.

Genus SONOROMERIS Silvestri

Sonoromeris Silvestri, 1929, Boll. Lab. Zool. Portici, vol. 22, p. 199.—
Loomis, 1943, Bull. Mus. Comp. Zool., vol. 92, No. 7, p. 373.
GENEROTYPE: *Sonoromeris prima* Silvestri, by original designation.
RANGE: Central California.
SPECIES: One.

Sonoromeris prima (Silvestri)

Apiomeris (Sonoromeris) prima Silvestri, 1929, Boll. Lab. Zool. Portici,
vol. 22, pp. 198–203, figs.
TYPE SPECIMEN: Probably in Silvestri's collection.
TYPE LOCALITY: Mill Valley, near San Francisco, California.
RANGE: Known only from type locality.

Genus TRICHOMERIS Loomis

Trichomeris Loomis, 1943, Bull. Mus. Comp. Zool., vol. 92, No. 7, p. 374
GENEROTYPE: *Trichomeris sinuata* Loomis, by original designation.
RANGE: Northern Alabama.
SPECIES: One.

Trichomeris sinuata Loomis

Trichomeris sinuata Loomis, 1943, Bull. Mus. Comp. Zool., vol. 92, No.
7, p. 374, figs. la–f.
TYPE: Mus. Comp. Zool.
TYPE LOCALITY: Monte Sano State Park, 6 miles southeast of Huntsville,
Madison County, Alabama.
RANGE: Known only from type locality.

Superorder HELMINTHOMORPHA

Helminthomorpha Pocock, 1887, Ann. Mag. Nat. Hist., ser. 5, vol. 20,
p. 294.—Bollman, 1893, U. S. Nat. Mus. Bull. 46, p. 155.—Silvestri,
1897, Ann. Mus. Civ. Stor. Nat. Genova, ser. 2, vol. 18, p. 646.
Eugnatha Attems, 1899, Denkschr. Akad. Wiss., Wien, vol. 67, p. 227.

KEY TO THE ORDERS OF HELMINTHOMORPHA

1. Body composed of 18 to 22 segments; sternites, pleurites, and tergites completely
fused without traces of sutures; tergites usually produced laterally into paranota;
eyes always absent; second legs of 7th segment of male not modified as gonopods.
POLYDESMIDA (p. 14)
Body composed of 30 or more (rarely 20, 26, or 28) segments; the body rings less
complete, the sternites being either free or set off by distinct sutures; eyes usually
present (secondarily lost in cave forms) 2

2. Terminal segment of body with 1 to 3 pairs of spinnerets; either one or both pairs of legs of the 7th segment of males modified into gonopods; sternites free from the pleurotergites, the latter usually with long setae . . . . Chordeumida (p. 84)
Terminal segment of body without spinnerets; either both pairs of legs of the 7th segment as gonopods, or one pair missing; sternites usually fused with pleurotergites 3
3. Stipites of gnathochilarium broadly in contact behind the laminae linguales.
Julida (p. 117)
Stipites of gnathochilarium separated for their entire length by the mentum and laminae linguales 4
4. Third segment open ventrally, the 4th and following segments closed; 5th segment with two pairs of legs 5
Third segment closed ventrally; 5th segment with a single pair of legs.
Spirobolida (p. 151)
5. Both anterior and posterior gonopods present and functional, posterior pair usually with long flagella; laminae linguales completely separated by the mentum.
Cambalida (p. 172)
Posterior pair of gonopods rudimentary or completely absent, anterior pair elaborate; laminae linguales not separated by the mentum (except in Choctellidae).
Spirostreptida (p. 169)

Order POLYDESMIDA

Polydesmidae Leach, 1815, Trans. Linn. Soc. London, vol. 11, p. 381.—
Latzel, 1884, Myr. Öst.-Ung. Monarch., vol. 2, p. 124—Bollman, 1893, U. S. Nat. Mus. Bull. 46, p. 159.
Polydesmoidea Pocock, 1887, Ann. Mag. Nat. Hist., ser. 5, vol. 20, p. 294.
—Cook, 1895, Ann. New York Acad. Sci., vol. 9, p. 4.—Attems, 1899, Denkschr. Akad. Wiss., Wien, vol. 67, p. 227.—Brölemann, 1916, Ann. Soc. Ent. France, vol. 84, p. 583.—Attems, 1937, Das Tierreich, Lief. 68, p. 1.
Merocheta Cook, 1895, Ann. New York Acad. Sci., vol. 9, p. 4.
Proterospermophora Verhoeff, 1900, Zool. Jahrb., Syst. Abt., vol. 13, p. 54; 1913, Zool. Anz., vol. 43, p. 57.
Polydesmida Chamberlin, 1938, Carnegie Inst. Washington, Publ. No. 491, p. 174; 1943, Bull. Univ. Utah, biol. ser., vol. 8, No. 3, p. 36.

KEY TO THE SUBORDERS OF POLYDESMIDA

1. Opening of sternal gonopod socket more or less constricted between the gonopods, the coxae of which are entirely free of each other . . . Strongylosomidea (p. 78)
Opening of sternal gonopod socket not medially constricted; coxae of gonopods connected to each other by a ligament or a pseudosternite, or else broadly in contact along the median surfaces . . . . Polydesmidea (p. 14)

Suborder POLYDESMIDEA

Polydesmidi + Leptodesmidi Brölemann, 1916, Ann. Soc. Ent. France, vol. 84, p. 527.
Polydesmidea Attems, 1926, in Kükenthal-Krumbach, Handbuch der Zoologie, vol. 4, p. 132; 1938, Des Tierreich, Lief. 69, p. 1; 1940, Das Tierreich, Lief. 70, p. 1.

KEY TO THE NORTH AMERICAN FAMILIES OF POLYDESMIDEA

1. Coxae of male gonopods smaller, usually concealed inside the body and never connected firmly with the margin of the sternal aperture, capable of extrusion from the body 2

    Coxae of male gonopods larger, often conspicuously enlarged, and partially external, usually attached to the margin of the socket and immovable 5

2. Dorsum very strongly arched, with lateral keels nearly vertical; prozonites obliterated on ventral sides; keels of 2nd, 3rd, or 4th segments enlarged, the body modified for rolling into a sphere 3

    Without any of the preceding modifications 4

3. Repugnatorial pores opening on upper surface of keels near the margin . . . . CYCLODESMIDAE (p. 15)

    Repugnatorial pores not detected; a large deep pit on each side of the tergites near the anterior base of the keels . . . . DESMONIDAE (p. 15)

4. Anal tergite broad, subquadrate . . . . EURYURIDAE (p. 55)

    Anal tergite subtriangular . . . . EURYDESMIDAE (p. 16)

5. Repugnatorial pores borne upon special stalks or processes, collum usually covering the head . . . . STYLODESMIDAE (p. 76)

    Repugnatorial pores not borne upon stalks; collum not concealing the head 6

6. Seminal canal of male gonopod widening into a distinct vesicle or ampulla near its distal extremity . . . . POLYDESMIDAE (p. 63)

    Seminal canal not distally widened or modified as above 7

7. Tubercules of tergites strongly developed (in our species); gonopods without prefemoral processes . . . . VANHOEFFENIIDAE (p. 77)

    Tubercules weakly developed or obliterated; prefemur of gonopods with two long slender processes . . . . NEARCTODESMIDAE (p. 59)

Family CYCLODESMIDAE Silvestri

Cyclodesmidae Silvestri, 1894, Ann. Mus. Civ. Stor. Nat. Genova, ser. 2, vol. 14, p. 747.

Genus ETHOCYCLUS Chamberlin and Mulaik

Ethocyclus Chamberlin and Mulaik, 1941, Journ. New York Ent. Soc., vol. 49, p. 58.

GENEROTYPE: *Ethocyclus atophus* Chamberlin and Mulaik, by original designation.

RANGE: Texas.

SPECIES: One.

Ethocyclus atophus Chamberlin and Mulaik

Ethocyclus atophus Chamberlin and Mulaik, 1941, Journ. New York Ent. Soc., vol. 49, p. 58.

TYPE: Collection of R. V. Chamberlin.

TYPE LOCALITY: Raven Ranch, Kerr County, Texas.

RANGE: Known only from type locality.

Family DESMONIDAE Cook

Desmonidae Cook, 1898, Pros. U. S. Nat. Mus., vol. 21, p. 463.

Genus **DESMONIELLA** Loomis

Desmoniella Loomis, 1943, Bull. Mus. Comp. Zool., vol. 92, No. 7, p. 400.
GENEROTYPE: *Desmoniella curta* Loomis, by original designation.
RANGE: Oklahoma.
SPECIES: One.

Desmoniella curta Loomis

Desmoniella curta Loomis, 1943, Bull. Mus. Comp. Zool., vol. 92, No. 7,
    p. 401, figs. 14a–c.
TYPE: Mus. Comp. Zool.
TYPE LOCALITY: Arbuckle Mountains, 2.3 miles south of Fittstown, Ponto-
toc County, Oklahoma.
RANGE: Known only from type locality.

Genus **DESMONUS** Cook

Desmonus Cook, 1898, Proc. U. S. Nat. Mus., vol. 21, p. 463.
GENEROTYPE: *Desmonus earlei* Cook, by original designation.
RANGE: Alabama to Kentucky, west to Arkansas.
SPECIES: Two.

Desmonus earlei Cook

Desmonus earlei Cook, 1898, Proc. U. S. Nat. Mus., vol. 21, p. 463, pl. 32,
    figs. 1a–n.
TYPE: U. S. Nat. Mus. (No. 681).
TYPE LOCALITY: Auburn, Lee County, Alabama.
RANGE: Known so far from the type locality, from several localities in
eastern Tennessee, and from central Kentucky.

Desmonus pudicus (Bollman)

Sphaeriodesmus pudicus Bollman, 1888, Ent. Amer., vol. 4, p. 3.
Desmonus pudicus Cook, 1898, Proc. U. S. Nat. Mus., vol. 21, p. 465, pl.
    32, figs. 2a–b.
TYPE: U. S. Nat. Mus. (No. 154).
TYPE LOCALITY: Little Rock, Pulaski County, Arkansas.
RANGE: Known only from Little Rock and Okolona, Arkansas.

Family **EURYDESMIDAE** Chamberlin

Chelodesmidae + Xystodesmidae Cook, 1895, Ann. New York Acad. Sci.,
    vol. 9, pp. 4, 5.
Leptodesminae Attems, 1899, Denkschr. Akad. Wiss., Wien, vol. 67, p. 369.
Leptodesmidae Attems, 1914, Arch. Naturg., Abt. A, vol. 80, p. 280; 1938,
    Das Tierreich, Lief. 69, p. 1.
Eurydesmidae Chamberlin, 1950, Zoologica, New York, vol. 35, p. 142.
Sigmocheiridae Causey, 1955, Proc. Biol. Soc. Washington, vol. 68, p. 93
    (in part, *Sigmocheir* and *Orophe* only).

As it does not seem possible to maintain as separate families, on the basis of characters thus far proposed, the two groups designated by Cook as the Chelodesmidae and Xystodesmidae, we here unite them pending a thorough study of all the "leptodesmoid" families. The proposal of a family Sigmocheiridae we regard as premature, particularly as its primary diagnostic character is also found in numerous typical eurydesmoids of the Neotropical region.

Genus AMPLOCHEIR Chamberlin

Amplocheir Chamberlin, 1949, Journ. Washington Acad. Sci., vol. 39, No. 3, p. 97.
GENEROTYPE: *Xystocheir sequoia* Chamberlin.
RANGE: California.
SPECIES: Two.

Amplocheir reducta Causey

Amplocheir reducta Causey, 1955, Proc. Biol. Soc. Washington, vol. 68, p. 92, fig. 4.
TYPE: Amer. Mus. Nat. Hist.
Type LOCALITY: Briceburg, Mariposa County, California.
RANGE: Known only from type locality.

Amplocheir sequoia (Chamberlin)

Xystocheir sequoia Chamberlin, 1941, Bull. Univ. Utah, biol. ser., vol. 6, No. 5, p. 15, fig. 28.
Amplocheir sequoia Chamberlin, 1949, Journ. Washington Acad. Sci., vol. 39, No. 3, p. 97.
TYPE: Collection of R. V. Chamberlin.
TYPE LOCALITY: Sequoia National Park, Tulare County, California.
RANGE: Known only from type locality.

Genus APHELORIA Chamberlin

Apheloria Chamberlin, 1921, Canadian Ent., vol. 53, p. 232.
Leptocircus (not Swainson 1833) Attems, 1931, Zoologica, Stuttgart, vol. 30, Lief. 3–4, p. 67 (generotype, *L. inexpectatus* Attems).
GENEROTYPE: *Fontaria montana* Bollman, by original designation.
RANGE: Eastern North America, from Vermont and southern Ontario south to North Carolina, Tennessee, and Arkansas, northwest to eastern Iowa.
SPECIES: Twenty-two named forms, of which three are regarded as subspecies of *trimaculata*.

Apheloria adela Chamberlin

Apheloria adela Chamberlin, 1939, Bull. Univ. Utah, biol. ser., vol. 5, No. 3, p. 10, fig. 34.

TYPE: Collection of R. V. Chamberlin.

TYPE LOCALITY: Ithaca, Tompkins County, New York.

RANGE: Known definitely only from the type locality, although possibly occurring southward in the Appalachians.

Apheloria ainsliei Chamberlin

Apheloria ainsliei Chamberlin, 1921, Canadian Ent., vol. 53, p. 232, pl. 9, fig. 1.

TYPE: Mus. Comp. Zool.

TYPE LOCALITY: Knox County, Tennessee.

RANGE: Known only from type locality.

Apheloria asburna Chamberlin

Apheloria asburna Chamberlin, 1949, Journ. Washington Acad. Sci., vol. 39, p. 101.

TYPE: Collection of R. V. Chamberlin.

TYPE LOCALITY: 20 miles north of Nashville, Davidson County, Tennessee.

RANGE: Known only from type locality.

Apheloria aspila Chamberlin

Apheloria aspila Chamberlin, 1939, Bull. Univ. Utah, biol. ser., vol. 5, No. 3, p. 10, fig. 31.

TYPE: Collection of R. V. Chamberlin.

TYPE LOCALITY: Soco Falls, northeast of Cherokee, Jackson County, North Carolina.

RANGE: Known definitely only from the type locality.

Apheloria butleriana (Bollman)

Fontaria butleriana Bollman, 1889, Proc. U. S. Nat. Mus., vol. 11, p. 407.

TYPE: U. S. Nat. Mus.

TYPE LOCALITY: Brookville, Franklin County, Indiana.

RANGE: Southern Indiana, eastern Kentucky; probably a western subspecies of *A. coriacea*.

Apheloria coriacea (Koch)

Fontaria coriacea Koch, 1847, *in* Krit. Rev. Insect. Deutschlands, vol. 3, p. 141; 1863, Die Myriapoden, vol. 1, p. 72, pl. 32, fig. 63.

Polydesmus (Fontaria) corrugatus Wood, 1864, Proc. Acad. Nat. Sci. Philadelphia, p. 6 (Trenton Falls, New York; types, U. S. Nat. Mus. and Mus. Comp. Zool.).

Apheloria coriacea Hoffman, 1949, Amer. Mus. Novitates, No. 1405, p. 3, figs. 1–4 (redescription).

TYPE: Original specimen not known to exist; neotypes in Amer. Mus. Nat. Hist. and U. S. Nat. Mus.

TYPE LOCALITY: "Virginien"; restricted by Hoffman to Swann's Point, near Scotland, Surry County, Virginia.

RANGE: Southeastern Virginia north as far as Massachusetts, west to Kentucky, Ohio, and Michigan.

Apheloria inexpectata (Attems)

Leptocircus inexpectatus Attems, 1931, Zoologica, Stuttgart, vol. 30, Lief. 3–4, p. 67, figs. 102–104.

TYPE: Probably in the Vienna Museum.

TYPE LOCALITY: North America, without further locality.

RANGE: No definite localities are known for this species, which may prove to be *A. iowa* or *A. reducta*.

Apheloria iowa Chamberlin

Apheloria iowa Chamberlin, 1939, Bull. Univ. Utah, biol. ser., vol. 5, No. 3, p. 10, fig. 28.

TYPE: Collection of R. V. Chamberlin.

TYPE LOCALITY: Mount Pleasant, Henry County, Iowa.

RANGE: Iowa and Illinois, probably continuous into Arkansas and Oklahoma.

Apheloria keuka Chamberlin

Apheloria keuka Chamberlin, 1939, Bull. Univ. Utah, biol. ser., vol. 5, No. 3, p. 10, fig. 32.

TYPE: Collection of R. V. Chamberlin.

TYPE LOCALITY: Ithaca, Tompkins County, New York.

RANGE: Finger Lakes region of central New York State.

Apheloria kleinpeteri Hoffman

Apheloria kleinpeteri Hoffman, 1949, Proc. U. S. Nat. Mus., vol. 99, p. 375, figs. 3, 4.

TYPE: U. S. Nat. Mus. (No. 1803).

TYPE LOCALITY: Burkes Garden, Tazewell County, Virginia.

RANGE: Known from Bland, Smyth, Tazewell, and Washington counties, Virginia, and from Mercer County, West Virginia.

Apheloria montana (Bollman)

Fontaria montana Bollman, 1887, Proc. U. S. Nat. Mus., vol. 10, p. 622.
Apheloria montana Chamberlin, 1921, Canadian Ent., vol. 53, p. 232, pl. 9, fig. 2.

TYPE: U. S. Nat. Mus.

TYPE LOCALITY: Wolf Creek, Cocke County, Tennessee.

RANGE: Eastern Tennessee.

Apheloria pinicola Chamberlin

Apheloria pinicola Chamberlin, 1947, Proc. Acad. Nat. Sci. Philadelphia, vol. 99, p. 26, figs. 6, 7.

TYPE: Acad. Nat. Sci. Philadelphia (No. 9945).

TYPE LOCALITY: Pine Mountain, Bell County, Kentucky.

RANGE: Known only from type locality.

Apheloria reducta Chamberlin

Apheloria reducta Chamberlin, 1939, Bull. Univ. Utah, biol. ser., vol. 5, No. 3, p. 11, fig. 35.

TYPE: Collection of R. V. Chamberlin.

TYPE LOCALITY: Imboden, Lawrence County, Arkansas.

RANGE: Recorded from about 14 Counties in the northwestern part of Arkansas and from southwest Missouri.

Apheloria roanea Chamberlin

Apheloria roanea Chamberlin, 1947, Proc. Acad. Nat. Sci. Philadelphia, vol. 99, p. 26, fig. 8.

TYPE: Acad. Nat. Sci. Philadelphia (No. 9946).

. TYPE LOCALITY: Harriman, Roane County, Tennessee.

RANGE: Known from type locality only.

Apheloria tigana Chamberlin

Apheloria tigana Chamberlin, 1939, Bull. Univ. Utah, biol. ser., vol. 5, No. 3, p. 11, fig. 29.

TYPE: Collection of R. V. Chamberlin.

TYPE LOCALITY: Raleigh, Wake County, North Carolina.

RANGE: Known also from Ashburnham, Davidson County, Tennessee, and from Mammoth Cave, Edmondson County, Kentucky.

Apheloria trimaculata trimaculata (Wood)

Polydesmus (Fontaria) trimaculatus Wood, 1864, Proc. Acad. Nat. Sci. Philadelphia, p. 6; 1865, Trans. Amer. Philos. Soc., vol. 13, p. 223, figs. 53, 54.

Fontaria lutzi Jacot, 1938, Amer. Midl. Nat., vol. 20, p. 571, fig. 1 (type locality: Keene, Cheshire County, New Hampshire; types in Boston Soc. Nat. Hist. and Peabody Mus., Yale Univ.).

Apheloria trimaculata Attems, 1938, Das Tierreich, Lief. 69, p. 170.

Apheloria trimaculata trimaculata Hoffman, 1951, Chicago Acad. Sci. Nat. Hist. Misc., No. 81, p. 2.

TYPE: Not known to be extant.

TYPE LOCALITY: Susquehanna County, Pennsylvania.

RANGE: Appalachian region from New Hampshire and Massachusetts south as far as Alleghany County, Virginia.

Apheloria trimaculata antrostomicola Hoffman

Apheloria antrostomicola Hoffman, 1949, Proc. U. S. Nat. Mus., vol. 99, p. 372, figs. 1, 2.

Apheloria trimaculata antrostomicola Hoffman, 1951, Chicago Acad. Sci. Nat. Hist. Misc. No. 81, p. 3.

TYPE: U. S. Nat. Mus. (No. 1802).

TYPE LOCALITY: Stull's Cave, about 9 miles southwest of Lowmoor, Alleghany County, Virginia.

RANGE: Known only from the vicinity of the type locality.

Apheloria trimaculata incarnata Hoffman

Apheloria trimaculata incarnata Hoffman, 1951, Chicago Acad. Sci., Nat. Hist. Misc., No. 81, p. 4, fig. 1a.

TYPE: U. S. Nat. Mus. (No. 1891).

TYPE LOCALITY: Gull Lake, Frontenac County, Ontario.

RANGE: Known from type locality only.

Apheloria trimaculata tortua Chamberlin

Apheloria tortua Chamberlin, 1949, Journ. Washington Acad. Sci., vol. 39, No. 3, p. 101, fig. 23 (March).

Apheloria picta Hoffman, 1949, Proc. U. S. Nat. Mus., vol. 99, p. 376, figs. 5, 6 (type locality: Mountain Lake, Giles County, Virginia; type: U. S. Nat. Mus. No. 1804; June).

Apheloria trimaculata tortua Hoffman, 1951, Chicago Acad. Sci., Nat. Hist. Misc., No. 81, p. 5.

TYPE: Collection of R. V. Chamberlin.

TYPE LOCALITY: Mountain Lake, Giles County, Virginia.

RANGE: High mountains in Bedford, Craig, and Giles counties, Virginia.

Apheloria unaka Chamberlin

Apheloria unaka Chamberlin, 1939, Bull. Univ. Utah, biol. ser., vol. 5, No. 3, p. 11, fig. 33.

TYPE: Collection of R. V. Chamberlin.

TYPE LOCALITY: Unaka Springs, Unicoi County, Tennessee.

RANGE: Also known from Hot Springs, Madison County, North Carolina.

Apheloria virginia Chamberlin

Apheloria virginia Chamberlin, 1939, Bull. Univ. Utah, biol. ser., vol. 5, No. 3, p. 12, fig. 30.

TYPE: Collection of R. V. Chamberlin.

TYPE LOCALITY: Chatham, Pittsylvania County, Virginia.

RANGE: Southcentral Virginia and adjacent North Carolina.

Apheloria waccamana Chamberlin

Apheloria waccamana Chamberlin, 1940, Ent. News, vol. 51, p. 284, fig. 3.

TYPE: Collection of R. V. Chamberlin.

TYPE LOCALITY: Pisgah National Forest, Buncombe County, North Carolina.

RANGE: Central and western North Carolina, north to Washington County, Virginia.

Genus BORARIA Chamberlin

Boraria Chamberlin, 1943, Proc. Biol. Soc. Washington, vol. 56, p. 143.
GENEROTYPE: *Aporiaria carolina* Chamberlin, by original designation.
RANGE: Southern Appalachians, from Virginia to Georgia.
SPECIES: Seven

Boraria brunnior (Chamberlin)

Aporiaria brunnior Chamberlin, 1943, Proc. Biol. Soc. Washington, vol. 56, p. 37, fig. 10.
TYPE: Chicago Nat. Hist. Mus.
TYPE LOCALITY: Great Smoky Mountains National Park, Sevier County, Tennessee.
RANGE: Known only from type locality.

Boraria carolina (Chamberlin)

Aporiaria carolina Chamberlin, 1939, Bull. Univ. Utah, biol. ser., vol. 5, No. 3, p. 6, fig. 10.
Boraria carolina Chamberlin, 1943, Proc. Biol. Soc. Washington, vol. 56, p. 144.—Hoffman, 1950, Journ. Elisha Mitchell Sci. Soc., vol. 66, p. 23, fig. 14.
TYPE: Collection of R. V. Chamberlin.
TYPE LOCALITY: Soco Falls, northeast of Cherokee, Jackson County, North Carolina.
RANGE: From Rabun County, Georgia, north through western North Carolina to Grayson and Patrick Counties, Virginia.

Boraria fumans (Chamberlin)

Aporiaria fumans Chamberlin, 1943, Proc. Biol. Soc. Washington, vol. 56, p. 37, fig. 9.
TYPE: Chicago Nat. Hist. Mus.
TYPE LOCALITY: Greenbrier Cove, Sevier County, Tennessee.
RANGE: Known only from type locality.

Boraria geniculata (Chamberlin)

Aporiaria geniculata Chamberlin, 1939, Bull. Univ. Utah, biol. ser., vol. 5, No. 3, p. 6, fig. 11.
TYPE: Collection of R. V. Chamberlin.
TYPE LOCALITY: Soco Falls, northeast of Cherokee, Jackson County, North Carolina.
RANGE: Known from about six localities in western North Carolina.

Boraria media (Chamberlin)

Nannaria media Chamberlin, 1918, Pysche, vol. 25, p. 125.
TYPE: Mus. Comp. Zool.

TYPE LOCALITY: Burbank, Carter County, Tennessee.
RANGE: Known only from the vicinity of Roan Mountain, North Carolina-Tennessee.

Boraria monticolens Chamberlin

Boraria monticolens Chamberlin, 1951, Great Basin Nat., vol. 11, p. 26, fig. 16.
TYPE: Collection of R. V. Chamberlin.
TYPE LOCALITY: Great Smoky Mountains National Park, Sevier County, Tennessee.
RANGE: Known only from type locality.

Boraria stricta (Brölemann)

Fontaria tennesseensis var. *stricta* Brölemann, 1896, Ann. Soc. Ent. France, vol. 65, p. 63, pl. 5, figs. 17, 18.
TYPE: Mus. Nat. Hist. Nat. Paris.
TYPE LOCALITY: North Carolina.
RANGE: No definite localities are known for this species.

Genus BRACHORIA Chamberlin

Brachoria Chamberlin, 1939, Bull. Univ. Utah, biol. ser., vol. 5, No. 3, p. 3.
Anfractogon Hoffman, 1948, Proc. Biol. Soc. Washington, vol. 61, p. 94 (generotype, *A. tenebrans* Hoffman).
GENEROTYPE: *Brachoria initialis* Chamberlin, by original designation.
RANGE: Southeastern United States, from West Virginia and Indiana south to Alabama and Mississippi.
SPECIES: Thirteen.

Brachoria benderi Causey

Brachoria benderi Causey, 1950, Ent. News, vol. 61, p. 193, figs. 1, 2.
TYPE: Acad. Nat. Sci. Philadelphia.
TYPE LOCALITY: Piney Woods, Rankin County, Mississippi.
RANGE: Known only from type locality.

Brachoria brachypus Chamberlin

Brachoria brachypus Chamberlin, 1947, Proc. Acad. Nat. Sci. Philadelphia, vol. 99, p. 26, fig. 9.
TYPE: Acad. Nat. Sci. Philadelphia (No. 9947).
TYPE LOCALITY: Harriman, Roane County, Tennessee.
RANGE: Known only from type locality.

Brachoria electa Causey

Brachoria electa Causey, 1955, Proc. Biol. Soc. Washington, vol. 68, p. 25, fig. 3.
TYPE: Amer. Mus. Nat. Hist.

Type Locality: Tyrone, Anderson County, Kentucky.
Range: Known only from type locality.

Brachoria ethotela Chamberlin

Brachoria ethotela Chamberlin, 1942, Bull. Univ. Utah, biol. ser., vol. 6, No. 8, p. 5, fig. 13.
Type: Collection of R. V. Chamberlin.
Type Locality: Marion, Smyth County, Virginia.
Range: Southwestern Virginia (Pulaski, Smyth, and Washington Counties) and northwestern North Carolina (Watauga County).

Brachoria eutypa Chamberlin

Brachoria eutypa Chamberlin, 1939, Bull. Univ. Utah, biol. ser., vol. 5, No. 3, p. 4, fig. 4.
Type: Collection of R. V. Chamberlin.
Type Locality: Russellville, Hamblen County, Tennessee.
Range: Known only from type locality.

Brachoria glendalea (Chamberlin)

Fontaria glendalea Chamberlin, 1918, Psyche, vol. 25, p. 28.
Type: Mus. Comp. Zool.
Type Locality: Glendale Hills, Nashville, Davidson County, Tennessee.
Range: Known only from type locality.

Brachoria hansonia Causey

Brachoria hansonia Causey, 1950, Ent. News, vol. 61, p. 6, fig. 1.
Type: Acad. Nat. Sci. Philadelphia.
Type Locality: Kentucky Ridge State Park, Pineville, Bell County, Kentucky.
Range: Known only from type locality.

Brachoria indianae (Bollman)

Fontaria indianae Bollman, 1889, Proc. U. S. Nat. Mus., vol. 11, p. 406.
Type: U. S. Nat. Mus.
Type Locality: Hagerstown and Brookville, Indiana. Here restricted to Brookville, Franklin County.
Range: Southern Indiana.

Brachoria initialis Chamberlin

Brachoria initialis Chamberlin, 1939, Bull. Univ. Utah, biol. ser., vol. 5, No. 3, p. 3, fig. 3.
Type: Collection of R. V. Chamberlin.
Type Locality: Mapleville, Chilton County, Alabama.
Range: Known only from type locality.

Brachoria ochra (Chamberlin)

Fontaria ochra Chamberlin, 1918, Psyche, vol. 25, p. 123.
TYPE: Mus. Comp. Zool.
TYPE LOCALITY: Agricultural College, Oktibbeha County, Mississippi.
RANGE: Known only from type locality.

Brachoria separanda Chamberlin

Brachoria separanda Chamberlin, 1947, Proc. Acad. Nat. Sci. Philadel-
phia, vol. 99, p. 28, fig. 10.
TYPE: Acad. Nat. Sci. Philadephia.
TYPE LOCALITY: Jennings, Garrett County, Maryland.
RANGE: Known elsewhere only from Parsons, Tucker County, West
Virginia.

Brachoria sequens Chamberlin

Brachoria sequens Chamberlin, 1939, Bull. Univ. Utah, biol. ser., vol. 5,
No. 3, p. 4, fig. 2.
TYPE: Collection of R. V. Chamberlin.
TYPE LOCALITY: Agricultural College, Oktibbeha County, Mississippi.
RANGE: Known only from type locality.

Brachoria tenebrans (Hoffman)

Anfractogon tenebrans Hoffman, 1948, Proc. Biol. Soc. Washington, vol.
61, p. 94, figs. 1–3.
TYPE: U. S. Nat. Mus. (No. 1811).
TYPE LOCALITY: Winston County, Alabama.
RANGE: Known only from type locality.

Genus CHEIRAUXUS Chamberlin

Cheirauxus Chamberlin, 1949, Journ. Washington Acad. Sci., vol. 39,
p. 97.
GENEROTYPE: *Cheirauxus sapiens* Chamberlin, by original designation.
RANGE: California.
SPECIES: One.

Cheirauxus sapiens Chamberlin

Cheirauxus sapiens Chamberlin, 1949, Journ. Washington Acad. Sci., vol.
39, p. 97, figs. 14, 15.
TYPE: Collection of R. V. Chamberlin.
TYPE LOCALITY: Palo Alto, Santa Clara County, California.
RANGE: Known only from type locality.

Genus CHEIROPUS Loomis

Cheiropus Loomis, 1944, Psyche, vol. 51, p. 171.
GENEROTYPE: *Cheiropus plancus* Loomis, by original designation.
RANGE: Georgia and Florida.
SPECIES: One.

Cheiropus plancus Loomis

Cheiropus plancus Loomis, 1944, Psyche, vol. 51, p. 171, fig. 3.
TYPE: Mus. Comp. Zool.
TYPE LOCALITY: Thomasville, Thomas County, Georgia.
RANGE: Known elsewhere only from Gainesville, Florida.

Genus CHEROKIA Chamberlin

Cherokia Chamberlin, 1949, Proc. Biol. Soc. Washington, vol. 62, p. 3.
GENEROTYPE: *Fontaria georgiana* Bollman, by original designation.
RANGE: Western Florida, north as far as Asheville, North Carolina.
SPECIES: Apparently one geographically variable species. Varying chiefly in color pattern, the forms of this genus are probably worthy of subspecific rank; for the purposes of this list, however, we treat them as local variants of a single polymorphic species.

Cherokia georgiana (Bollman)

Fontaria georgiana Bollman, 1889, Proc. U. S. Nat. Mus., vol. 11, p. 344.
Fontaria tallulah Bollman, 1889, Proc. U. S. Nat. Mus., vol. 11, p. 344
  (type locality: Tallulah Falls, Georgia; type: U. S. Nat. Mus.).
Fontaria ducilla Chamberlin, 1939, Bull. Univ. Utah, biol. ser., vol. 5, No.
  3, p. 7, fig. 12 (type locality: Soco Falls, Jackson County, North
  Carolina; type: collection of R. V. Chamberlin).
Mimuloria furcifer Chamberlin, 1940, Ent. News, vol. 51, p. 282, fig. 1
  (type locality: Pisgah National Forest, near Asheville, North Caro-
  line; type: collection of R. V. Chamberlin).
Dynoria parvior Chamberlin, 1947, Proc. Biol. Soc. Washington, vol. 60,
  p. 10, fig. 4 (type locality: Neel Gap, Georgia; type: collection of
  R. V. Chamberlin).
Cherokia georgiana Chamberlin, 1949, Proc. Biol. Soc. Washington, vol.
  62, p. 3.—Hoffman, 1950, Journ. Elisha Mitchell Sci. Soc., vol. 66,
  p. 23, figs. 9–12.
TYPE: U. S. Nat. Mus. (No. 780).
TYPE LOCALITY: Macon, Bibb County, Georgia.
RANGE: From western Florida, north through Georgia and eastern Ala-
bama into the southern Blue Ridge as far as the French Broad River.

Genus CHIPUS Loomis

Chipus Loomis, 1953, Journ. Washington Acad. Sci., vol. 43, No. 12, p. 421.
GENEROTYPE: *Chipus unicus* Loomis, by original designation.
RANGE: Idaho.
SPECIES: One.

Chipus unicus Loomis

Chipus unicus Loomis, 1953, Journ. Washington Acad. Sci., vol. 43, No.
  12, p. 421, fig. 18.

Type: U. S. Nat. Mus. (No. 2092).
Type Locality: Emerald Creek, St. Joe National Forest, Idaho.
Range: Known only from type locality.

Genus CHONAPHE Cook

Chonaphe Cook, 1904, *in* Harriman Alaska Exped., vol. 8, p. 56.
Generotype: *Polydesmus armatus* Harger, by original designation.
Range: Washington, Oregon, northern Idaho.
Species: Four.

Chonaphe armata (Harger)

Polydesmus armatus Harger, 1872, Amer. Journ. Sci. Arts, vol. 4, p. 120.
Chonaphe armata Cook, 1904, *in* Harriman Alaska Exped., vol. 8, p. 56,
   pl. 4, figs. 2a–c.
Type: Not known to exist.
Type Locality: John Day River Valley, Oregon.
Range: Oregon.

Chonaphe cygneia Chamberlin

Chonaphe cygneia Chamberlin, 1949, Proc. Biol. Soc. Washington, vol. 63
   [sic,=62], p. 125, fig. 1.
Type: Collection of R. V. Chamberlin.
Type Locality: White Swan, Yakima County, Washington.
Range: Known only from type locality.

Chonaphe patriotica Chamberlin

Chonaphe patriotica Chamberlin, 1949, Proc. Biol. Soc. Washington, vol.
   63 [sic,=62], p. 127, figs. 2, 3.
Type: Collection of R. V. Chamberlin.
Type Locality: Fourth of July Canyon, Kootenai County, Idaho.
Range: Known only from type locality.

Chonaphe remissa Chamberlin

Chonaphe remissa Chamberlin, 1949, Proc. Biol. Soc. Washington, vol. 63
   [sic,=62], p. 127, figs. 4, 5.
Type: Collection of R. V. Chamberlin.
Type Locality: Puyallup, Pierce County, Washington.
Range: Known only from type locality.

Genus CIBULARIA Chamberlin and Hoffman

Cibularia Chamberlin and Hoffman, 1950, Chicago Acad. Sci., Nat. Hist.
   Misc. No. 71, p. 4.
Generotype: *Fontaria tuobita* Chamberlin, by original designation.
Range: Central New Mexico; Arkansas.
Species: Two.

Cibularia profuga Causey

Cibularia profuga Causey, 1955, Proc. Biol. Soc. Washington, vol. 68, p. 29, fig. 7.

TYPE: Amer. Mus. Nat. Hist.

TYPE LOCALITY: Mount Ida, Montgomery County, Arkansas.

RANGE: Known only from type locality.

Cibularia tuobita (Chamberlin)

Fontaria tuobita Chamberlin, 1910, Ann. Ent. Soc. Amer., vol. 3, No. 4, p. 243, pl. 35, figs. 7, 8.

Nannaria ursa Chamberlin, 1938, Proc. Biol. Soc. Washington, vol. 51, p. 207 (type locality: Camp Mary White, near Cloudcroft, New Mexico; type: collection of R. V. Chamberlin).

Cibularia tuobita Chamberlin and Hoffman, 1950, Chicago Acad. Sci. Nat. Hist. Misc. No. 71, p. 5.

TYPE: Mus. Comp. Zool.

TYPE LOCALITY: Sacramento Mountains at Cloudcroft, Otero County, New Mexico.

RANGE: Otero and Lincoln Counties in central New Mexico.

Genus CLEPTORIA Chamberlin

Cleptoria Chamberlin, 1939, Bull. Univ. Utah, biol. ser., vol. 5, No. 3, p. 9.

GENEROTYPE: *Cleptoria macra* Chamberlin, by original designation.

RANGE: Georgia and South Carolina, in the Piedmont.

SPECIES: Three.

Cleptoria macra Chamberlin

Cleptoria macra Chamberlin, 1939, Bull. Univ. Utah, biol. ser., vol. 5, No. 3, p. 9, figs. 36, 37.

TYPE: Collection of R. V. Chamberlin.

TYPE LOCALITY: Taylors, Greenville County, South Carolina.

RANGE: Known only from type locality.

Cleptoria rileyi (Bollman)

Fontaria rileyi Bollman, 1889, Proc. U. S. Nat. Mus., vol. 11, p. 345.

Cleptoria rileyi Chamberlin, 1939, Bull. Univ. Utah, biol. ser., vol. 5, No. 3, p. 9.

TYPE: U. S. Nat. Mus.

TYPE LOCALITY: Macon, Bibb County, Georgia.

RANGE: Known only from type locality.

Cleptoria shelfordi Loomis

Cleptoria shelfordi Loomis, 1944, Psyche, vol. 51, p. 172, fig. 4.

TYPE: Mus. Comp. Zool.

TYPE LOCALITY: De La Howe Forest, Station 11, Lincoln County, Georgia.

RANGE: Known only from the type locality.

Genus DELOCHEIR Chamberlin

Delocheir Chamberlin, 1949, Journ. Washington Acad. Sci., vol. 39, p. 99.
GENEROTYPE: *Xystocheir taibona* Chamberlin, by original designation.
RANGE: Central California.
SPECIES: Three.

Delocheir conservata Chamberlin

Delocheir conservata Chamberlin, 1949, Journ. Washington Acad. Sci., vol. 39, p. 99, figs. 16, 17.
TYPE: Collection of R. V. Chamberlin.
TYPE LOCALITY: Hastings Reservation, Monterey County, California.
RANGE: Known only from the type locality.

Delocheir dalea Chamberlin

Delocheir dalea Chamberlin, 1949, Journ. Washington Acad. Sci., vol. 39, p. 99, fig. 19.
TYPE: Collection of R. V. Chamberlin.
TYPE LOCALITY: Brookdale, Santa Cruz County, California.
RANGE: Known only from the type locality.

Delocheir taibona (Chamberlin)

Xystocheir taibona Chamberlin, 1912, Ann. Ent. Soc. Amer., vol. 5, p. 170, pl. 10, figs. 1, 2.
Delocheir taibona Chamberlin, 1949, Journ. Washington Acad. Sci., vol. 39, p. 99.
TYPE: Present location unknown.
TYPE LOCALITY: Vicinity of Monterey Bay, California.
RANGE: Monterey and adjoining Counties, California.

Genus DELTOTARIA Causey

Deltotaria Causey, 1942, Ent. News, vol. 53, p. 165.
Phanoria Chamberlin, 1949, Journ. Washington Acad. Sci., vol. 39, p. 101 (generotype: *P. philia* Chamberlin).
GENEROTYPE: *Deltotaria brimleii* Causey, by original designation.
RANGE: Southern Appalachians in North Carolina, Tennessee, and northern Georgia.
SPECIES: Four.

Deltotaria brimleardia Causey

Deltotaria brimleardia Causey, 1950, Ent. News, vol. 61, p. 7, figs. 2, 3.
TYPE: Acad. Nat. Sci. Philadelphia.
TYPE LOCALITY: Great Smoky Mountains National Park, Tennessee.
RANGE: Known only from the type locality.

Deltotaria brimleii Causey

Deltotaria brimleii Causey, 1942, Ent. News, vol. 53, p. 165, figs. 1, 2.
TYPE: Acad. Nat. Sci. Philadelphia.
TYPE LOCALITY: Swannanoa, Buncombe County, North Carolina.
RANGE: Known only from type locality.

Deltotaria philia (Chamberlin)

Phanoria philia Chamberlin, 1949, Journ. Washington Acad. Sci., vol.
    39, p. 101, fig. 25.
TYPE: Collection of R. V. Chamberlin.
TYPE LOCALITY: Clarkesville, Habersham County, Georgia.
RANGE: Known only from type locality.

Deltotaria tela Causey

Deltotaria tela Causey, 1950, Ent. News, vol. 61, p. 38, figs. 3–5.
TYPE: Acad. Nat. Sci. Philadelphia.
TYPE LOCALITY: Bent Creek Forest Experiment Station, southwest of Asheville, Buncombe County, North Carolina.
RANGE: Known only from type locality.

Genus DICELLARIUS Chamberlin

Dicellarius Chamberlin, 1920, Proc. Biol. Soc. Washington, vol. 33, p. 97.
Spathoria Chamberlin, 1939, Bull. Univ. Utah, biol. ser., vol. 5, No. 3, p. 6
    (generotype: *Fontaria lamellidens* Chamberlin).
GENEROTYPE: *Leptodesmus okefenokensis* Chamberlin, by original designation.
RANGE: Gulf Coastal Plain, Florida to Mississippi.
SPECIE: Three.

Dicellarius bimaculatus (McNeill)

Polydesmus bimaculatus McNeill, 1887, Proc. U. S. Nat. Mus., vol. 10, p.
    323, pl. 11, figs. 3–5.
TYPE: U. S. Nat. Mus. (No. 8).
TYPE LOCALITY: Pensacola, Escambia County, Florida.
RANGE: Known only from type locality.

Dicellarius lamellidens (Chamberlin)

Fontaria lamellidens Chamberlin, 1931, Ent. News, vol. 42, p. 78.
Spathoria lamellidens Chamberlin, 1939, Bull. Univ. Utah, biol. ser., vol.
    5, No. 3, p. 6, fig. 9.
TYPE: Collection of R. V. Chamberlin.
TYPE LOCALITY: Biloxi, Harrison County, Mississippi.
RANGE: Known only from type locality.

Dicellarius okefenokensis (Chamberlin)

Leptodesmus okefenokensis Chamberlin, 1918, Ann. Ent. Soc. Amer., vol. 11, p. 370.

Dicellarius okefenokensis Chamberlin, 1920, Proc. Biol. Soc. Washington, vol. 33, p. 97.

Epeloria nannoides Chamberlin, 1949, Journ. Washington Acad. Sci., vol. 39, p. 101, fig. 4 (type locality: Gainesville, Florida; type: collection of R. V. Chamberlin).

TYPE: Mus. Comp. Zool.

TYPE LOCALITY: Billys Island, Okefenokee Swamp, Charlton County, Georgia.

RANGE: Southeastern Georgia and adjacent northern Florida.

Genus DIXIORIA Chamberlin

Dixioria Chamberlin, 1947, Proc. Acad. Nat. Sci. Philadelphia, vol. 99, p. 28.

GENEROTYPE: *Dixioria dentifer* Chamberlin [=*Fontaria pela* Chamberlin] by original designation.

RANGE: Southern Blue Ridge in Virginia, Tennessee, and North Carolina.

SPECIE: One, with two named subspecies.

Dixioria pela pela (Chamberlin)

Fontaria pela Chamberlin, 1918, Psyche, vol. 25, p. 123.

Dixioria dentifer Chamberlin, 1947, Proc. Acad. Nat. Sci. Philadelphia, vol. 99, p. 28, fig. 13 (type locality: Cranberry, Avery County, North Carolina; type: Amer. Mus. Nat. Hist.).

TYPE: Mus. Comp. Zool.

TYPE LOCALITY: Burbank, Carter County, Tennessee.

RANGE: Vicinity of Roan Mountain, in Carter and Unicoi Counties, Tennessee, and Avery and Mitchell Counties, North Carolina.

Dixioria pela coronata (Hoffman)

Deltotaria coronata Hoffman, 1949, Proc. U. S. Nat. Mus., vol. 99, p. 380, figs. 7, 8.

TYPE: U. S. Nat. Mus. (No. 1805).

TYPE LOCALITY: Mount Rogers, Grayson County, Virginia.

RANGE: The Iron Mountain in Grayson, Smyth, and Washington Counties, Virginia.

Genus DYNORIA Chamberlin

Dynoria Chamberlin, 1939, Bull. Univ. Utah, biol. ser., vol. 5, No. 3, p. 7.

GENEROTYPE: *Dynoria icana* Chamberlin, by original designation.

RANGE: Northern Georgia and adjacent South Carolina.

SPECIES: Two.

Dynoria icana Chamberlin

Dynoria icana Chamberlin, 1939, Bull. Univ. Utah, biol. ser., vol. 5, No. 3, p. 7, figs. 13, 14.

TYPE: Collection of R. V. Chamberlin.

TYPE LOCALITY: Tallulah Falls, Habersham County, Georgia.

RANGE: Known from the type locality, from Saluda, South Carolina, and from Clayton, Georgia.

Dynoria medialis Chamberlin

Dynoria medialis Chamberlin, 1949, Proc. Biol. Soc. Washington, vol. 62, p. 3, figs. 5, 6.

TYPE: Collection of R. V. Chamberlin.

TYPE LOCALITY: Atlanta, De Kalb County, Georgia.

RANGE: Known only from type locality.

Genus EPELORIA Chamberlin

Epeloria Chamberlin, 1939, Bull. Univ. Utah, biol. ser., vol. 5, No. 3, p. 3.

GENEROTYPE: *Epeloria talapoosa* Chamberlin, by original designation.

RANGE: Georgia.

SPECIES: Six.

Epeloria atlanta Chamberlin

Epeloria atlanta Chamberlin, 1946, Ent. News, vol. 57, p. 151, fig. 6.

TYPE: Collection of R. V. Chamberlin.

TYPE LOCALITY: Atlanta, De Kalb County, Georgia.

RANGE: Known only from type locality.

Epeloria bifida (Wood) [4]

Polydesmus (*Fontaria*) *bifidus* Wood, 1864, Proc. Acad. Nat. Sci. Philadelphia, p. 7; 1865, Trans. Amer. Philos. Soc., vol. 13, p. 223, fig. 52.

TYPE: Not known to exist.

TYPE LOCALITY: "Georgia and Texas."

RANGE: No definite localities yet known.

Epeloria dela Chamberlin

Epeloria dela Chamberlin, 1946, Proc. Biol. Soc. Washington, vol. 59, p. 139, figs. 1, 2.

TYPE: Collection of R. V. Chamberlin.

TYPE LOCALITY: Morgan, Morgan County, Georgia.

RANGE: Known only from type locality.

Epeloria ficta Chamberlin

Epeloria ficta Chamberlin, 1943, Proc. Biol. Soc. Washington, vol. 56, p. 37, fig. 11.

---

[4] Tentatively referred to this genus. The species may prove to be a form of *Thrinaxoria*.

TYPE: Chicago Nat. Hist. Mus.
TYPE LOCALITY: Thomasville, Thomas County, Georgia.
RANGE: Known only from type locality.

Epeloria leiacantha Chamberlin

Epeloria leiacantha Chamberlin, 1946, Proc. Biol. Soc., Washington, vol. 59, p. 139, fig. 3.
TYPE: Collection of R. V. Chamberlin.
TYPE LOCALITY: Spring Creek, Decatur County, Georgia.
RANGE: Known elsewhere from Fort Benning, Georgia.

Epeloria talapoosa Chamberlin

Epeloria talapoosa Chamberlin, 1939, Bull. Univ. Utah, biol. ser., vol. 5, No. 3, p. 3, fig. 1.
TYPE: Collection of R. V. Chamberlin.
TYPE LOCALITY: Talapoosa, Haralson County, Georgia.
RANGE: Known only from type locality.

Genus FALLORIA Hoffman

Falloria Hoffman, 1948, Proc. Biol. Soc. Washington, vol. 61, p. 93.
GENEROTYPE: *Apheloria bidens* Causey, by original designation.
RANGE: Great Smoky Mountains, Tennessee.
SPECIES: One.

Falloria bidens (Causey)

Apheloria bidens Causey, 1942, Ent. News, vol. 53, p. 169, fig. 9.
TYPE: Acad. Nat. Sci. Philadelphia.
TYPE LOCALITY: Chimneys, Great Smoky Mountains National Park, Sevier County, Tennessee.
RANGE: Known only from type locality.

Genus FONTARIA Gray

Fontaria Gray, 1832, Insecta, *in* Griffith, The animal kingdom . . . by the Baron Cuvier, vol. 15, p. 787, pl. 135, fig. 1.—Pocock, 1909, Diplopoda, *in* Biol. Centr.-Amer., p. 188.—Hoffman, 1952, Ent. News, vol. 63, p. 72.
Stelgipus Loomis, 1944, Psyche, vol. 51, p. 173 (generotype: *S. agrestis* Loomis).
GENEROTYPE: *Julus virginiensis* Drury, by monotypy.
RANGE: South Carolina, Georgia.
SPECIES: Two.

Fontaria agrestis (Loomis)

Stelgipus agrestis Loomis, 1944, Psyche, vol. 51, p. 173, fig. 5.
TYPE: Mus. Comp. Zool.
TYPE LOCALITY: Waynesboro, Burke County, Georgia.

RANGE: Known also from Wadmalaw Island, South Carolina. May be identical with *F. virginiensis.*

Fontaria virginiensis (Drury)

Julus virginiensis Drury, 1770, Illustrations of natural history, vol. 1, pl. 43, fig. 8.

Fontaria virginiensis Gray, 1832, Insecta, *in* Griffith, The animal kingdom,
. . . by the Baron Cuvier, vol. 15, p. 787, pl. 135, fig. 1.—Hoffman, 1952, Ent. News, vol. 63, p. 72, fig. 1.

TYPE: British Mus. (Nat. Hist.).

TYPE LOCALITY: Georgia.

RANGE: Known only from type locality.

Genus HARPAPHE Cook

Harpaphe Cook, 1904, *in* Harriman Alaska Exped., vol. 8, p. 59.

Paimokia Chamberlin, 1941, Bull. Univ. Utah, biol. ser., vol. 6, No. 5, p. 13 (generotype: *P. modestior* Chamberlin.)

GENEROTYPE: *Polydesmus haydenianus* Wood, by original designation.

RANGE: California, Oregon, Washington.

SPECIES: Nine recognized here, in a purely provisional arrangement. The genus is badly in need of study.

Harpaphe clara Chamberlin

Harpaphe clara Chamberlin, 1949, Proc. Biol. Soc. Washington, vol. 63 [sic,=62], p. 128, figs. 6, 7.

TYPE: Collection of R. V. Chamberlin.

TYPE LOCALITY: Steven's Creek, Santa Clara County, California.

RANGE: Recorded from Santa Clara and Santa Cruz Counties, California.

Harpaphe haydeniana (Wood)

Polydesmus (Leptodesmus) haydenianus Wood, 1864, Proc. Acad. Nat. Sci. Philadelphia, p. 10.

Harpaphe haydeniana Cook, 1904, *in* Harriman Alaska Exped., vol. 8, p. 59, pl. 4, figs. 4a–c.

Fontaria Simoni Brölemann, 1896, Ann. Soc. Ent. France, vol. 65, p. 65, pl. 5, figs. 19, 20 (type locality: Washington State; type: Mus. Hist. Nat., Paris).

TYPE: Not known to exist.

TYPE LOCALITY: Oregon.

RANGE: Oregon, Washington, Vancouver Island.

Harpaphe inlignea Chamberlin

Harpaphe inlignea Chamberlin, 1949, Proc. Biol. Soc. Washington, vol. 63 [sic,=62], p. 128, fig. 8.

TYPE: Collection of R. V. Chamberlin.

TYPE LOCALITY: Inwood, Shasta County, California.

RANGE: Known only from type locality.

Harpaphe intaminata (Karsch)

Polydesmus (Oxyurus) intaminatus Karsch, 1881, Arch. Naturg., vol. 47, p. 41.

Harpaphe intaminata Cook, 1904, *in* Harriman Alaska Exped., vol. 8, p. 60.

Paimokia scotia Chamberlin, 1941, Bull. Univ. Utah, biol. ser., vol. 6, No. 5, p. 13, fig. 26 (type locality: Santa Cruz County, California; type: collection of R. V. Chamberlin.

Pachydesmus cummingsiensis Verhoeff, 1944, Bull. Southern California Acad. Sci., vol. 43, p. 64, fig. 14 (type locality: Cummings, Mendocino County, California; type: Verhoeff collection).

TYPE: Berlin Museum.

TYPE LOCALITY: "California."

RANGE: Central California.

Harpaphe maculifer (Chamberlin)

Paimokia maculifer Chamberlin, 1941, Bull. Univ. Utah, biol. ser., vol. 6, No. 5, p. 14.

TYPE: Collection of R. V. Chamberlin.

TYPE LOCALITY: 9 miles north of Woodlake, Tulare County, California.

RANGE: Known only from type locality.

Harpaphe modestior (Chamberlin)

Paimokia modestior Chamberlin, 1941, Bull. Univ. Utah, biol. ser., vol. 6, No. 5, p. 13, fig. 25.

TYPE: Collection of R. V. Chamberlin.

TYPE LOCALITY: 4.7 miles north of Badger, Fresno County, California.

RANGE: Known only from type locality.

Harpaphe penulta Chamberlin

Harpaphe penulta Chamberlin, 1949, Proc. Biol. Soc. Washington, vol. 63 [sic,=62], p. 128, fig. 9.

TYPE: Collection of R. V. Chamberlin.

TYPE LOCALITY: 9 miles south of Belknap Springs, Lane County, Oregon.

RANGE: Reported from four localities in Lane County, Oregon.

Harpaphe pottera Chamberlin

Harpaphe pottera Chamberlin, 1949, Proc. Biol. Soc. Washington, vol. 63 [sic,=62], p. 129, fig. 11.

TYPE: Collection of R. V. Chamberlin.

TYPE LOCALITY: Potter Creek, Mendocino County, California.

RANGE: Mendocino and Shasta Counties, California.

Harpaphe telodonta (Chamberlin)

Paimokia telodonta Chamberlin, 1943, Bull. Univ. Utah, biol. ser., vol. 8, No. 2, p. 17, fig. 33.

Harpaphe telodonta Chamberlin, 1949, Proc. Biol. Soc. Washington, vol. 63 [sic,=62], p. 129, fig. 11.

TYPE: Collection of R. V. Chamberlin.

TYPE LOCALITY: Arcata, Humboldt County, California.

RANGE: Known only from type locality.

Genus HYBAPHE Cook

Hybaphe Cook, 1904, *in* Harriman Alaska Exped., vol. 8, p. 58.

GENEROTYPE: *Hybaphe tersa* Cook, by original designation.

RANGE: Washington; northern California.

SPECIES: Two.

Hybaphe curtipes Cook

Hybaphe curtipes Cook, 1904, *in* Harriman Alaska Exped., vol. 8, p. 59.

TYPE: U. S. Nat. Mus. (No. 790).

TYPE LOCALITY: Pullman, Whitman County, Washington.

RANGE: Known only from type locality.

Hybaphe tersa Cook

Hybaphe tersa Cook, 1904, *in* Harriman Alaska Exped., vol. 8, p. 58, pl. 4, fig. 3a—Causey, 1954, Pan-Pacific Ent., vol. 30, No. 3, p. 222, fig. 1.

TYPE: U. S. Nat. Mus. (No. 789).

TYPE LOCALITY: Almota, Whitman County, Washington.

RANGE: Recorded also from Shasta County, California.

Genus ISAPHE Cook

Isaphe Cook, 1904, *in* Harriman Alaska Exped., vol. 8, p. 57.

GENEROTYPE: *Isaphe convexa* Cook, by original designation.

RANGE: Northern Idaho; California?

SPECIES: Two.

Isaphe convexa Cook

Isaphe convexa Cook, 1904, *in* Harriman Alaska Exped., vol. 8, p. 58, pl. 4, figs. 1a, b.

TYPE: U. S. Nat. Mus. (No. 788).

TYPE LOCALITY: Kootenai County, Idaho.

RANGE: Known only from type locality.

Isaphe simplex Chamberlin

Isaphe simplex Chamberlin, 1918, Pomona Coll. Journ. Ent. and Zool., vol. 10, No. 1, p. 9.

TYPE: Mus. Comp. Zool.

TYPE LOCALITY: California.

RANGE: No definite localities known.

Genus HOWELLARIA Hoffman

Howellaria Hoffman, 1950, Journ. Elisha Mitchell Sci. Soc., vol. 66, p. 26.
GENEROTYPE: *Aporiaria deturkiana* Causey, by original designation.
RANGE: Western North Carolina and eastern Tennessee.
SPECIES: One.

Howellaria deturkiana (Causey)

Aporiaria deturkiana Causey, 1942, Ent. News, vol. 53, p. 169, fig. 8.
Howellaria deturkiana Hoffman, 1950, Journ. Elisha Mitchell Sci. Soc., vol. 66, p. 26, figs. 7, 8, 13.
TYPE: Acad. Nat. Sci. Philadelphia.
TYPE LOCALITY: Highlands, Macon County, North Carolina.
RANGE: Type locality and Great Smoky Mountains in Sevier County, Tennessee, and Haywood County, North Carolina; probably also in the intervening Balsam Mountains.

Genus MIMULORIA Chamberlin

Mimuloria Chamberlin, 1928, Ent. News, vol. 39, p. 155.
Castanaria Causey, 1950, Chicago Acad. Sci. Nat. Hist. Misc. No. 73, p. 1 (generotype: *C. depalmai* Causey).
GENEROTYPE: *Mimuloria missouriensis* Chamberlin, by original designation.
RANGE: Ozark region; Indiana, Ohio.
SPECIES: Five.

Mimuloria castanea (McNeill)

Polydesmus castaneus McNeill, 1887, Proc. U. S. Nat. Mus., vol. 10, p. 329, pl. 12, fig. 8.
Mimuloria castanea Causey, 1952, Chicago Acad. Sci. Nat. Hist. Misc. No. 106, p. 8, fig. 6.
TYPE: U. S. Nat. Mus.
TYPE LOCALITY: Bloomington, Monroe County, Indiana.
RANGE: Southern Indiana.

Mimuloria davidcauseyi (Causey)

Nannaria davidcauseyi Causey, 1950, Ent. News, vol. 61, p. 194, figs. 3, 4.
Mimuloria davidcauseyi Causey, 1952, Chicago Acad. Sci. Nat. Hist. Misc. No. 106, p. 8.
TYPE: Acad. Nat. Sci. Philadelphia.
TYPE LOCALITY: Near Jasper, Newton County, Arkansas.
RANGE: Known only from type locality.

Mimuloria depalmai (Causey)

Castanaria depalmai Causey, 1950, Chicago Acad. Sci. Nat. Hist. Misc. No. 73, p. 1, fig. 1.

TYPE: Acad. Nat. Sci. Philadelphia.
TYPE LOCALITY: 2 miles south of Lake Leatherwood, Carroll County, Arkansas.
RANGE: Known only from type locality.

Mimuloria missouriensis Chamberlin

Mimuloria missouriensis Chamberlin, 1928, Ent. News, vol. 39, p. 155.
TYPE: Collection of R. V. Chamberlin.
TYPE LOCALITY: St. Charles, Missouri.
RANGE: Known only from type locality.

Mimuloria ohionis (Loomis and Hoffman)

Fontaria castanea (Not McNeill) Williams and Hefner, 1928, Bull. Ohio
    Biol. Surv. No. 18, p. 106, fig. 9b.
Nannaria ohionis Loomis and Hoffman, 1948, Proc. Biol. Soc. Wash-
    ington, vol. 61, p. 53.
Mimuloria ohionis Causey, 1952, Chicago Acad. Sci. Nat Hist. Misc. No.
    106, p. 8, fig. 6.
TYPE: Collection of Miami Univ.
TYPE LOCALITY: "Southern Ohio."
RANGE: Known only from type locality.

Genus MONTAPHE Chamberlin

Montaphe Chamberlin, 1949, Proc. Biol. Soc. Washington, vol. 63
    [sic,=62], p. 127.
GENEROTYPE: *Leptodesmus elrodi* Chamberlin, by original designation.
RANGE: Montana.
SPECIES: One.

Montaphe elrodi (Chamberlin)

Leptodesmus (Chonapke) elrodi Chamberlin, 1913, Canadian Ent., vol.
    45, p. 424, fig. 17.
Montaphe elrodi Chamberlin, 1949, Proc. Biol. Soc. Washington, vol. 63
    [sic,=62], p. 127.
TYPE: Mus. Comp. Zool.
TYPE LOCALITY: Flathead Lake, Flathead County, Montana.
RANGE: Known only from type locality and from Evans, Stevens County, Washington.

Genus MOTYXIA Chamberlin

Motyxia Chamberlin, 1941, Bull. Univ. Utah, biol. ser., vol. 6, No. 5, p. 15.
GENEROTYPE: *Motyxia kerna* Chamberlin, by original designation.
RANGE: Southern California.
SPECIES: Six.

Motyxia exilis Loomis

Motyxia exilis Loomis, 1953, Journ. Washington Acad. Sci., vol. 43, p. 422, fig. 20.

TYPE: U. S. Nat. Mus. (No. 2094).

TYPE LOCALITY: Woodford, near Tehachapi, Kern County, California.

RANGE: Known only from type locality.

Motyxia expansa Loomis

Motyxia expansa Loomis, 1953, Journ. Washington Acad. Sci., vol. 43, p. 422, fig. 19.

TYPE: U. S. Nat. Mus. (No. 2093).

TYPE LOCALITY: Fort Tejon, Kern County, California.

RANGE: Known only from type locality.

Motyxia kerna Chamberlin

Motyxia kerna Chamberlin, 1941, Bull. Univ. Utah, biol. ser., vol. 6, No. 5, p. 15, fig. 29.

TYPE: Collection of R. V. Chamberlin.

TYPE LOCALITY: 12 miles northeast of Hammond, Tulare County, California.

RANGE: Known from type locality only.

Motyxia monica Chamberlin

Motyxia monica Chamberlin, 1944, Proc. Biol. Soc. Washington, vol. 57, p. 113, figs. 1–3.

TYPE: Collection of R. V. Chamberlin.

TYPE LOCALITY: Meadow Canyon, Santa Monica Mountains, Los Angeles County, California.

RANGE: Known only from type locality.

Motyxia pior Chamberlin

Motyxia pior Chamberlin, 1941, Bull. Univ. Utah, biol. ser., vol. 6, No. 5, p. 16.

TYPE: Collection of R. V. Chamberlin.

TYPE LOCALITY: 12 miles east of Hammond, Tulare County, California.

RANGE: Known only from type locality.

Motyxia tejona Chamberlin

Motyxia tejona Chamberlin, 1947, Proc. Acad. Nat. Sci. Philadelphia, vol. 99, p. 25, fig. 4.

TYPE: Acad. Nat. Sci. Philadelphia.

TYPE LOCALITY: Fort Tejon, Kern County, California.

RANGE: Known only from type locality.

Genus NANNARIA Chamberlin

Nannaria Chamberlin, 1918, Psyche, vol. 25, p. 124.

GENEROTYPE: *Nannaria minor* Chamberlin, by original designation.

RANGE: Eastern United States, chiefly in the Appalachian region from Georgia to New York.

SPECIES: Seventeen.

Nannaria austricola Hoffman

Nannaria austricola Hoffman, 1950, Journ. Elisha Mitchell Sci. Soc., vol. 66, p. 26, figs. 26, 27.

TYPE: U. S. Nat. Mus. (No. 1879).

TYPE LOCALITY: Highlands, Macon County, North Carolina.

RANGE: Known only from type locality and adjacent Rabun County, Georgia.

Nannaria cayugae Chamberlin

Nannaria cayugae Chamberlin, 1949, Proc. Biol. Soc. Washington, vol. 62, p. 4, fig. 3.

TYPE: Collection of R. V. Chamberlin.

TYPE LOCALITY: Ithaca, Tompkins County, New York.

RANGE: Known only from type locality.

Nannaria conservata Chamberlin

Nannaria conservata Chamberlin, 1940, Canadian Ent., vol. 72, p. 56.

TYPE: Collection of R. V. Chamberlin.

TYPE LOCALITY: Duke Forest, Orange County, North Carolina.

RANGE: Known only from type locality.

Nannaria equalis Chamberlin

Nannaria equalis Chamberlin, 1949, Proc. Biol. Soc. Washington, vol. 62, p. 4, fig. 4.

TYPE: Collection of R. V. Chamberlin.

TYPE LOCALITY: Knoxville, Knox County, Tennessee.

RANGE: Known only from type locality.

Nannaria ericacea Hoffman

Nannaria ericacea Hoffman, 1949, Proc. U. S. Nat. Mus., vol. 99, p. 381, figs. 9, 10.

TYPE: U. S. Nat. Mus. (No. 1784).

TYPE LOCALITY: Clifton Forge, Alleghany County, Virginia.

RANGE: Known from Alleghany, Botetourt, Craig, and Montgomery Counties, Virginia.

Nannaria fowleri Chamberlin

Nannaria fowleri Chamberlin, 1947, Proc. Acad. Nat. Sci. Philadelphia, vol. 99, p. 29, fig. 14.

TYPE: Acad. Nat. Sci. Philadelphia (No. 9951).

TYPE LOCALITY: Jennings, Garrett County, Maryland.

RANGE: Known only from type locality.

Nannaria infesta Chamberlin

Nannaria infesta Chamberlin, 1918, Psyche, vol. 25, p. 126.
TYPE: Herbarium of Cryptogamic Botany, Harvard University.
TYPE LOCALITY: Cranberry, Avery County, North Carolina.
RANGE: Known only from type locality.

Nannaria laminata Hoffman

Nannaria laminata Hoffman, 1949, Proc. U. S. Nat. Mus., vol. 99, p.
383, figs. 11, 12.
TYPE: U. S. Nat. Mus. (No. 1806).
TYPE LOCALITY: 2 miles south of Glen Lyn, Mercer County, West
Virginia.
RANGE: Known only from type locality.

Nannaria minor Chamberlin

Nannaria minor Chamberlin, 1918, Psyche, vol. 25, p. 124.
TYPE: Mus. Comp. Zool.
TYPE LOCALITY: Burbank, Carter County, Tennessee.
RANGE: Known only from type locality.

Nannaria morrisoni Hoffman

Nannaria morrisoni Hoffman, 1948, Journ. Washington Acad. Sci., vol.
38, p. 348, figs. 3, 4.
TYPE: U. S. Nat. Mus. (No. 1834).
TYPE LOCALITY: 2 miles northwest of Crozet, Albemarle County, Virginia.
RANGE: Blue Ridge Mountains from Jefferson County, West Virginia,
south as far as Rockbridge County, Virginia.

Nannaria pulchella (Bollman)

Fontaria pulchella Bollman, 1889, Proc. U. S. Nat. Mus., vol. 11, p. 316.
TYPE: U. S. Nat. Mus.
TYPE LOCALITY: Strawberry Plains, Jefferson County, Tennessee.
RANGE: Known only from type locality.

Nannaria scutellaria Causey

Nannaria scutellaria Causey, 1942, Ent. News, vol. 53, p. 168, figs. 6, 7.
TYPE: Acad. Nat. Sci. Philadelphia.
TYPE LOCALITY: Chimneys, Great Smoky Mountains National Park,
Sevier County, Tennessee.
RANGE: Known only from type locality.

Nannaria shenandoa Hoffman

Nannaria shenandoa Hoffman, 1949, Proc. Biol. Soc. Washington, vol. 62,
p. 82, figs. 1–4.
TYPE: U. S. Nat. Mus. (No. 1848).
TYPE LOCALITY: Shenandoah Mountain, Rockingham County, Virginia.
RANGE: Known only from type locality.

Nannaria simplex Hoffman

Nannaria simplex Hoffman, 1949, Proc. U. S. Nat. Mus., vol. 99, p. 384, figs. 13, 14.

TYPE: U. S. Nat. Mus. (No. 1807).

TYPE LOCALITY: Clifton Forge, Alleghany County, Virginia.

RANGE: Known so far only from several localities in Alleghany County, Virginia.

Nannaria tennesseensis (Bollman)

Fontaria tennesseensis Bollman, 1889, Proc. U. S. Nat. Mus. vol. 11, p. 340.

TYPE: U. S. Nat. Mus.

TYPE LOCALITY: Mossy Creek, Jefferson County, Tennessee.

RANGE: Reported only from the type locality.

Nannaria terricola (Williams and Hefner)

Fontaria terricola Williams and Hefner, 1928, Bull. Ohio Biol. Surv., No. 18, p. 106, fig. 9c.

Nannaria terricola Loomis and Hoffman, 1948, Proc. Biol. Soc. Washington, vol. 61, p. 53.

TYPE: U. S. Nat. Mus. (No. 2269).

TYPE LOCALITY: Probably Oxford, Ohio.

RANGE: Known also from Grant County, Indiana.

Nannaria wilsoni Hoffman

Nannaria wilsoni Hoffman, 1949, Proc. U. S. Nat. Mus., vol. 99, p. 386, figs. 15, 16.

TYPE: U. S. Nat. Mus. (No. 1808).

TYPE LOCALITY: Mountain Lake, Giles County, Virginia.

RANGE: Known so far from Giles, Montgomery, Floyd, and Patrick Counties, Virginia.

Genus OROPHE Chamberlin

Orophe Chamberlin, 1951, Chicago Acad. Sci. Nat. Hist. Misc. No. 87, p. 2.

GENEROTYPE: *Orophe cabinetus* Chamberlin, by original designation.

RANGE: Western Montana.

SPECIES: One.

Orophe cabinetus Chamberlin

Orophe cabinetus Chamberlin, 1951, Chicago Acad. Sci. Nat. Hist. Misc. No. 87, p. 4, figs. 8, 9.

TYPE: California Acad. Sci.

TYPE LOCALITY: Clark's Peak, Cabinet National Forest, Montana.

RANGE: Known only from the type locality and vicinity.

Genus PACHYDESMUS Cook

Pachydesmus Cook, 1895, Ann. New York Acad. Sci., vol. 9, p. 5.

GENEROTYPE: *Polydesmus crassicutis* Wood, by original designation.

RANGE: Southeastern United States, from South Carolina and Tennessee west to Louisiana.

SPECIES: Eight listed here, but these probably are actually geographic races of but two full species.

Pachydesmus clarus (Chamberlin)

Fontaria clara Chamberlin, 1918, Ann. Ent. Soc. Amer., vol. 11, p. 372.

Pachydesmus kisatchinsis Chamberlin, 1942, Bull. Univ. Utah, biol. ser., vol. 6, No. 8, p. 4, fig. 8 (type locality: Kisatchi, Louisiana; type: collection of R. V. Chamberlin).

TYPE: Mus. Comp. Zool.

TYPE LOCALITY: Creston, Natchitoches Parish, Louisiana.

RANGE: Northwestern Parishes of Louisiana.

Pachydesmus crassicutis (Wood)

Polydesmus crassicutis Wood, 1864, Proc. Acad. Nat. Sci. Philadelphia, p. 7; 1865, Trans. Amer. Philos. Soc., vol. 13, p. 224, fig. 55.

Fontaria crassicutis Brölemann, 1900, Mém. Soc. Zool. France, vol. 13, p. 101, pl. 6, figs. 28, 29.

TYPE: Location unknown.

TYPE LOCALITY: Mississippi, without further location.

RANGE: Southern Mississippi and Louisiana.

Pachydesmus denticulatus Chamberlin

Pachydesmus denticulatus Chamberlin, 1946, Ent. News, vol. 57, p. 152, figs. 8, 9.

TYPE: Collection of R. V. Chamberlin.

TYPE LOCALITY: Atlanta, Georgia.

RANGE: Known only from type locality.

Pachydesmus duplex Chamberlin

Pachydesmus duplex Chamberlin, 1939, Bull. Univ. Utah, biol. ser., vol. 5, No. 3, p. 5, fig. 8.

TYPE: Collection of R. V. Chamberlin.

TYPE LOCALITY: Grenada, Grenada County, Mississippi.

RANGE: Known only from type locality.

Pachydesmus incursus Chamberlin

Pachydesmus incursus Chamberlin, 1939, Bull. Univ. Utah, biol. ser., vol. 5, No. 3, p. 5, fig. 7.

TYPE: Collection of R. V. Chamberlin.

TYPE LOCALITY: Taylors, Greenville County, South Carolina.

RANGE: Known from Greenville and Pickens Counties, in western South Carolina.

Pachydesmus laticollis (Attems)

Fontaria laticollis Attems, 1900, Denkschr. Akad. Wiss., Wien, vol. 68, p. 258, pl. 13, fig. 312; 1938, Das Tierreich, Lief. 69, p. 154, fig. 176.

TYPE: Vienna Museum.

TYPE LOCALITY: Illinois (probably in error as no other forms of this genus have been found farther north than southern Tennessee).

RANGE: No definite localities known.

Pachydesmus louisianus (Chamberlin)

Fontaria louisiana Chamberlin, 1918, Canadian Ent., vol. 50, p. 363.

TYPE: Mus. Comp. Zool.

TYPE LOCALITY: Covington, St. Tammany Parish, Louisiana.

RANGE: Known only from type locality.

Pachydesmus retrorsus Chamberlin

Pachydesmus retrorsus Chamberlin, 1921, Canadian Ent., vol. 53, p. 231, pl. 9, figs. 3, 4.

TYPE: Mus. Comp. Zool.

TYPE LOCALITY: Knox County, Tennessee.

RANGE: Known from several localities in eastern Tennessee and extreme Northern Alabama.

Genus PLEUROLOMA Rafinesque

Pleuroloma Rafinesque, 1820, Annals of nature, . . ., p. 8.—Hoffman and Crabill, 1953, Florida Ent., vol. 36, p. 79.

Zinaria Chamberlin, 1939, Bull. Univ. Utah, biol. ser., vol. 5, No. 3, p. 4.— Causey, 1951, Proc. Arkansas Acad. Sci., vol. 4, p. 77 (generotype: *Zinaria cala* Chamberlin).

GENEROTYPE: *Pleuroloma flavipes* Rafinesque, by monotypy.

RANGE: North America east of the Great Plains.

SPECIES: Twelve, most of which will probably be shown to be only geographic races of *P. flavipes*.

Pleuroloma brunnea (Bollman)

Fontaria virginiensis brunnea Bollman, 1887, Amer. Nat., vol. 21, p. 82.

Fontaria virginiensis castanea Bollman, 1893, U. S. Nat. Mus. Bull. 46, p. 132 (error for *F. v. brunnea*).

Zinaria brunnea Causey, 1951, Proc. Arkansas Acad. Sci., vol. 4, p. 80, pl. 1, figs. 1b, 3d, and pl. 2, fig. 8d.

TYPE: U. S. Nat. Mus.

TYPE LOCALITY: Fort Snelling, Hennipin County, Minnesota.

RANGE: Southeastern Minnesota.

Pleuroloma busheyi (Causey)

Zinaria busheyi Causey, 1951, Proc. Arkansas Acad. Sci., vol. 4, p. 84, pl. 1, figs. 1f, 4, 7, and pl. 2, fig. 8j.

Type: Acad. Nat. Sci. Philadelphia.
Type Locality: Upland, Grant County, Indiana.
Range: Known only from type locality.

Pleuroloma butleri (McNeill)

Polydesmus butleri McNeill, 1888, Bull. Brookville Soc. Nat. Hist., No. 3, p. 8.
Fontaria virginiensis Bollman, 1889, Proc. U. S. Nat. Mus., vol. 11, p. 6.
Zinaria butleri Chamberlin, 1943, Bull. Univ. Utah, biol. ser., vol. 8, No. 2, p. 16.
Type: U. S. Nat. Mus.
Type Locality: Brookville, Franklin County, Indiana.
Range: Central Indiana, exact limits unknown.

Pleuroloma cala (Chamberlin)

Zinaria cala Chamberlin, 1939, Bull. Univ. Utah, biol. ser., vol. 5, No. 3, p. 4, fig. 6.
Type: Collection of R. V. Chamberlin.
Type Locality: East of Deer Park, Lake County, Florida.
Range: Peninsular Florida, northeast as far as Screven County, Georgia.

Pleuroloma flavipes Rafinesque

Pleuroloma flavipes Rafinesque, 1820, Annals of nature, . . . , p. 8.
—Hoffman and Crabill, 1953, Florida Ent., vol. 36, p. 80.
Type: Not known to exist.
Type Locality: Near Catskill, Greene County, New York.
Range: Probably general over New England.

Pleuroloma iowa Chamberlin

Pleuroloma iowa Chamberlin, 1942, Canadian Ent., vol. 74, p. 16.
Type: Collection of R. V. Chamberlin.
Type Locality: Ames, Story County, Iowa.
Range: Known only from Iowa.

Pleuroloma mima (Chamberlin)

Zinaria mima Chamberlin, 1949, Journ. Washington Acad. Sci., vol. 39, p. 101, fig. 26.
Type: Collection of R. V. Chamberlin.
Type Locality: Greene County, Pennsylvania.
Range: Known only from the type locality.

Pleuroloma miribilia (Causey)

Zinaria miribilia Causey, 1951, Proc. Arkansas Acad. Sci., vol. 4, p. 85, pl. 1, fig. 1d, and pl. 2, fig. 8f.
Type: Acad. Nat. Sci. Philadelphia.

TYPE LOCALITY: 12 miles northeast of Piggott, Clay County, Arkansas.
RANGE: Known only from type locality.

Pleuroloma proxima (Causey)

Zinaria proxima Causey, 1951, Proc. Arkansas Acad. Sci., vol. 4, p. 86,
   pl. 1, figs. 1g, 2a, 3c, and pl. 2, figs. 8e, 12.
TYPE: Acad. Nat. Sci. Philadelphia.
TYPE LOCALITY: Ann Arbor, Michigan.
RANGE: Known only from type locality.

Pleuroloma rubrilata (Hoffman)

Zinaria rubrilata Hoffman, 1949, Proc. Biol. Soc. Washington, vol. 62,
   p. 84.
TYPE: U. S. Nat. Mus. (No. 1849).
TYPE LOCALITY: 1 mile north of Kilmarnock, Lancaster County, Virginia.
RANGE: Known only from type locality and vicinity.

Pleuroloma urbana (Chamberlin)

Zinaria urbana Chamberlin, 1939, Bull. Univ. Utah, biol. ser., vol. 5,
   No. 3, p. 5, fig. 5.
TYPE: Collection of R. V. Chamberlin.
TYPE LOCALITY: Urbana, Champaign County, Illinois.
RANGE: Champaign and adjoining Counties Illinois.

Pleuroloma warreni (Causey)

Zinaria warreni Causey, 1951, Proc. Arkansas Acad. Sci., vol. 4, p. 83, figs.
   1c, 3b, 6, 8c, 10.
TYPE: Acad. Nat. Sci. Philadelphia.
TYPE LOCALITY: Carroll County, Arkansas.
RANGE: Also known from Cherokee and Latimer Counties, Oklahoma.

Genus RHYSODESMUS Cook

Rhysodesmus Cook, 1895, Ann. New York Acad. Sci., vol. 9, p. 5.—Pocock,
   1909, Diplopoda, *in* Biol Centr.-Amer., p. 188.—Attems, 1938, Das
   Tierreich, Lief. 69, p. 138.—Chamberlin, 1943, Bull. Univ. Utah,
   biol. ser., vol. 8, No. 3, p. 36.
Aporiaria Chamberlin, 1938, Proc. Biol. Soc. Washington, vol. 51, p. 207
   (generotype: *A. texicolens* Chamberlin).
GENEROTYPE: *Polydesmus limax* Saussure, by original designation.
RANGE: Southwestern Texas and New Mexico south through México to
Yucatán and Guatemala.
SPECIES: Sixty-one, of which two named forms (others occur) are known
from our limits.

Rhysodesmus anamesus (Chamberlin and Mulaik)

Aporiaria anamesa Chamberlin and Mulaik, 1941, Journ. New York Ent.
   Soc., vol. 49, p. 57.

TYPE: Collection of R. V. Chamberlin.
TYPE LOCALITY: Camp Mary White, near Cloudcroft, Otero County, New Mexico.
RANGE: Known only from type locality.

Rhysodesmus texicolens (Chamberlin)

Aporiaria texicolens Chamberlin, 1938, Proc. Biol. Soc. Washington, vol. 51, p. 207.
Rhysodesmus texicolens Chamberlin, 1943, Proc. Biol. Soc. Washington, vol. 56, p. 143.
TYPE: Collection of R. V. Chamberlin.
TYPE LOCALITY: Edinburg, Hidalgo County, Texas.
RANGE: Known only from type locality.

Genus RUDILORIA Causey

Rudiloria Causey, 1955, Proc. Biol. Soc. Washington, vol. 68, p. 28.
GENEROTYPE: *Rudiloria mohicana* Causey, by original designation.
RANGE: Southern Ohio.
SPECIES: One.

Rudiloria mohicana Causey

Rudiloria mohincana [sic] Causey, 1955, Proc. Biol. Soc. Washington, vol. 68, p. 28, fig. 6.
TYPE: Amer. Mus. Nat. Hist.
TYPE LOCALITY: Mohican State Park, Ashland County, Ohio.
RANGE: Known only from type locality.

Genus SEMIONELLUS Chamberlin

Semionellus Chamberlin, 1920, Proc. Biol. Soc. Washington, vol. 33, p. 97.
GENEROTYPE: *Polydesmus placidus* Wood, by original designation.
RANGE: Eastern United States.
SPECIES: One.

Semionellus placidus (Wood)

Polydesmus (Leptodesmus) placidus Wood, 1864, Proc. Acad. Nat. Sci. Philadelphia, p. 9.
Polydesmus (Leptodesmus) floridus Wood, 1864, Proc. Acad. Nat. Sci. Philadelphia, p. 9 (type locality: Michigan; type: probably lost).
Leptodesmus borealis Bollman, 1893, U. S. Nat. Mus. Bull. 46, p. 183 (type locality: Winona, Minnesota; type: U. S. Nat. Mus.).
Semionellus placidus Chamberlin, 1920, Proc. Biol. Soc. Washington, vol. 33, p. 97; 1947, Proc. Acad. Nat. Sci. Philadelphia, vol. 99, p. 24, fig. 3.
Chonaphe michigana Chamberlin, 1946, Proc. Biol. Soc. Washington, vol. 59, p. 31, fig. 1 (type locality: Midland County, Michigan; type: collection of R. V. Chamberlin).

Trichomorpha placida Attems, 1938, Das Tierreich, Lief. 69, p. 119.
TYPE: Probably lost.
TYPE LOCALITY: Michigan, without further indication.
RANGE: Minnesota and Michigan east to New York, south in the mountains through western Maryland and Virginia to Fort Benning, Georgia. Very sporadic in occurrence.

Genus SIGIRIA Chamberlin

Sigiria Chamberlin, 1939, Bull. Univ. Utah, biol. ser., vol. 5, No. 3, p. 9.
GENEROTYPE: *Sigiria scorpio* Chamberlin [=*rubromarginata* Bollman] by original designation.
RANGE: Western North Carolina.
SPECIES: Three; the association of these species based upon unpublished studies involving annectant and as yet unnamed species.

Sigiria intermedia (Hoffman)

Apheloria intermedia Hoffman, 1948, Journ. Washington Acad. Sci., vol. 38, p. 346, figs. 1, 2.
TYPE: U. S. Nat. Mus. (No. 1833).
TYPE LOCALITY: Asheville, Buncombe County, North Carolina.
RANGE: Known only from type locality.

Sigiria nigrimontis (Chamberlin)

Deltotaria nigrimontis Chamberlin, 1947, Proc. Acad. Nat. Sci. Philadelphia, vol. 99, p. 28, figs. 11, 12.
TYPE: Amer. Mus. Nat. Hist.
TYPE LOCALITY: Black Mountain, Buncombe County, North Carolina.
RANGE: The Black Mountains, in Buncombe and Yancey Counties, North Carolina.

Sigiria rubromarginata (Bollman)

Fontaria rubromarginata Bollman, 1888, Proc. U. S. Nat. Mus., vol. 10, p. 622.
Sigiria scorpio Chamberlin, Bull. Univ. Utah, biol. ser., vol. 5, No. 3, p. 9, figs. 26, 27 (type locality: Madison County, North Carolina; type: Collection of R. V. Chamberlin).
Sigiria rubromarginata Hoffman, 1950, Journ. Elisha Mitchell Sci. Soc., vol. 66, p. 25.
TYPE: U. S. Nat. Mus. (No. 320).
TYPE LOCALITY: Balsam, Jackson County, North Carolina.
RANGE: Western North Carolina, south and west of the French Broad River; Madison, Jackson, Swain, Haywood Counties.

Genus SIGMOCHEIR Chamberlin

Sigmocheir Chamberlin, 1951, Chicago Acad. Sci. Nat. Hist. Misc. No. 87, p. 4.

GENEROTYPE: *Sigmocheir calaveras* Chamberlin, by original designation.
RANGE: California.
SPECIES: One.

Sigmocheir calaveras Chamberlin

Sigmocheir calaveras Chamberlin, 1951, Chicago Acad. Sci. Nat. Hist. Misc. No. 87, p. 5, figs. 10, 11.
TYPE: Collection of R. V. Chamberlin.
TYPE LOCALITY: Crystal-Stanislaus Cave, Calaveras County, California.
RANGE: Known only from type locality.

Genus SIGMORIA Chamberlin

Sigmoria Chamberlin, 1939, Bull. Univ. Utah, biol. ser., vol. 5, No. 3, p. 7.—Hoffman, 1950, Amer. Mus. Novitates, No. 1462, p. 1.
GENEROTYPE: *Sigmoria munda* Chamberlin, by original designation.
RANGE: Southern Appalachians from West Virginia to South Carolina; central Tennessee; eastern Texas.
SPECIES: Fifteen.

Sigmoria aberrans Chamberlin

Sigmoria aberrans Chamberlin, 1939, Bull. Univ. Utah, biol. ser., vol. 5, No. 3, p. 8, figs. 24, 25.
TYPE: Collection of R. V. Chamberlin.
TYPE LOCALITY: Linville Falls, Avery County, North Carolina.
RANGE: Northwestern North Carolina (Avery, Watauga, and Ashe Counties) and adjacent southwestern Virginia (Patrick, Washington, Grayson, and Buchanan Counties), at elevations below 3,000 feet.

Sigmoria brachygon Chamberlin

Sigmoria brachygon Chamberlin, 1940, Ent. News, vol. 51, p. 283, fig. 2.
TYPE: Collection of R. V. Chamberlin.
TYPE LOCALITY: Glen Bald, Buncombe County, North Carolina.
RANGE: Known only from type locality.

Sigmoria conclusa Chamberlin

Sigmoria conclusa Chamberlin, 1939, Bull. Univ. Utah, biol. ser., vol. 5, No. 3, p. 8, figs. 22, 23.
TYPE: Collection of R. V. Chamberlin.
TYPE LOCALITY: Altapass, Mitchell County, North Carolina.
RANGE: Known only from type locality.

Sigmoria divergens Chamberlin

Sigmoria divergens Chamberlin, 1939, Bull. Univ. Utah, biol. ser., vol. 5, No. 3, p. 8, figs. 19–21.
TYPE: Collection of R. V. Chamberlin.
TYPE LOCALITY: Landrum, Spartanburg County, South Carolina.
RANGE: Known only from type locality.

Sigmoria evides (Bollman)

Fontaria evides Bollman, 1888, Proc. U. S. Nat. Mus., vol. 10, p. 621.
Sigmoria evides Chamberlin, 1939, Bull. Univ. Utah, biol. ser., vol. 5, No. 3, p. 7.
TYPE: U. S. Nat. Mus.
TYPE LOCALITY: Mossy Creek [Jefferson City], Jefferson County Tennessee.
RANGE: Known only from type locality.

Sigmoria furcifera Hoffman

Sigmoria furcifera Hoffman, 1949, Proc. U. S. Nat. Mus., vol. 99, p. 387, figs. 17, 18.
TYPE: U. S. Nat. Mus. (No. 1809).
TYPE LOCALITY: Near Pineville, Wyoming County, West Virginia.
RANGE: Known from several localities in extreme southern West Virginia.

Sigmoria gracilipes Chamberlin

Sigmoria gracilipes Chamberlin, 1947, Proc. Acad. Nat. Sci. Philadelphia, vol. 99, p. 29, fig. 15.
TYPE: Acad. Nat. Sci. Philadelphia (No. 9952).
TYPE LOCALITY: Pine Mountain, Bell County, Kentucky.
RANGE: Known only from type locality.

Sigmoria houstoni Chamberlin

Sigmoria houstoni Chamberlin, 1943, Proc. Biol. Soc. Washington, vol. 56, p. 144, fig. 1.
TYPE: Collection of R. V. Chamberlin.
TYPE LOCALITY: Houston, Harris County, Texas.
RANGE: Known only from type locality.

Sigmoria latior (Brölemann)

Fontaria latior Brölemann, 1900, Mém. Soc. Zool. France, vol. 13, p. 123, pl. 6, figs. 37–42.
Sigmoria latior Hoffman, 1950, Amer. Mus. Novitates No. 1462, p. 5.
TYPE: Mus. Hist. Nat., Paris.
TYPE LOCALITY: North Carolina, without further locality.
RANGE: Known only from a single locality, Tryon, Polk County, North Carolina.

Sigmoria mariona Chamberlin

Sigmoria mariona Chamberlin, 1939, Bull. Univ. Utah, biol. ser., vol. 5, No. 3, p. 9, figs. 17, 18.
TYPE: Collection of R. V. Chamberlin.
TYPE LOCALITY: Marion, McDowell County, North Carolina.
RANGE: Catawba River Valley, in McDowell and Burke Counties, North Carolina.

Sigmoria mimetica (Chamberlin)

Fontaria mimetica Chamberlin, 1918, Psyche, vol. 25, p. 29.
Sigmoria mimetica Hoffman, 1950, Amer. Mus. Novitates No. 1462, p. 6.
TYPE: Mus. Comp. Zool.
TYPE LOCALITY: Hillsboro Hills, near Nashville, Davidson County,
Tennessee.
RANGE: Known only from type locality.

Sigmoria munda Chamberlin

Sigmoria munda Chamberlin, 1939, Bull. Univ. Utah, biol. ser., vol. 5, No.
3, p. 8, figs. 15, 16.
TYPE: Collection of R. V. Chamberlin.
TYPE LOCALITY: Hot Springs, Madison County, North Carolina.
RANGE: Madison and Buncombe Counties, North Carolina.

Sigmoria nigrescens Hoffman

Sigmoria nigrescens Hoffman, 1950, Journ. Elisha Mitchell Sci. Soc., vol.
66, p. 28, figs. 28–32.
TYPE: U. S. Nat. Mus. (No. 1880).
TYPE LOCALITY: 1 mile west of intersection of South Carolina Highway
288 with U. S. Highway 178, near Rocky Bottom, Pickens County, South
Carolina.
RANGE: Known only from type locality.

Sigmoria stenogon Chamberlin

Sigmoria stenogon Chamberlin, 1942, Bull. Univ. Utah, biol. ser., vol. 6,
No. 8, p. 5, fig. 12.
TYPE: Collection of R. V. Chamberlin.
TYPE LOCALITY: Bennett Gap Road, Pisgah National Forest, Transylvania
County, North Carolina.
RANGE: Known only from type locality.

Sigmoria zyga Chamberlin

Sigmoria zyga Chamberlin, 1949, Proc. Biol. Soc. Washington, vol. 63
[sic,=62], p. 3, fig. 2.
TYPE: Collection of R. V. Chamberlin.
TYPE LOCALITY: Between Hot Springs and Paint Rock, Madison County,
North Carolina.
RANGE: Known only from type locality.

Genus THRINAXORIA Chamberlin and Hoffman

Thrinaxoria Chamberlin and Hoffman, 1950, Chicago Acad. Sci. Nat. Hist.
Misc. No. 71, p. 4.
GENEROTYPE: *Fontaria lampra* Chamberlin, by original designation.
RANGE: Gulf Coast region.
SPECIES: One.

52   U. S. NATIONAL MUSEUM BULLETIN 212

Thrinaxoria lampra (Chamberlin)

Fontaria lampra Chamberlin, 1918, Ann. Ent. Soc. Amer., vol. 11, p. 371.
Zinaria aberrans Chamberlin, 1942, Bull. Univ. Utah, biol. ser., vol. 6, No.
    8, p. 4, fig. 7 (type locality: Shreveport, Louisiana; type: collection of
    R. V. Chamberlin).
Thrinaxoria lampra Chamberlin and Hoffman, 1950, Chicago Acad. Sci.
    Nat. Hist. Misc. No. 71, p. 4.
TYPE: Mus. Comp. Zool.
TYPE LOCALITY: Creston, Natchitoches Parish, Louisiana.
RANGE: Known from Creston and Shreveport, Louisiana, and from Tusca-
loosa, Alabama.

Genus TUBAPHE Causey

Tubaphe Causey, 1954, Pan-Pacific Ent., vol. 30, p. 222.
GENEROTYPE: *Tubaphe levii* Causey, by original designation.
RANGE: Washington.
SPECIES: One.

Tubaphe levii Causey

Tubaphe levii Causey, 1954, Pan-Pacific Ent., vol. 30, p. 223, figs. 2–4.
TYPE: Amer. Mus. Nat. Hist.
TYPE LOCALITY: Graves Creek Camp Ground, Olympic National Forest,
Jefferson County, Washington.
RANGE: Known only from type locality.

Genus TUCORIA Chamberlin

Tucoria Chamberlin, 1943, Bull. Univ. Utah, biol. ser., vol. 8, No. 2, p. 17.
GENEROTYPE: *Fontaria kentuckiana* Causey, by original designation.
RANGE: Kentucky.
SPECIES: Four.

Tucoria calceata Causey

Tucoria calceata Causey, 1955, Proc. Biol. Soc. Washington, vol. 68, p. 28,
    figs. 4, 5.
TYPE: Amer. Mus. Nat. Hist.
TYPE LOCALITY: Tyrone, Anderson County, Kentucky.
RANGE: Known only from type locality.

Tucoria kentuckiana (Causey)

Fontaria kentuckiana Causey, 1942, Ent. News, vol. 53, p. 167, figs. 3, 4.
TYPE: Acad. Nat. Sci. Philadelphia.
TYPE LOCALITY: Cumberland Falls State Park, Cumberland County,
Kentucky.
RANGE: Known only from type locality.

Tucoria splendida (Causey)

Cleptoria splendida Causey, 1942, Ent. News, vol. 53, p. 167, fig. 5.
Tucoria splendida Chamberlin, 1943, Bull. Univ. Utah, biol. ser., vol. 8, No. 2, p. 17.
Tucoria dynama Chamberlin, 1947, Proc. Acad. Nat. Sci. Philadelphia, vol. 99, p. 29, fig. 16 (type locality: Pine Mountain, Bell County, Kentucky; type: Acad. Nat. Sci. Philadelphia, No. 9953).
TYPE: Acad. Nat. Sci. Philadelphia (No. 11261).
TYPE LOCALITY: Pine Mountain State Park, Bell County, Kentucky.
RANGE: Known only from type locality.

Tucoria viridicolens Hoffman

Tucoria viridicolens Hoffman, 1948, Journ. Washington Acad. Sci., vol. 38, p. 349, figs. 5, 6.
TYPE: U. S. Nat. Mus. (No. 1835).
TYPE LOCALITY: Trace Creek, Greensville, Greene County, Kentucky.
RANGE: Known only from type locality.

Genus **WAIMOKIA** Chamberlin

Waimokia Chamberlin, 1941, Bull. Univ. Utah, biol. ser., vol. 6, No. 5, p. 14.
GENEROTYPE: *Waimokia placera* Chamberlin, by original designation.
RANGE: California.
SPECIES: One.

Waimokia placera Chamberlin

Waimokia placera Chamberlin, 1941, Bull. Univ. Utah, biol. ser., vol. 6, No. 5, p. 14, fig. 27.
TYPE: Collection of R. V. Chamberlin.
TYPE LOCALITY: 9 miles north of Placerville, Tulare County, California.
RANGE: Known only from type locality.

Genus **XYSTOCHEIR** Cook

Xystocheir Cook, 1904, *in* Harriman Alaska Exped., vol. 8, p. 53.
Luminodesmus Loomis and Davenport, 1951, Journ. Washington Acad. Sci., vol. 41, p. 270 (generotype: *L. sequoiae* Loomis and Davenport).
GENEROTYPE: *Polydesmus dissectus* Wood, by original designation.
RANGE: Pacific Coast States.
SPECIES: Eight.

Xystocheir acuta Cook

Xystocheir acuta Cook, 1904, *in* Harriman Alaska Exped., vol. 8, p. 54.
TYPE: U. S. Nat. Mus.
TYPE LOCALITY: California, probably near Palo Alto.
RANGE: Known definitely only from Berkeley, California.

Xystocheir cooki Causey

Xystocheir cooki Causey, 1955, Proc. Biol. Soc. Washington, vol. 68, p. 91, fig. 3.

TYPE: Amer. Mus. Nat. Hist.

TYPE LOCALITY: Redwood Canyon, Sequoia National Park, Tulare County, California.

RANGE: Known only from type locality.

Xystocheir dissecta (Wood)

Polydesmus dissectus Wood, 1867, Proc. Acad. Nat. Sci. Philadelphia, p. 129.

Xystocheir dissecta Cook, 1904, *in* Harriman Alaska Exped., vol. 8, p. 55.

Xystocheir obtusa Cook, 1904, *in* Harriman Alaska Exped., vol. 8, p. 53, pl. 3, figs. 1a–c (type locality: not known; type: U. S. Nat. Mus., No. 795).

TYPE: Not known to exist.

TYPE LOCALITY: Fort Tejon, Kern County, California.

RANGE: Known only from type locality.

Xystocheir francisca Chamberlin

Xystocheir francisca Chamberlin, 1949, Journ. Washington Acad. Sci., vol. 39, p. 99, fig. 20.

TYPE: Collection of R. V. Chamberlin.

TYPE LOCALITY: San Francisco, California.

RANGE: Also known from Berkeley, California.

Xystocheir furcifer (Karsch)

Polydesmus (Fontaria) furcifer Karsch, 1881, Arch. Naturg., vol. 47, p. 39, pl. 3, fig. 12.

Xystocheir furcifer Cook, 1904, *in* Harriman Alaska Exped., vol. 8, p. 54.

TYPE: Berlin Museum.

TYPE LOCALITY: California.

RANGE: No definite localities known.

Xystocheir milpetas Chamberlin

Xystocheir milpetas Chamberlin, 1949, Journ. Washington Acad. Sci., vol. 39, p. 99, figs. 21, 22.

TYPE: Collection of R. V. Chamberlin.

TYPE LOCALITY: Milpetas, Santa Clara County, California.

RANGE: Known only from type locality.

Xystocheir sequoiae (Loomis and Davenport)

Lumizodesmus sequoiae Loomis and Davenport, 1951, Journ. Washington Acad. Sci., vol. 41, p. 271, fig. 1.

TYPE: U. S. Nat. Mus.

TYPE LOCALITY: Camp ground above Camp Nelson at junction of Belknap Creek and south fork of the middle fork of the Tulare River, Sequoia National Forest, Tulare County, California.
RANGE: Known only from type locality.

Xystocheir tularea Chamberlin

Xystocheir tularea Chamberlin, 1949, Journ. Washington Acad. Sci., vol. 39, p. 101, fig. 27.
TYPE: Collection of R. V. Chamberlin.
TYPE LOCALITY: Sugar Loaf Mountain, Tulare County, California.
RANGE: Known only from type locality.

Eurydesmidae of uncertain generic position

Fontaria luminosa Kenyon

Fontaria luminosa Kenyon, 1893, Publ. Nebraska Acad. Sci., vol. 3, p. 16.
TYPE: Unknown.
TYPE LOCALITY: Omaha, Nebraska.
Most likely to prove to be a species of *Apheloria*.

Fontaria oblonga Koch

Fontaria oblonga Koch, 1847, *in* Krit. Rev. Insect. Deutschlands, vol. 3, p. 175; 1863, Die Myriapoden, vol. 1, p. 73, pl. 32, fig. 64.
TYPE: Unknown.
TYPE LOCALITY: Pennsylvania.
This species may be, as Bollman suggested, related to *Mimuloria castanea*, but as the type was probably immature, it seems impossible to identify it with certainty.

Strongylosoma eruca Wood

Strongylosoma eruca Wood, 1864, Proc. Acad. Nat. Sci. Philadelphia, p. 8; 1865, Trans. Amer. Philos. Soc., vol. 13, p. 227.
Chonaphe eruca Cook, 1904, *in* Harriman Alaska Exped., vol. 8, p. 57.
TYPE: Probably not extant.
TYPE LOCALITY: Oregon.
Cook's assignation of this species to *Chonaphe* was wholly tentative, and he stated ". . . the generic position of this species cannot be determined with confidence from Wood's description of his badly preserved alcoholic specimens."

Family EURYURIDAE Pocock

Euryurinae Pocock, 1909, Diplopoda, *in* Biol. Centr.-Amer., p. 147.
Euryuridae Chamberlin, 1918, Bull. Mus. Comp. Zool., vol. 62, p. 249.
— Hoffman, 1954, Journ. Washington Acad. Sci., vol. 44, p. 49.

KEY TO THE NORTH AMERICAN SUBFAMILIES OF EURYURIDAE

1. Tibiotarsus of male gonopod expanded into a broad sheath, which shields or partially
   encloses the solenomerite, and which often has one or more small processes of its
   own . . . . APHELIDESMINAE (p. 56)
   Tibiotarsus of male gonopod very slender or completely rudimentary; no separate
   solenomerite present . . . . EURYURINAE (p. 56)

Subfamily APHELIDESMINAE Brölemann

Aphelidesminae Brölemann, 1916, Ann. Soc. Ent. France, vol. 84,
    p. 584.—Hoffman, 1954, Journ. Washington Acad. Sci., vol. 44, p. 57.

Genus APHELIDESMUS Brölemann

Trachelorachis Silvestri, 1898, Bull. Mus. Zool. Anat. Comp. Univ. Torino,
    vol. 13, No. 324, p. 5 (preoccupied by Trachelorachis Agassiz 1846,
    an emendation of Trachelorachys Hope 1841) (generotype, T. rivicola
    Silvestri).
Aphelidesmus Brölemann, 1898, Ann. Soc. Ent. France, vol. 67, p. 266.—
    Attems, 1937, Das Tierreich, Lief. 68, p. 128.
Trachelacantha Berg, 1899, Comun. Mus. Nac. Buenos Aires, vol. 1, No. 3,
    p. 77 (new name for Trachelorachis Silvestri).
GENEROTYPE: Aphelidesmus hermaphroditus Brölemann, by original
designation.
RANGE: Northeastern Brasil and British Guiana west to Ecuador, north
through Central America and Mexico to southern Texas.
SPECIES: Twenty-nine, of which but one is known within our limits.

Aphelidesmus tertius (Chamberlin)

Semionellus tertius Chamberlin, 1948, Ent. News, vol. 59, p. 269, figs. 1, 2.
TYPE: Collection of R. V. Chamberlin.
TYPE LOCALITY: Near Kerrville, Kerr County, Texas.
RANGE: Known only from type locality.

Subfamily EURYURINAE Hoffman

Euryurinae Hoffman, 1954, Journ. Washington Acad. Sci., vol. 44, p. 57.

Genus EURYURUS Koch

Euryurus Koch, 1847, in Krit. Rev. Insect. Deutschlands, vol. 3, p. 591.
Eutheatus Attems, 1938, Das Tierreich, Lief. 69, p. 294 (new name for
    Euryurus Koch, thought by Attems to be preoccupied by the nomen
    nudum Euryurus Rafinesque, 1815).
GENEROTYPE: Polydesmus erythropygus Brandt, by subsequent designa-
tion of Silvestri, 1896.
RANGE: Eastern United States.
SPECIES: Three, which are probably only geographic races of a single
polytypic species.

Euryurus australis Bollman

Euryurus erythropygus australis Bollman, 1889, Proc. U. S. Nat. Mus., vol. 11, p. 346.

Euryurus falcipes Loomis, 1943, Bull. Mus. Comp. Zool., vol. 92, No. 7, p. 403, fig. 15 (type locality: Torreya State Park, Liberty County, Florida; type: Mus. Comp. Zool.).

Euryurus australis Hoffman, 1951, Proc. U. S. Nat. Mus., vol. 102, p. 238.

TYPE: U. S. Nat. Mus.

TYPE LOCALITY: Indian Springs, Bibb County, Georgia.

RANGE: Western Florida north to extreme western South Carolina and central Kentucky.

Euryurus erythropygus (Brandt)

Polydesmus erythropygus Brandt, 1841, Recueil, p. 134.

Euryurus maculatus Koch, 1847, *in* Krit. Rev. Insect. Deutchlands, vol. 3, p. 138 (type locality and present location of type both unknown).

Polydesmus carolinensis Saussure, 1859, Linnaea Ent., vol. 13, p. 325 (type locality: "Carolina"; type: Geneva Museum).

Polydesmus (Euryurus) erythropygus Saussure and Humbert, 1872, Études sur les myriapodes, *in* Miss. Sci. Mexique, Zool., pt. 6, sect. 2, p. 26.

TYPE: Formerly in the Berlin Museum; present location unknown.

TYPE LOCALITY: Georgetown, Georgetown County, South Carolina.

RANGE: North and South Carolina, eastern Tennessee. Exact limits of range not known.

Euryurus leachii (Gray)

Polydesmus leachii Gray, 1832, *in* Griffith, The animal kingdom, . . . by the Baron Cuvier, vol. 15, plate 135, fig. 3.

Euryurus aculeatus Causey, 1952, Chicago Acad. Sci. Nat. Hist. Misc. No. 106, p. 9, fig. 8 (type locality: Giant City State Park, Madison County, Illinois; type: Amer. Mus. Nat. Hist.).

TYPE: British Mus. (Nat. Hist.).

TYPE LOCALITY: Unknown.

RANGE: Illinois and southern Wisconsin, east to Ohio, western Pennsylvania, and northern Kentucky.

Genus AUTURUS Chamberlin

Auturus Chamberlin, 1942, Bull. Univ. Utah, biol. ser., vol. 6, No. 8, p. 7.

GENEROTYPE: *Auturus phanus* Chamberlin, by original designation.

RANGE: Mississippi Valley from Minnesota to Louisiana, east to Georgia.

SPECIES: Ten.

Auturus becki Chamberlin

Auturus becki Chamberlin, 1951, Great Basin Nat., vol. 11, No. 1–2, p. 29, fig. 2.

TYPE: Collection of R. V. Chamberlin.

TYPE LOCALITY: Suwanee River, Florida.

RANGE: Known only from type locality.

Auturus dixianus Chamberlin

Auturus dixianus Chamberlin, 1942, Bull. Univ. Utah, biol. ser., vol. 6, No. 8, p. 8.

TYPE: Collection of R. V. Chamberlin.

TYPE LOCALITY: Covington, St. Tammany Parish, Louisiana.

RANGE: Known only from type locality.

Auturus evides (Bollman)

Paradesmus evides Bollman, 1887, Ent. Amer., vol. 2, p. 229.

Auturus evides Chamberlin, 1942, Bull. Univ. Utah, biol. ser., vol. 6, No. 8, p. 7.

TYPE: U. S. Nat. Mus.

TYPE LOCALITY: Winona, Winona County, Minnesota.

RANGE: Minnesota, eastern Iowa, northern Illinois.

Auturus florus Causey

Auturus florus Causey, 1950, Ent. News, vol. 61, p. 37, figs. 1, 2.

TYPE: Acad. Nat. Sci. Philadelphia (No. 11264).

TYPE LOCALITY: Hemmed-in-Hollow, Compton, Newton County, Arkansas.

RANGE: Known only from type locality.

Auturus georgianus Chamberlin

Auturus georgianus Chamberlin, 1942, Bull. Univ. Utah, biol. ser., vol. 6, No. 8, p. 8, fig. 22.

TYPE: Collection of R. V. Chamberlin.

TYPE LOCALITY: 13 miles south of Savannah, Chatham County, Georgia.

RANGE: Known only from type locality.

Auturus louisianus (Chamberlin)

Euryurus louisiana Chamberlin, 1918, Ann. Ent. Soc. Amer., vol. 11, p. 371.

Auturus louisianus Chamberlin, 1942, Bull. Univ. Utah, biol. ser., vol. 6, No. 8, p. 7.

TYPE: Mus. Comp. Zool.

TYPE LOCALITY: Creston, Natchitoches Parish, Louisiana.

RANGE: Known only from type locality.

Auturus mcclurkini Causey

Auturus mcclurkini Causey, 1955, Proc. Biol. Soc. Washington, vol. 68, p. 23, fig. 1.

TYPE: Amer. Mus. Nat. Hist.
TYPE LOCALITY: Jackson, Madison County [Stated to be Jackson County in the original description], Tennessee.
RANGE: Known only from type locality.

Auturus mimetes Chamberlin

Auturus mimetes Chamberlin, 1942, Bull. Univ. Utah, biol. ser., vol. 6, No. 8, p. 8, fig. 21.
TYPE: Collection of R. V. Chamberlin.
TYPE LOCALITY: Near Selma, Jefferson County, Missouri.
RANGE: Ozark region of Missouri, known from the type locality and from Chadwick, Christian County.

Auturus phanus Chamberlin

Auturus phanus Chamberlin, 1942, Bull. Univ. Utah, biol. ser., vol. 6, No. 8, p. 7, fig. 20.
TYPE: Collection of R. V. Chamberlin.
TYPE LOCALITY: Greensburg, St. Helena Parish, Louisiana.
RANGE: Known only from type locality.

Auturus scotius Chamberlin

Auturus scotius Chamberlin, 1942, Bull. Univ. Utah, biol. ser., vol. 6, No. 8, p. 9, fig. 23.
TYPE: Collection of R. V. Chamberlin.
TYPE LOCALITY: Darlington, St. Helena Parish, Louisiana.
RANGE: Known only from type locality.

Genus SINGULIURUS Causey

Singuliurus Causey, 1955, Proc. Biol. Soc. Washington, vol. 68, p. 23.
GENEROTYPE: *Singuliurus mississippiensis* Causey, by original designation.
RANGE: Mississippi.
SPECIES: One.

Singuliurus mississippiensis Causey

Singuliurus mississippiensis Causey, 1955, Proc. Biol. Soc. Washington, vol. 68, p. 23, fig. 2.
TYPE: Amer. Mus. Nat. Hist.
TYPE LOCALITY: Van Cleave, Jackson County, Mississippi.
RANGE: Known only from type locality.

Family NEARCTODESMIDAE Chamberlin and Hoffman

Nearctodesmidae Chamberlin and Hoffman, 1950, Chicago Acad. Sci. Nat. Hist. Misc. No. 71, p. 1.

Genus ERGODESMUS Chamberlin

Ergodesmus Chamberlin, 1949, Journ. Washington Acad. Sci., vol. 39, No. 3, p. 94.

GENEROTYPE: *Ergodesmus compactus* Chamberlin, by original designation.

RANGE: Washington.

SPECIES: One.

Ergodesmus compactus Chamberlin

Ergodesmus compactus Chamberlin, 1949, Journ. Washington Acad. Sci., vol. 39, No. 3, p. 94, fig. 1.

TYPE: Collection of R. V. Chamberlin.

TYPE LOCALITY: Between Goldendale and Mayfield, Klickitat County, Washington.

RANGE: Known also from Richland and Orondo, Washington.

Genus KEPOLYDESMUS Chamberlin

Kepolydesmus Chamberlin, 1910, Ann. Ent. Soc. America, vol. 3, No. 4, p. 246; 1949, Journ. Washington Acad. Sci., vol. 39, No. 3, p. 94.

GENEROTYPE: *Kepolydesmus anderisus* Chamberlin.

RANGE: Northwestern United States.

SPECIES: Four.

Kepolydesmus anderisus Chamberlin

Kepolydesmus anderisus Chamberlin, 1910, Ann. Ent. Soc. Amer., vol. 3, No. 4, p. 246, pl. 36, figs. 6–9, pl. 37, figs. 1–4.

TYPE: Collection of R. V. Chamberlin.

TYPE LOCALITY: Kendrick, Latah County, Idaho.

RANGE: Also recorded from Roselake, Fourth of July Canyon, Kootenai County, Idaho.

Kepolydesmus hesperus Chamberlin

Kepolydesmus hesperus Chamberlin, 1949, Journ. Washington Acad. Sci., vol. 39, No. 3, p. 94, fig. 3.

TYPE: Collection of R. V. Chamberlin.

TYPE LOCALITY: Ashland, Jackson County, Oregon.

RANGE: Known from Jackson and Douglas Counties, Oregon.

Kepolydesmus mimus Chamberlin

Kepolydesmus mimus Chamberlin, 1947, Proc. Biol. Soc. Washington, vol. 60, p. 10, fig. 3.

TYPE: Collection of R. V. Chamberlin.

TYPE LOCALITY: Martha Creek, Carson, Skamania County, Washington.

RANGE: Known only from type locality.

Kepolydesmus pungo Chamberlin

Kepolydesmus pungo Chamberlin, 1949, Journ. Washington Acad. Sci., vol. 39, p. 95, fig. 4.

TYPE: Collection of R. V. Chamberlin.

TYPE LOCALITY: Horsetail Falls, Oregon.

RANGE: Known also from Latourell Falls, Oregon.

Genus NEARCTODESMUS Silvestri

Nearctodesmus Silvestri, 1910, Zool. Anz., vol. 35, p. 364.—Chamberlin, 1949, Journ. Washington Acad. Sci., vol. 39, p. 96.

GENEROTYPE: *Polydesmus cerasinus* Wood, by original designation.

RANGE: Northwestern North America.

SPECIES: Thirteen.

Nearctodesmus amissus Chamberlin

Nearctodesmus amissus Chamberlin, 1949, Journ. Washington Acad. Sci., vol. 39, p. 96, fig. 5.

TYPE: Collection of R. V. Chamberlin.

TYPE LOCALITY: Oregon, without further locality.

RANGE: Oregon and Vancouver, British Columbia.

Nearctodesmus boydi Chamberlin

Nearctodesmus boydi Chamberlin, 1951, Chicago Acad. Sci. Nat. Hist. Misc. No. 87, p. 2, figs. 6, 7.

TYPE: Prov. Mus. British Columbia.

TYPE LOCALITY: Lake Cowichan, Vancouver Island, British Columbia.

RANGE: Known only from type locality.

Nearctodesmus brunnior Chamberlin

Nearctodesmus brunnior Chamberlin, 1949, Journ. Washington Acad. Sci., vol. 39, p. 96, fig. 6.

TYPE: Collection of R. V. Chamberlin.

TYPE LOCALITY: 9 miles north of Crescent, Del Norte County, California.

RANGE: Known only from type locality.

Nearctodesmus campicolens Chamberlin

Nearctodesmus campicolens Chamberlin, 1949, Journ. Washington Acad. Sci., vol. 39, p. 96, fig. 7.

TYPE: Collection of R. V. Chamberlin.

TYPE LOCALITY: Red Wood Fort, Route 101, Prairie Creek Park, Mendocino County, California.

RANGE: Known only from type locality.

Nearctodesmus carli Chamberlin

Nearctodesmus carli Chamberlin, 1951, Chicago Acad. Sci. Nat. Hist. Misc. No. 87, p. 2, figs. 4, 5.

TYPE: Prov. Mus. British Columbia.

TYPE LOCALITY: Scott Island, British Columbia.

RANGE: Known from Santine, Cox, Lanz, Triangle, and Scott Islands, British Columbia.

Nearctodesmus cerasinus (Wood)

Polydesmus cerasinus Wood, 1864, Proc. Acad. Nat. Sci. Philadelphia, p. 6.

Nearctodesmus cerasinus Silvestri, 1910, Zool. Anz., vol. 35, p. 364.

TYPE: Lost.

TYPE LOCALITY: Oregon.

RANGE: Northern California to British Columbia.

Nearctodesmus cochlearius Causey

Nearctodesmus cochlearius Causey, 1954, Ann. Ent. Soc. Amer., vol. 47, p. 82, figs. 4–6.

TYPE: Amer. Mus. Nat. Hist.

TYPE LOCALITY: Seattle, King County, Washington.

RANGE: Known only from type locality.

Nearctodesmus insulanus (Chamberlin)

Kepolydesmus insulanus Chamberlin, 1941, Bull. Univ. Utah, biol. ser., vol. 6, No. 4, p. 25, fig. 47.

TYPE: Collection of R. V. Chamberlin.

TYPE LOCALITY: Vancouver Island, British Columbia.

RANGE: Known only from type locality.

Nearctodesmus malkini Chamberlin

Nearctodesmus malkini Chamberlin, 1951, Chicago Acad. Sci. Nat. Hist. Misc. No. 87, p. 1, 2.

TYPE: California Acad. Sci.

TYPE LOCALITY: Brookings, Curry County, Oregon.

RANGE: Known only from type locality.

Nearctodesmus olympus Causey

Nearctodesmus olympus Causey, 1954, Ann. Ent. Soc. Amer., vol. 47, p. 84, figs. 7, 8 .

TYPE: Amer. Mus. Nat. Hist.

TYPE LOCALITY: Olympic Hot Springs, Clallam County, Washington.

RANGE: Known only from type locality.

Nearctodesmus pseustes Chamberlin

Nearctodesmus pseustes Chamberlin, 1949, Journ. Washington Acad. Sci., vol. 39, p. 96, fig. 8.

TYPE: Collection of R. V. Chamberlin.

TYPE LOCALITY: Boyer (location unknown), Oregon.

RANGE: Known also from Comstock, Oregon.

Nearctodesmus renigens Chamberlin

Nearctodesmus renigens Chamberlin, 1949, Journ. Washington Acad. Sci., vol. 39, p. 97, fig. 9.

TYPE: Collection of R. V. Chamberlin.

TYPE LOCALITY: Oregon: probably near Corvallis.

RANGE: Known only from type locality.

Nearctodesmus salix Chamberlin

Nearctodesmus salix Chamberlin, 1949, Journ. Washington Acad. Sci., vol. 39, p. 97, fig. 10.

TYPE: Collection of R. V. Chamberlin.

TYPE LOCALITY: 12 miles west of Willow Creek, Lassen County, California.

RANGE: Known only from type locality.

Family POLYDESMIDAE Leach

Polydesmidae (in part) Leach, 1815, Trans. Linn. Soc. London, vol. 11, p. 381.—Meinert, 1868, Naturh. Tidsskr., ser. 3, vol. 5, p. 23.— Wood, 1865, Trans. Amer. Philos. Soc., vol. 13, p. 212.

Polydesminae Bollman, 1893, U. S. Nat. Mus. Bull. 46, p. 159.

Polydesmidae Porath, 1872, Öfvers. Vet.-Akad. Förh., No. 5, p. 9.—Cook, 1895, Ann. New York Acad. Sci., vol. 9, p. 5.—Attems, 1940, Das Tierreich, Lief. 70, p. 1.

Genus ANTRIADESMUS Loomis

Antriadesmus Loomis, 1943, Bull. Mus. Comp. Zool., vol. 92, p. 408.

GENEROTYPE: *Antriadesmus fragilis* Loomis, by original designation.

RANGE: Central Kentucky.

SPECIES: One.

Antriadesmus fragilis Loomis

Antriadesmus fragilis Loomis, 1943, Bull. Mus. Comp. Zool., vol. 92, p. 409, fig. 18a–b and pl. 1, fig. 6.

TYPE: Mus. Comp. Zool.

TYPE LOCALITY: White's Cave, Edmondson County, Kentucky.

RANGE: Known only from type locality.

Genus BRACHYDESMUS Heller

Brachydesmus Heller, 1858, Sitz.-ber. Akad. Wiss., Wien, vol. 26, p. 318.— Attems, 1940, Das Tierreich, Lief. 70, p. 86.

GENEROTYPE: *Brachydesmus subterraneus* Heller, by monotypy.

RANGE: Palearctic and Nearctic areas.

SPECIES: About 105 species and subspecies have been described from the Old World, of which at least one, *B. superus* Latzel, has been introduced into this country, where it has become widely distributed in the eastern and middle-western States.   From the western States four species, as listed below, have been referred to the genus.   For these species, a closer comparative study seems indicated.

Brachydesmus californicus Chamberlin

Brachydesmus californicus Chamberlin, 1918, Pomona Coll. Journ. Ent. Zool., vol. 10, No. 1, p. 9.

TYPE: Mus. Comp. Zool.

TYPE LOCALITY: Stanford, Santa Clara County, California.

RANGE: Known only from the type locality.

Brachydesmus cavicola (Packard)

Polydesmus cavicola Packard, 1877, Bull. U. S. Geol. Geogr. Surv. Terr. (Hayden), vol. 3, p. 161, figs. 6, 6a–d.

TYPE: Not known to exist.

TYPE LOCALITY: Clinton's Cave, Tooele County, Utah.

RANGE: Known only from type locality.

Brachydesmus hastingsus Chamberlin

Brachydesmus hastingsus Chamberlin, 1941, Bull. Univ. Utah, biol. ser., vol. 6, No. 4, p. 27, figs. 18, 19.

TYPE: Collection of R. V. Chamberlin.

TYPE LOCALITY: Hastings Reservation, Monterey County, California.

RANGE: Known only from the type locality.

Brachydesmus superus Latzel

Brachydesmus superus Latzel, 1884, Myr. Öst.-Ung. Monarch., vol. 2, p. 130, pl. 6, figs. 68, 69.—Jawlowski, 1939, Frag. Faun. Mus. Zool. Polonici, vol. 4, p. 150.—Attems, 1940, Das Tierreich, Lief. 70, p. 120.

Brachydesmus gladiolus Williams and Hefner, 1928, Bull. Ohio Biol. Surv., No. 18, p. 113, fig. 12c (type locality: Allen County, Ohio: location of types unknown).

Brachydesmus pallidus Loomis, 1939, Bull. Mus. Comp. Zool., vol. 86, p. 191, fig. 14 (type locality: Charleston, West Virginia; type: Mus. Comp. Zool.).

Brachydesmus dux Chamberlin, 1940, Ent. News, vol. 51, p. 284, fig. 4 (type locality: Durham, North Carolina; type: collection of R. V. Chamberlin).

TYPE: Present location unknown.

TYPE LOCALITY: Prater, near Wien, Austria.

RANGE: General over eastern Europe, widely distributed elsewhere by commerce.   In the United States it is often abundant in gardens and cultivated areas, having been collected in North Carolina, Virginia, Pennsylvania, West Virginia, Ohio, and Michigan.

Brachydesmus yosemitensis Causey

Brachydesmus (*Brachydesmus*) *yosemitensis* Causey, 1954, Pan-Pacific Ent., vol. 30, No. 3, p. 224, fig. 5.

TYPE: Amer. Mus. Nat. Hist.

TYPE LOCALITY: Vernal Falls, Yosemite National Park, California.

RANGE: Known only from the type locality.

Genus CHAETASPIS Bollman

Chaetaspis Bollman, 1887, Ent. Amer., vol. 3, p. 45.

GENEROTYPE: *Chaetaspis albus* Bollman, by monotypy.

RANGE: Central eastern United States.

SPECIES: Two.

Chaetaspis albus Bollman

Chaetaspis albus Bollman, 1887, Ent. Amer., vol. 3, p. 46.

TYPE: Collection of Indiana Univ.

TYPE LOCALITY: Bloomington, Monroe County, Indiana.

RANGE: Recorded from Kentucky and Indiana.

Chaetaspis ohionis Causey

Chaetaspis albus (not Bollman, 1887) Williams and Hefner, 1928, Bull. Ohio Biol. Surv., No. 18, p. 110, fig. 12a.

Chaetaspis ohionis Causey, 1950, Ent. News, vol. 61, No. 7, p. 197.

TYPE: Collection of Miami (Ohio) Univ.

TYPE LOCALITY: Washington and Athens Counties, Ohio.

RANGE: Known only from type locality.

Genus DIXIDESMUS Chamberlin

Dixidesmus Chamberlin, 1943, Bull. Univ. Utah, biol. ser., vol. 8, No. 2, p. 18.

GENEROTYPE: *Dixidesmus tallulanus* Chamberlin, by original designation.

RANGE: Eastern United States, dominantly in the Appalachian region.

SPECIES: Eleven.

Dixidesmus branneri (Bollman)

Polydesmus branneri Bollman, 1887, Proc. U. S. Nat. Mus., vol. 11, p. 620.—Loomis, 1943, Bull. Mus. Comp. Zool., vol. 92, No. 7, p. 405, fig. 16, and pl. 1, fig. 4.

Polydesmus conlatus Chamberlin, 1943, Proc. Biol. Soc. Washington, vol. 56, p. 36, fig. 5 (type locality: Gatlinburg, Tennessee; type: collection of R. V. Chamberlin).

TYPE: U. S. Nat. Mus.

TYPE LOCALITY: Mossy Creek [Jefferson City], Jefferson County, Tennessee.

RANGE: From the Great Smokies north to eastern Kentucky and central-western Virginia.

Dixidesmus catskillus Chamberlin

Dixidesmus catskillus Chamberlin, 1947, Proc. Acad. Nat. Sci. Philadelphia, vol. 99, p. 24, fig. 2.

TYPE: Acad. Nat. Sci. Philadelphia (No. 9943).

TYPE LOCALITY: Catskill, Greene County, New York.

RANGE: Known only from type locality.

Dixidesmus christianus Chamberlin

Dixidesmus christianus Chamberlin, 1946, Proc. Biol. Soc. Washington, vol. 59, p. 142, fig. 4.

TYPE: Collection of R. V. Chamberlin.

TYPE LOCALITY: Pass Christian, Harrison County, Mississippi.

RANGE: Known only from type locality.

Dixidesmus echinogon (Chamberlin)

Polydesmus echinogon Chamberlin, 1942, Bull. Univ. Utah, biol. ser., vol. 6, No. 8, p. 10, fig. 33.

Dixidesmus echinogon Chamberlin, 1943, Bull. Univ. Utah, biol. ser., vol. 8, No. 2, p. 18.

TYPE: Collection of R. V. Chamberlin.

TYPE LOCALITY: Shawanese (Harvey's Lake), Luzerne County, Pennsylvania.

RANGE: Thus far recorded only from type locality and Elmira, Chemung County, New York.

Dixidesmus erasus (Loomis)

Polydesmus erasus Loomis, 1943, Bull. Mus. Comp. Zool., vol. 92, No. 7, p. 406, fig. 17, and pl. 5, fig. 4.

Dixidesmus humilidens Chamberlin, 1943, Bull. Univ. Utah, biol. ser., vol. 8, No. 2, p. 20, fig. 36 (type locality: Gainesville, Hall County, Georgia; type: collection of R. V. Chamberlin).

Dixidesmus erasus Causey, 1952, Chicago Acad. Sci. Nat. Hist. Misc. No. 106, p. 7.

TYPE: Mus. Comp. Zool.

TYPE LOCALITY: Huntsville, Madison County, Alabama.

RANGE: Northern Georgia and Alabama, north through Tennessee and Kentucky to Pope County, Illinois.

Dixidesmus gausodicrorhachus Johnson

Dixidesmus gausodicrorhachus Johnson, 1954, Chicago Acad. Sci. Nat. Hist. Misc. No. 137, p. 1, fig. 1a–d.

TYPE: U. S. Nat. Mus. (No. 2117).

TYPE LOCALITY: West side of Garnet Lake, Mackinaw County, Michigan.

RANGE: Recorded from 19 Counties in northern Michigan.

Dixidesmus nitidus (Bollman)

Polydesmus nitidus Bollman, 1887, Ent. Amer., vol. 3, p. 45.
TYPE: Collection of Indiana Univ.
TYPE LOCALITY: Pensacola, Escambia County, Florida.
RANGE: Known only from the type locality.

Dixidesmus penicillus Chamberlin

Dixidesmus penicillus Chamberlin, 1943, Bull. Univ. Utah, biol. ser., vol. 8, No. 2, p. 19, fig. 35.
TYPE: Collection of R. V. Chamberlin.
TYPE LOCALITY: Clarksville, Habersham County, Georgia.
RANGE: Known only from Clarksville and Neel Gap, in northern Georgia.

Dixidesmus phanus Chamberlin

Dixidesmus phanus Chamberlin, 1951, Great Basin Nat., vol. 11, No. 1–2, p. 27, fig. 1.
TYPE: Collection of R. V. Chamberlin.
TYPE LOCALITY: Suwannee River, Florida.
RANGE: Known only from type locality.

Dixidesmus sylvicolens Chamberlin

Dixidesmus sylvicolens Chamberlin, 1943, Bull. Univ. Utah, biol. ser., vol. 8, No. 2, p. 20, fig. 33.
TYPE: Collection of R. V. Chamberlin.
TYPE LOCALITY: 7 miles north of Sylvania, Screven County, Georgia.
RANGE: Known only from type locality.

Dixidesmus tallulanus Chamberlin

Dixidesmus tallulanus Chamberlin, 1943, Bull. Univ. Utah, biol ser., vol. 8, No. 2, p. 19, fig. 34.
TYPE: Collection of R. V. Chamberlin.
TYPE LOCALITY: Between Clayton and Tallulah Falls, Rabun County, Georgia.
RANGE: Known also from western North Carolina (Macon County) and the Great Smokies in Tennessee (Sevier County).

Genus POLYDESMUS Latreille

Polydesmus Latreille, 1802, Histoire naturelle . . . des crustacés et des insectes, vol. 3, p. 44.—Attems, 1940, Das Tierreich, Lief. 70, p. 3.
GENEROTYPE: *Julus complanatus* Linnaeus, by monotypy.
RANGE: Palearctic region. The American representatives were introduced and have become established in many places throughout the country.
SPECIES: About 145 species and subspecies have been described, of which five have been found in North America.

Polydesmus angustus Latzel

Polydesmus complanatus angustus Latzel, 1884, Bull. Soc. Sci. Nat. Rouen, ann. 19, ser. 2, pp. 262, 267.

Polydesmus verhoeffi var. *angustatus* Attems, 1940, Das Tierreich, Lief. 70, p. 12.

TYPE: Vienna Museum.

TYPE LOCALITY: Normandie, France.

RANGE: Generally distributed over western Europe. In America it has been found in Louisiana and also at Mexico City.

Polydesmus complanatus (Linnaeus)

Julus complanatus Linnaeus, 1761, Fauna Svecica, ed. 2, p. 502.

Polydesmus complanatus Latreille, 1802, Histoire naturelle . . . des crustacés et des insectes, vol. 3, p. 44.—Attems, 1940, Das Tierreich, Lief. 70, p. 6, fig. 2.—Chamberlin, 1951, Great Basin Nat., vol. 11, p. 27.

TYPE: Not known to exist.

TYPE LOCALITY: Europe.

RANGE: Europe and eastern North America (e. g., New Jersey), where introduced and established.

Polydesmus denticulatus Koch

Polydesmus denticulatus+scabratus Koch, 1847, *in* Krit, Rev. Insect. Deutschlands, vol. 3, pp. 135, 136.—Latzel, 1884, Myr. Öst.-Ung. Monarch., vol. 2, p. 141, pl. 5, figs. 59, 60.—Palmén, 1952, Ann. Zool. Soc. 'Vanamo', vol. 15, No. 1, p. 14.

TYPE: Location unknown.

TYPE LOCALITY: Germany.

RANGE: Europe, from France to Sweden and Norway. Known in North America from Newfoundland.

Polydesmus inconstans Latzel

Polydesmus inconstans Latzel, 1884, Bull. Soc. Sci. Nat. Rouen, ser. 2, ann. 19, p. 269, pl. 1, fig. 3.—Palmén, 1952, Ann. Zool. Soc. 'Vanamo', vol. 15, p. 13.

Polydesmus distractus Latzel, 1888, Bull. Soc. Hist. Nat. Toulouse, Proc. Verb., p. lxxxv.

Polydesmus coriaceus var. *borealis* Porat, 1889, Ent. Tidskr., vol. 10, p. 71.

Polydesmus rhenanus Verhoeff, 1891, Berliner Ent. Zeitschr., vol. 36, p. 121, pl. 5, fig. 1.

Polydesmus coriaceus (not Porat) Schubart, 1934, *in* Dahl, Die Tierwelt Deutschlands, Teil 28, p. 165, fig. 264.—Chamberlin, 1947, Proc. Acad. Nat. Sci. Philadelphia, vol. 99, p. 22.

Polydesmus testi Bollman, 1888, Proc. U. S. Nat. Mus., vol. 10, p. 617 (type locality: Indianapolis, Indiana; type: U. S. Nat. Mus.).

Polydesmus socarnius Chamberlin, 1910, Ann. Ent. Soc. Amer., vol. 3, p. 252 (type locality: Salt Lake City, Utah; location of type unknown).

Polydesmus hortus Williams and Hefner, 1928, Bull. Ohio Biol. Surv., No. 18, p. 113, fig. 13d (type locality: Athens County, Ohio; no types designated).

Polydesmus pronomeutes Chamberlin, 1942, Bull. Univ. Utah, biol. ser., vol. 6, No. 8, p. 9, fig. 29 (type locality: Fort Collins, Colorado; type: collection of R. V. Chamberlin).

Polydesmus wheeleri Causey, 1950, Ent. News, vol. 61, p. 197, figs. 6, 7 (type locality: Grand Fork, North Dakota; type: Acad. Nat. Sci. Philadelphia).

TYPE: Vienna Museum.

TYPE LOCALITY: Europe.

RANGE: Widespread in Europe; introduced into North America, where it occurs across the continent in cultivated areas from Newfoundland and the New England States as far west as Oregon and British Columbia.

Polydesmus (Hormobrachium) racovitzai Brölemann

Polydesmus racovitzai Brölemann, 1910, Arch Zool. Expér. Gén., ser. 5, vol. 5, p. 352, figs. 27–33.

Polydesmus (Hormobrachium) racovitzai Attems, 1940, Das Tierreich, Lief. 70, p. 48, fig. 63.—Causey, 1954, Ann. Ent. Soc. Amer., vol. 47, p. 82.

TYPE: Probably Paris Museum.

TYPE LOCALITY: Pyrenees Mountains at Banyuls-sur-Mer, France.

RANGE: Southern Europe. Introduced into North America at Seattle, Washington.

Genus PSEUDOPOLYDESMUS Attems

Pseudopolydesmus Attems, 1899, Denkschr. Akad. Wiss., Wien, vol. 67, p. 270; 1940, Das Tierreich, Lief. 70, p. 139.—Chamberlin, 1943, Bull. Univ. Utah, biol. ser., vol. 8, No. 2, p. 17.

GENEROTYPE: *Polydesmus canadensis* Newport, by monotypy.

RANGE: North America east of the Rocky Mountains.

SPECIES: Eleven.

Pseudopolydesmus caddo Chamberlin

Pseudopolydesmus caddo Chamberlin, 1949, Journ. Washington Acad. Sci., vol. 39, p. 97, fig. 11.

TYPE: Collection of R. V. Chamberlin.

TYPE LOCALITY: 5 miles northwest of Shreveport, Caddo Parish, Louisiana.

RANGE: Known also from Reelfoot Lake, Obion County, Tennessee.

Pseudopolydesmus euthetus (Chamberlin)

Polydesmus euthetus Chamberlin, 1942, Bull. Univ. Utah, biol. ser., vol. 6, No. 8, p. 11, fig. 36.

TYPE: Collection of R. V. Chamberlin.

TYPE LOCALITY: Buder Park, 1 mile southwest of Valley Park, St. Louis County, Missouri.

RANGE: Known only from type locality.

Pseudopolydesmus minor (Bollman)

Polydesmus minor Bollman, 1888, Ent. Amer., vol. 4, p. 2.

TYPE: U. S. Nat. Mus.

TYPE LOCALITY: Little Rock, Pulaski County, Arkansas.

RANGE: Arkansas, western Tennessee, and southern Illinois.

Pseudopolydesmus natchitoches (Chamberlin)

Polydesmus natchitoches Chamberlin, 1942, Bull. Univ. Utah, biol. ser., vol. 6, No. 8, p. 10, figs. 34, 35.

TYPE: Collection of R. V. Chamberlin.

TYPE LOCALITY: 2 miles south of Saline, Natchitoches Parish, Louisiana.

RANGE: Central Louisiana.

Pseudopolydesmus neoterus (Chamberlin)

Polydesmus neoterus Chamberlin, 1942, Bull. Univ. Utah, biol. ser., vol. 6, No. 8, p. 10, fig. 30.

TYPE: Collection of R. V. Chamberlin.

TYPE LOCALITY: New Orleans, Louisiana.

RANGE: Known only from type locality.

Pseudopolydesmus paludicolus Hoffman

Pseudopolydesmus paludicolus Hoffman, 1950, Virginia Journ. Sci., new ser., vol. 1, p. 222, fig. 4.

TYPE: U. S. Nat. Mus. (No. 1871).

TYPE LOCALITY: Sand Bridge, 5 miles south of Virginia Beach, Princess Anne County, Virginia.

RANGE: Known only from type locality.

Pseudopolydesmus paroicus (Chamberlin)

Polydesmus paroicus Chamberlin, 1942, Bull. Univ. Utah, biol. ser., vol. 6, No. 8, p. 11, figs. 37, 38.

TYPE: Collection of R. V. Chamberlin.

TYPE LOCALITY: 1.5 miles north of Clay, Jackson Parish, Louisiana.

RANGE: Known only from type locality.

Pseudopolydesmus pinetorum (Bollman)

Polydesmus pinetorum Bollman, 1888, Ent. Amer., vol. 4, p. 3.

Polydesmus americanus Carl, 1902, Rev. Suisse Zool., vol. 10, p. 611, fig. 37 (type locality: Texas; type: Geneva Museum).

Polydesmus hubrichti Chamberlin, 1943, Ent. News, vol. 54, p. 15, figs. 1, 2 (type locality: St. Louis, Missouri; type: collection of R. V. Chamberlin).

Polydesmus modocus Chamberlin, 1943, Proc. Biol. Soc. Washington, vol. 56, p. 36, fig. 6 (type locality: between Modoc and Roots, Randolph County, Illinois; type: Chicago Nat. Hist. Mus.).

Pseudopolydesmus pinetorum Causey, 1952, Chicago Acad. Sci. Nat. Hist. Misc. No. 106, p. 6 (synonymy, distribution).

TYPE: U. S. Nat. Mus.

TYPE LOCALITY: Little Rock, Pulaski County, Arkansas.

RANGE: From eastern Texas and Louisiana north through Oklahoma and Arkansas to central Missouri and Illinois. The terminal populations are probably subspecifically distinct.

Pseudopolydesmus planicolens (Chamberlin)

Polydesmus planicolens Chamberlin, 1942, Canadian Ent., vol. 74, p. 16, fig. 2.

TYPE: Collection of R. V. Chamberlin.

TYPE LOCALITY: Ames, Story County, Iowa.

RANGE: Known only from type locality.

Pseudopolydesmus scopus (Chamberlin)

Polydesmus scopus Chamberlin, 1942, Canadian Ent., vol. 74, p. 16, fig. 1.

TYPE: Collection of R. V. Chamberlin.

TYPE LOCALITY: 6 miles south of Boone, Boone County, Iowa.

RANGE: Known only from type locality.

Pseudopolydesmus serratus (Say)

Polydesmus serratus Say, 1821, Journ. Acad. Nat. Sci. Philadelphia, vol. 2, p. 106.

Polydesmus canadensis Newport, 1844, Ann. Mag. Nat. Hist., vol. 13, p. 265.—Wood, 1865, Trans. Amer. Philos, Soc., vol. 13, p. 216, fig. 43.—Attems, 1940, Das Tierreich, Lief. 70, p. 140. (type locality: Albany River, Hudson's Bay, Canada; type: British Museum).

Polydesmus pensylvanicus Koch, 1847, *in* Krit. Rev. Insect. Deutschlands, vol. 3, p. 133; 1863, Die Myriapoden, vol. 2, p. 18, pl. 69, fig. 142 (type locality: Pennsylvania; type: unknown).

Polydesmus glaucescens Koch, 1847, *in* Krit. Rev. Insect. Deutschlands, vol. 3, p. 133; 1863, Die Myriapoden, vol. 1, p. 59, pl. 26, fig. 51 (type locality: North America; type: unknown).

TYPE: Not known to exist.

TYPE LOCALITY: "Eastern shore of Virginia."

RANGE: Northeastern North America, from Maine to Minnesota, south in the mountains to North Carolina; also recorded from Louisiana.

Genus SCYTONOTUS Koch

Scytonotus Koch, 1847, *in* Krit. Rev. Insect. Deutschlands, vol. 3, p. 57.—
    Cook and Cook, 1894, Ann. New York Acad. Sci., vol. 8, p. 233.
Lasiolathus Loomis, 1943, Journ. Washington Acad. Sci., vol. 33, p. 318
    (generotype: *L. virginicus* Loomis).
GENEROTYPE: *Scytonotus scabricollis* Koch [=*Polydesmus granulatus*
Say, 1821].
RANGE: North America, except southeastern and southwestern United
States; most species occur in the Pacific Northwest.
SPECIES: Nine.

Scytonotus amandus (Chamberlin)

Polydesmus amandus Chamberlin, 1910, Ann. Ent. Soc. America, vol. 3,
    p. 249, pl. 38, figs. 4–6; pl. 39, fig. 1.
Archipolydesmus amandus Attems, 1940, Das Tierreich, Lief. 70, p. 154.
TYPE: Present location unknown.
TYPE LOCALITY: Mill Creek Canyon, Salt Lake County, Utah.
RANGE: Canyons of Wasatch Mountains in Utah and Idaho.

Scytonotus bergrothi Chamberlin

Scytonotus bergrothi Chamberlin, 1911, Canadian Ent., vol. 43, p. 262,
    fig. 16.
Scytonotus pallidus Attems, 1931, Zoologica, Stuttgart, vol. 30, Lief. 3–4,
    p. 145, figs. 234–39 (type locality: Vancouver Island, British Colum-
    bia; type: Vienna Museum).
TYPE: Present location unknown.
TYPE LOCALITY: Bremerton, Kitsap County, Washington.
RANGE: Vicinity of Puget Sound. Vancouver Island; Port Ludlow, Ta-
coma, Bremerton, Muckilteo, and Port Blackely, Washington.

Scytonotus columbianus Chamberlin

Scytonotus columbianus Chamberlain, 1920, Canadian Ent., vol. 52, p.
    166, figs. 16, 17.
TYPE: Mus. Comp. Zool.
TYPE LOCALITY: British Columbia, without precise locality.
RANGE: Known only from the original collection.

Scytonotus granulatus (Say)

Polydesmus granulatus Say, 1821, Journ. Acad. Nat. Sci. Philadelphia,
    vol. 2, p. 107.
Scytonotus scabricollis Koch, 1847, *in* Krit. Rev. Insect. Deutschlands, vol.
    3, p. 130; 1863, Die Myriapoden, vol. 2, pl. 80, fig. 163. (type lo-
    cality: North America; type: unknown).
Scytonotus laevicollis Koch, 1847, *in* Krit. Rev. Insect. Deutschlands, vol. 3,
    p. 131; 1863, Die Myriapoden, vol. 2, pl. 80, fig. 164 (type locality:
    Pennsylvania; type: unknown).

Stenonia hispida Sager, 1856, Proc. Acad. Nat. Sci. Philadelphia, vol. 8, p. 109 (type locality: vicinity of Detroit, Michigan; type: unknown).

Polydesmus setiger Wood, 1865, Trans. Amer. Philos. Soc., vol. 13, p. 213 (type locality: Pennsylvania; type: Acad. Nat. Sci. Philadelphia).

Scytonotus granulatus Bollman, 1893, U. S. Nat. Mus. Bull. 46, p. 108.— Cook and Cook, 1894, Ann. New York Acad. Sci., vol. 8, p. 233, pls. 6–9.—Hoffman, 1950, Virginia Journ. Sci., new ser., vol. 1, p. 219, fig. 1.

TYPE: Not known to exist.

TYPE LOCALITY: Vicinity of Philadelphia, Pennsylvania.

RANGE: New York south to North Carolina, west to Iowa and Missouri.

Scytonotus insulanus Attems

Scytonotus insulanus Attems, 1931, Zoologica, Stuttgart, vol. 30, Lief. 3–4, p. 147, figs. 240–245; 1940, Das Tierreich, Lief. 70 p., 157, figs. 229–31.

TYPE: Vienna Museum.

TYPE LOCALITY: Nanaimo, Vancouver Island, British Columbia.

RANGE: Known also from Juneau, Alaska.

Scytonotus orthodox Chamberlin

Scytonotus orthodox Chamberlin, 1925, Pan-Pacific Ent., vol. 2, p. 61.

TYPE: Collection of R. V. Chamberlin.

TYPE LOCALITY: Logan Canyon, Cache County, Utah.

RANGE: Known also from Cour d'Alene, Kootenai County, Idaho, and the Bear Lake region of Idaho and Utah.

Scytonotus piger Chamberlin

Scytonotus piger Chamberlin, 1910, Ann. Ent. Soc. America, vol. 3, p. 244, pl. 36, figs. 1–5.

TYPE: Present location unknown.

TYPE LOCALITY: Mill Creek Canyon, Salt Lake County, Utah.

RANGE: Wasatch Mountains, Utah.

Scytonotus simplex Chamberlin

Scytonotus simplex Chamberlin, 1941, Bull. Univ. Utah, biol, ser., vol. 6, No. 5, p. 16, fig. 30.

TYPE: Collection of R. V. Chamberlin.

TYPE LOCALITY: John Day Creek, Douglas County, Oregon.

RANGE: Known only from type locality.

Scytonotus virginicus (Loomis)

Lasiolathus virginicus Loomis, 1943, Journ. Washington Acad. Sci., vol. 33, p. 319, fig. 1.

Scytonotus virginicus Hoffman, 1950, Virginia Journ. Sci., new ser., vol. 1, p. 220, fig. 2.

TYPE: Mus. Comp. Zool.

TYPE LOCALITY: Thornton Gap, Page and Rappahannock Counties, Virginia.

RANGE: Apparently restricted to the Blue Ridge Province, from northern Virginia south as far as Linville Falls, North Carolina.

Genus SPEODESMUS Loomis

Speodesmus Loomis, 1939, Bull. Mus. Comp. Zool., vol. 86, p. 187.
GENEROTYPE: *Speodesmus echinourus* Loomis, by original designation.
RANGE: Texas.
SPECIES: One.

Speodesmus echinourus Loomis

Speodesmus echinourus Loomis, 1939, Bull. Mus. Comp. Zool., vol. 86, p. 188, fig. 13a–g.
TYPE: Mus. Comp. Zool.
TYPE LOCALITY: Prassel Ranch Cave, Kerrville, Kerr County, Texas.
RANGE: Caves in Kerr, Kendall, and Hays Counties, Texas.

Genus SPEORTHUS Chamberlin

Speorthus Chamberlin, 1952, Ent. News, vol. 63, p. 12.
GENEROTYPE: *Speorthus tuganbius* Chamberlin, by original designation.
RANGE: New Mexico.
SPECIES: One.

Speorthus tuganbius Chamberlin

Speorthus tuganbius Chamberlin, 1952, Ent. News, vol. 63, p. 12.
TYPE: Collection of R. V. Chamberlin.
TYPE LOCALITY: Carlsbad Caverns, New Mexico.
RANGE: Known only from type locality.

Genus TIDESMUS Chamberlin

Tidesmus Chamberlin, 1943, Proc. Biol. Soc. Washington, vol. 56, p. 35.
GENEROTYPE: *Tidesmus episcopus* Chamberlin, by original designation.
RANGE: California and Nevada.
SPECIES: Two.

Tidesmus episcopus Chamberlin

Tidesmus episcopus Chamberlin, 1943, Proc. Biol. Soc. Washington, vol. 56, p. 35, figs. 1–3.
TYPE: Chicago Nat. Hist. Mus.
TYPE LOCALITY: Bishop's Road, Reservoir Hill, Los Angeles County, California.
RANGE: Known only from type locality.

Tidesmus hubbsi Chamberlin

Tidesmus hubbsi Chamberlin, 1943, Proc. Biol. Soc. Washington, vol. 56, p. 36, fig. 4.

TYPE: Collection of R. V. Chamberlin.

TYPE LOCALITY: Cave Valley, Lincoln County, Nevada.

RANGE: Known only from type locality.

Genus UTADESMUS Chamberlin and Hoffman

Utadesmus Chamberlin and Hoffman, 1950, Chicago Acad. Sci. Nat. Hist. Misc. No. 71, p. 3.

GENEROTYPE: *Brachydesmus henriensis* Chamberlin, by original designation.

RANGE: Southern Utah and central New Mexico.

SPECIES: Two.

Utadesmus henriensis (Chamberlin)

Brachydesmus henriensis Chamberlin, 1930, Pan-Pacific Ent., vol. 6, p. 118, 2 figs.

Utadesmus henriensis Chamberlin and Hoffman, 1950, Chicago Acad. Sci. Nat. Hist. Misc. No. 71, p. 3.

TYPE: Collection of R. V. Chamberlin.

TYPE LOCALITY: Mount Ellen, Henry Mountains, Utah.

RANGE: Known only from type locality.

Utadesmus hoffi Chamberlin and Hoffman

Utadesmus hoffi Chamberlin and Hoffman, 1950, Chicago Acad. Sci. Nat. Hist. Misc. No. 71, p. 3, figs. 1, 2.

TYPE: U. S. Nat. Mus. (No. 2015).

TYPE LOCALITY: Sandia Mountains, near Albuquerque, New Mexico.

RANGE: Known only from the Sandia Mountains.

Polydesmidae of uncertain systematic position

Polydesmus moniliaris Koch

Polydesmus moniliaris Koch, 1847, *in* Krit. Rev. Insect. Deutschlands, vol. 3, p. 135.

TYPE: Not known to exist.

TYPE LOCALITY: Pennsylvania.

The exact identity of Koch's species has never been made known, despite which fact the name has been used by several American authors in reporting specimens from northeastern United States. It seems likely that the name may have been based upon introduced specimens of *P. inconstans* or some other synanthropic species.

Polydesmus sastianus Chamberlin

Polydesmus sastianus Chamberlin, 1910, Ann. Ent. Soc. Amer., vol. 3, p. 251.

TYPE: Present location unknown.

TYPE LOCALITY: Shasta Springs, Siskiyou County, California. Based on a female.

Polydesmus bonikus Chamberlin

Polydesmus bonikus Chamberlin, 1912, Ann. Ent. Soc. Amer., vol. 5, p. 168, pl. 10, fig. 3.

TYPE: Present location unknown.

TYPE LOCALITY: Madison, Washington.

Scytonotus cavernarum Bollman

Scytonotus cavernarum Bollman, 1887, Ent. Amer., vol. 3, p. 46.

TYPE: Present location unknown.

TYPE LOCALITY: Mayfield's Cave, Monroe County, Indiana.

Described from a single female. It is not possible to determine from the description whether the species is really a scytonotid.

Scytonotus nodulosus Koch

Scytonotus nodulosus Koch, 1847, *in* Krit. Rev. Insect. Deutschlands, vol. 3, p. 131.—Bollman, 1893, U. S. Nat. Mus. Bull. 46, p. 151.

TYPE: Not known to exist.

TYPE LOCALITY: Pennsylvania.

We have no suggestions to offer on the status of this form. It appears from the drawings later published by Koch (Die Myriapoden, 1863, pl. 80, fig. 164) to be more like a polydesmid than a scytonotid.

Family STYLODESMIDAE Cook

Stylodesmidae Cook, 1895, Ann. New York Acad. Sci., vol. 9, p. 5.— Chamberlin, 1943, Bull. Univ. Utah, biol. ser., vol. 8, No. 3, p. 62.— Schubart, 1945, Arq. Mus. Nac. Brasil, vol. 38, p. 81.

Stiodesmidae Cook, 1896, Brandtia, No. 5, p. 25.—Loomis, 1944, Psyche, vol. 51, p. 175.

Genus ILYMA Chamberlin

Ilyma Chamberlin, 1941, Bull. Univ. Utah, biol. ser., vol. 6, No. 4, p. 24.

GENEROTYPE: *Ilyma orizaba* Chamberlin, by original designation.

RANGE: Southern Mexico; Gulf Coast States?

SPECIES: Five, one within our limits.

Ilyma cajuni Loomis

Ilyma cajuni Loomis, 1944, Psyche, vol. 51, p. 175, fig. 6.

TYPE: Mus. Comp. Zool.

TYPE LOCALITY: Venice, Plaquemines Parish, Louisiana.
RANGE: Known only from type locality. This is possibly an introduced and now established species.

Genus PSOCHODESMUS Cook

Psochodesmus Cook, 1896, Brandtia, No. 5, p. 25.
GENEROTYPE: *Psochodesmus crescentis* Cook, by original designation.
RANGE: Florida and the West Indies.
SPECIES: Three, one within our limits.

Psochodesmus crescentis Cook

Psochodesmus crescentis Cook, 1896, Brandtia, No. 5, p. 25.—Loomis, 1934, Smithsonian Misc. Coll., vol. 89, No. 14, p. 54, fig. 27a,b.
TYPE: U. S. Nat. Mus.
TYPE LOCALITY: Crescent City, Putnam County, Florida.
RANGE: The southern two-thirds of the Florida Peninsula.

Family VANHOEFFENIIDAE Attems

Vanhoeffeniidae Attems, 1914, Arch. Naturg., Abt. A, vol. 80, p. 158; 1940, Das Tierreich, Lief. 70, p. 162.

Jeekel (1956, Beaufortia, vol. 51, p. 77) places *Vanhoeffenia* as a junior synonym of *Gnomeskelus* Attems, a genus of the family Sphaeriotrichopidae. As that family name has several years priority over the name Vanhoeffeniidae, the latter name must be placed into synonymy. The considerable number of polydesmoid genera not confamilial with *Gnomeskelus* and previously placed in the Vanhoeffeniidae, now need a new family name. Because of the very confused condition of the taxonomy of the small polydesmoids, it is felt that no ends would be served by the premature selection of some of the possibly available names, or by the proposal of a new one for the American genera.

Genus OPHIODESMUS Cook

Ophiodesmus Cook, 1895, Ann. New York Acad. Sci., vol. 9, p. 5.
GENEROTYPE: *Strongylosoma verhoeffi* Brölemann, by original designation.
RANGE: Europe from France and England to Sweden, and in North America known from Newfoundland, where probably introduced.
SPECIES: Two, one occurring in North America.

Ophiodesmus albonanus (Latzel)

Paradesmus albonanus Latzel, 1895, Mitt. Naturh. Mus. Hamburg, vol. 12, p. 107, fig. 1.
Ophiodesmus albonanus Lohmander, 1925, Göteborgs Vetensk. Handl., ser. 4, vol. 30, p. 20, fig. 6.—Palmén, 1952, Ann. Zool. Soc. 'Vanamo', vol. 15, No. 1, p. 14.

TYPE: Hamburg Museum.
TYPE LOCALITY: Hamburg, Germany.
RANGE: Northern Germany; Sweden; introduced into Newfoundland.

Suborder STRONGYLOSOMIDEA Brölemann

Strongylosomidi Brölemann, 1916, Ann. Soc. Ent. France, vol. 84, p. 526.
Strongylosomidea Attems, 1937, Das Tierreich, Lief. 68, p. 23.

KEY TO NORTH AMERICAN FAMILIES OF STRONGYLOSOMIDEA

1. Gonopods of male very simple, the acropodite not definitely set off from a prefemur, and never sheathed; gonopod aperture large . . . EURYMERODESMIDAE (p. 78)
   Gonopods of male commonly more or less complicated, with the acropodite definitely set off from a prefemur, and with a separate solenomerite
   STRONGYLOSOMIDAE (p. 83)

Family EURYMERODESMIDAE Causey

Eurymerodesmidae Causey, 1951, Proc. Arkansas Acad. Sci., vol. 4, p. 69.

Genus EURYMERODESMUS Brölemann

Eurymerodesmus Brölemann, 1900, Mém. Soc. Zool. France, vol. 13, p. 101.
GENEROTYPE: *Polydesmus hispidipes* Wood, by monotypy.
RANGE: Eastern United States, from Illinois and Iowa south to Texas and Oklahoma, east to Florida.
SPECIES: Twenty-one, many of which appear to be but geographic races of a polytypic species.

Eurymerodesmus amplus Causey

Eurymerodesmus amplus Causey, 1952, Chicago Acad. Sci. Nat. Hist. Misc. No. 106, p. 4, fig. 3.
TYPE: Amer. Mus. Nat. Hist.
TYPE LOCALITY: Ruston, Lincoln Parish, Louisiana.
RANGE: Known only from type locality.

Eurymerodesmus angularis Causey

Eurymerodesmus angularis Causey, 1951, Proc. Arkansas Acad. Sci., vol. 4, p. 69, figs. 1–3.
TYPE: Acad. Nat. Sci. Philadelphia.
TYPE LOCALITY: Prairie County, Arkansas.
RANGE: Known only from type locality.

Eurymerodesmus bentonus Causey

Eurymerodesmus bentonus Causey, 1950, Ohio Journ. Sci., vol. 50, p. 268, fig. 5.
TYPE: Acad. Nat. Sci. Philadelphia.
TYPE LOCALITY: Monte Ne, Benton County, Arkansas.
RANGE: Known only from type locality.

Eurymerodesmus birdi Chamberlin

Eurymerodesmus birdi Chamberlin, 1931, Ent. News, vol. 42, p. 101, pl. 2, figs. 6–8.

TYPE: Collection of R. V. Chamberlin.

TYPE LOCALITY: Murray County, Oklahoma.

RANGE: Recorded from Murray, Seminole, Pittsburg, and Hughes Counties, Oklahoma, and from Sebastin, Logan, and Miller Counties, Arkansas.

Eurymerodesmus booneus Chamberlin

Eurymerodesmus booneus Chamberlin, 1942, Canadian Ent., vol. 74, p. 16.

TYPE: Collection of R. V. Chamberlin.

TYPE LOCALITY: 3 miles west of Boone, Boone County, Iowa.

RANGE: Known only from type locality.

Eurymerodesmus christianus Chamberlin

Eurymerodesmus christianus Chamberlin, 1946, Proc. Biol. Soc. Washington, vol. 59, p. 140, fig. 5.

TYPE: Collection of R. V. Chamberlin.

TYPE LOCALITY: Pass Christian, Harrison County, Mississippi.

RANGE: Known only from type locality.

Eurymerodesmus compressus Causey

Eurymerodesmus compressus Causey, 1952, Ent. News, vol. 63, No. 7, p. 169, figs. 1–4.

TYPE: Acad. Nat. Sci. Philadelphia.

TYPE LOCALITY: Junction City, Union County, Arkansas.

RANGE: Known only from type locality.

Eurymerodesmus creolus Chamberlin

Eurymerodesmus creolus Chamberlin, 1942, Bull. Univ. Utah, biol. ser., vol. 6, No. 8, p. 6, fig. 16.

TYPE: Collection of R. V. Chamberlin.

TYPE LOCALITY: 5 miles northwest of Shreveport, Caddo Parish, Louisiana.

RANGE: Known only from type locality.

Eurymerodesmus dubius Chamberlin

Eurymerodesmus dubius Chamberlin, 1943, Proc. Biol. Soc. Washington, vol. 56, p. 38, fig. 8.

TYPE: Chicago Nat. Hist. Mus.

TYPE LOCALITY: Delight, Pike County, Arkansas.

RANGE: Recorded from Pike, Clark, Dallas, Hot Springs, Saline, and Sevier Counties, Arkansas.

Eurymerodesmus goodi Causey

Eurymerodesmus goodi Causey, 1952, Chicago Acad. Sci. Nat. Hist. Misc. No. 106, p. 3, fig. 1.

TYPE: Amer. Mus. Nat. Hist.

TYPE LOCALITY: 16 miles southeast of Mena, Polk County, Arkansas.

RANGE: Known only from type locality.

Eurymerodesmus louisianae Chamberlin

Eurymerodesmus louisianae Chamberlin, 1942, Bull. Univ. Utah, biol. ser., vol. 6, No. 8, p. 6, fig. 17.

TYPE: Collection of R. V. Chamberlin.

TYPE LOCALITY: 2 miles south of Saline, Natchitoches Parish, Louisiana.

RANGE: Known only from type locality.

Eurymerodesmus melacis Chamberlin and Mulaik

Eurymerodesmus melacis Chamberlin and Mulaik, 1941, Journ. New York Ent. Soc., vol. 49, p. 59.

TYPE: Collection of R. V. Chamberlin.

TYPE LOCALITY: Raven Ranch, Kerr County, Texas.

RANGE: Recorded from Kerr, Kendall, and Concho Counties, Texas.

Eurymerodesmus mundus Chamberlin

Eurymerodesmus mundus Chamberlin, 1931, Ent. News, vol. 42, p. 102, pl. 2, figs. 3–5.

TYPE: Collection of R. V. Chamberlin.

TYPE LOCALITY: University, Norman, Cleveland County, Oklahoma.

RANGE: Recorded from Cleveland, Latimer, Caddo, and McLain Counties, Oklahoma, and Sevier County, Arkansas.

Eurymerodesmus newtonus Chamberlin

Eurymerodesmus newtonus Chamberlin, 1942, Bull. Univ. Utah, biol. ser., vol. 6, No. 8, p. 6, fig. 14.

TYPE: Collection of R. V. Chamberlin.

TYPE LOCALITY: 12 miles south of Jasper, Newton County, Arkansas.

RANGE: Known only from type locality.

Eurymerodesmus oliphantus Chamberlin

Eurymerodesmus oliphantus Chamberlin, 1942, Bull. Univ. Utah, biol. ser., vol. 6, No. 8, p. 6, fig. 15.

TYPE: Collection of R. V. Chamberlin.

TYPE LOCALITY: 15 miles south of Oliphant, Jackson County, Arkansas.

RANGE: Known only from type locality.

Eurymerodesmus planus Causey

Eurymerodesmus planus Causey, 1950, Ent. News, vol. 61, p. 196, fig. 5.

TYPE: Acad. Nat. Sci. Philadelphia.

TYPE LOCALITY: Piney Woods, Rankin County, Mississippi.

RANGE: Known only from type locality.

Eurymerodesmus sanbernardiensis Causey

Eurymerodesmus sanbernardiensis Causey, 1952, Ent. News, vol. 63, p. 174, figs. 6, 7.

TYPE: Acad. Nat. Sci. Philadelphia.

TYPE LOCALITY: Banks of San Bernardo River, Fort Bend County, Texas.

RANGE: Known only from type locality.

Eurymerodesmus schmidti Chamberlin

Eurymerodesmus schmidti Chamberlin, 1943, Proc. Biol. Soc. Washington, vol. 56, p. 38, fig. 7.

Eurymerodesmus plishneri Causey, 1950, Ohio Journ. Sci., vol. 50, p. 271, fig. 8 (type locality: Fayetteville, Washington County, Arkansas; type: Acad. Nat. Sci. Philadelphia).

TYPE: Chicago Nat. Hist. Mus.

TYPE LOCALITY: Rich Mountain, Polk County, Arkansas.

RANGE: Recorded from Washington, Carroll, and Polk Counties, Arkansas.

Eurymerodesmus spectabilis Causey

Eurymerodesmus spectabilis Causey, 1950, Ohio Journ. Sci., vol. 50, p. 270, figs. 6, 7.

TYPE: Acad. Nat. Sci. Philadelphia.

TYPE LOCALITY: 3 miles east of Magnolia, Columbia County, Arkansas.

RANGE: Known only from type locality, and from Union County, Arkansas, and Clairborne Parish, Louisiana.

Eurymerodesmus varius (McNeill)

Polydesmus varius McNeill, 1887, Proc. U. S. Nat. Mus., vol. 10, p. 323.

Eurymerodesmus minimus Loomis, 1943, Journ. Washington Acad. Sci., vol. 33, p. 320, fig. 2 (type locality: Marianna, Jackson County, Florida; type: Mus. Comp. Zool.).

Eurymerodesmus varius Causey, 1954, Tulane Stud. Zool., vol. 2, No. 4, p. 67.

TYPE: U. S. Nat. Mus.

TYPE LOCALITY: Pensacola, Escambia County, Florida.

RANGE: Known from Escambia and Marianna Counties in the Florida Panhandle and from Mobile County, Alabama.

Eurymerodesmus wellesleybentonus Causey

Eurymerodesmus wellesleybentonus Causey, 1952, Ent. News, vol. 63, p. 171, fig. 5.

TYPE: Acad. Nat. Sci. Philadelphia.

TYPE LOCALITY: Helena, Phillips County, Arkansas.

RANGE: Known only from type locality.

Genus KEWANIUS Chamberlin

Kewanius Chamberlin, 1938, Proc. Biol. Soc. Washington, vol. 51, p. 208.
GENEROTYPE: *Eurymerodesmus simplex* Chamberlin, by original designation.
RANGE: Louisiana:
SPECIES: One.

Kewanius simplex (Chamberlin)

Eurymerodesmus simplex Chamberlin, 1920, Proc. Biol. Soc. Washington, vol. 33, p. 98.
TYPE: Mus. Comp. Zool.
TYPE LOCALITY: Louisiana, probably near New Orleans.
RANGE: No definite localities known.

Genus PARESMUS Chamberlin

Paresmus Chamberlin, 1942, Bull. Univ. Utah, biol. ser., vol. 6, No. 8, p. 7.
GENEROTYPE: *Paresmus paroicus* Chamberlin, by original designation.
RANGE: Arkansas and Louisiana.
SPECIES: Five.

Paresmus columbus Causey

Paresmus columbus Causey, 1950, Ohio Journ. Sci., vol. 50, p. 272, figs. 10, 11.
TYPE: Acad. Nat. Sci. Philadelphia.
TYPE LOCALITY: Magnolia, Columbia County, Arkansas.
RANGE: Known only from type locality.

Paresmus impurus (Wood)

Polydesmus impurus Wood, 1867, Proc. Acad. Nat. Sci. Philadelphia, p. 43.
Paresmus impurus Causey, 1952, Ent. News, vol. 63, p. 174, figs. 8, 9.
TYPE: Acad. Nat: Sci. Philadelphia.
TYPE LOCALITY: Texas.
RANGE: No definite localities known.

Paresmus paroicus Chamberlin

Paresmus paroicus Chamberlin, 1942, Bull. Univ. Utah, biol. ser., vol. 6, No. 8, p. 7, figs. 18, 19.
TYPE: Collection of R. V. Chamberlin.
TYPE LOCALITY: 1½ miles north of Clay, border of Lincoln and Jackson Parishes, Louisiana.
RANGE: Known only from type locality.

Paresmus polkensis Causey

Paresmus polkensis Causey, 1952, Chicago Acad. Sci. Nat. Hist. Misc. No. 106, p. 5, fig. 4.

TYPE: Amer. Mus. Nat. Hist.

TYPE LOCALITY: 11 miles north of Mena, Polk County, Arkansas.

RANGE: Known only from type locality.

Paresmus pulaski Causey

Paresmus pulaski Causey, 1950, Ohio Journ. Sci., vol. 50, p. 271, fig. 9.

TYPE: Acad. Nat. Sci. Philadelphia.

TYPE LOCALITY: Sweet Home, Pulaski County, Arkansas.

RANGE: Known only from Grant and Pulaski Counties, Arkansas.

Family STRONGYLOSOMIDAE Cook

Strongylosomatidae Cook, 1895, Ann. New York Acad. Sci., vol. 9, p. 5.

Strongylosomidae Pocock, 1909, Diplopoda, in Biol. Centr.-Amer., p. 158.—Attems, 1937, Das Tierreich, Lief. 68, p. 24 (monograph of family).

Genus ORTHOMORPHA Bollman

Paradesmus Saussure, 1859, Linnaea Ent., vol. 13, p. 325. (preoccupied).

Orthomorpha Bollman, 1893, U. S. Nat. Mus. Bull. 46, p. 159.—Attems, 1937, Das Tierreich, Lief. 68, p. 59.

Asiomorpha Verhoeff, 1939, Zool. Anz., vol. 127, p. 117 (generotype, Paradesmus coarctatus Saussure, by original designation).

Brasilogonopus Verhoeff, 1943, Arq. Mus. Nac. Brasil, vol. 37, p. 274 (generotype, B. attemsi Verhoeff [=coarctatus Saussure] by monotypy).

GENEROTYPE: Polydesmus (Paradesmus) beaumonti LeGillou, by subsequent designation of Pocock, 1909.

RANGE: Indo-Australian region; also introduced by commerce into most other warmer lands of the world.

SPECIES: About 20.

Orthomorpha coarctata (Saussure)

Polydesmus coarctatus Saussure, 1860, Mém. Soc. Phys. Hist. Nat. Genève, vol. 15, p. 297, pl. 3, fig. 18.

Polydesmus vicarius Karsch, 1881, Arch. Naturg., vol. 47, p. 38, pl. 3, fig. 8 (type locality: Mayotti, Africa; type: Berlin Museum).

Strongylosoma poeyi Bollman, 1887, Ent. Amer., vol. 3, p. 82 (type locality: Havana, Cuba: type: U. S. Nat. Mus. No. 1227).

Orthomorpha coarctata Bollman, 1893, U. S. Nat. Mus. Bull. 46, p. 196.

Brasilogonopus attemsi Verhoeff, 1943, Arq. Mus. Nac. Brasil, vol. 37, p. 275 (type locality: Minas Gerais, Brasil; type: Verhoeff collection).

TYPE: Location unknown.

TYPE LOCALITY: French Guiana (unquestionably introduced from the Malayan Archipelago).

RANGE: Throughout the Malayan and East Indian areas, Madagascar, West Africa, tropical South America, Central America, and México, and the West Indies; widely dispersed through commerce. In the United States it is occasional in greenhouses and has been taken in the open in Texas and Louisiana.

Genus OXIDUS Cook

Oxidus Cook, 1911, Proc. U. S. Nat. Mus., vol. 40, p. 628.

Kalorthomorpha Attems, 1914, Arch. Naturg., Abt. A, vol. 80, p. 191; 1937, Das Tierreich, Lief. 68, p. 80.

GENEROTYPE: *Fontaria gracilis* Koch, by original designation.

RANGE: Indo-Australian region; introduced widely by commerce into other parts of the world.

SPECIES: About 20 listed by Attems.

Oxidus gracilis (Koch)

Fontaria gracilis Koch, 1847, *in* Krit. Rev. Insect. Deutschlands, vol. 3, p. 142.

Paradesmus dasys Bollman, 1888, Proc. U. S. Nat. Mus., vol. 10, p. 619 (type locality: Baltimore, Maryland; type: U. S. Nat. Mus.).

Kepolydesmus sontus Chamberlin, 1910, Ann. Ent. Soc. Amer., vol. 3, p. 247, pl. 38, figs. 5–7 (type locality: Los Angeles, California; location of types unknown).

Oxidus gracilis Cook, 1911, Proc. U. S. Nat. Mus., vol. 40, p. 631.

Orthomorpha (*Kalorthomorpha*) *gracilis* Attems, 1914, Arch. Naturg., Abt. A, vol. 80, p. 191; 1937, Das Tierreich, Lief. 68, p. 82, fig. 101.

TYPE: Present location unknown.

TYPE LOCALITY: Originally described from a greenhouse in Austria.

RANGE: Tropicopolitan. Introduced by commerce and well established in southern and western United States, and found throughout the country in greenhouses.

Order CHORDEUMIDA

Chordeumidae Koch, 1847, *in* Krit. Rev. Insect. Deutschlands, vol. 3, pp. 49, 119.—Latzel, 1884, Myr. Öst.-Ung. Monarch., vol. 2, p. 171.

Craspedosomidae Saussure and Humbert, 1872, Études sur les myriapodes, *in* Miss. Sci. Mexique, Zool., pt. 6, sect. 2, p. 56.

Craspedosomatidae Cook and Collins, 1895, Ann. New York Acad. Sci., vol. 9, p. 1.

Chordeumoidea Pocock, 1894, Chilopoda, Symphyla and Diplopoda . . . , *in* Weber, Zool. Erg. Reise, Niederl. Ost-Ind., vol. 3, p. 341.—Silvestri, 1896, Ann. Mus. Civ. Stor. Nat. Genova, ser. 2, vol. 16, p. 158.—Pocock, 1903, Diplopoda, *in* Biol. Centr.-Amer., p. 51.

Coelocheta+Merocheta Cook, 1896, Amer. Nat., vol. 30, p. 683.—Silvestri, 1897, Ann. Mus. Civ. Stor. Nat. Genova, ser. 2, vol. 18, p. 3.

Nematophora Verhoeff, 1913, Zool. Anz., vol. 43, p. 52.—Attems, 1926, *in* Kükenthal-Krumbach, Handbuch der Zoologie, vol. 4, p. 154.— Schubart, 1945, Arq. Mus. Nac. Brasil, vol. 38, p. 8.

Chordeumida Chamberlin, 1943, Bull. Univ. Utah, biol. ser., vol. 8, No. 3, pp. 5, 34.

The four suborders into which this order is divided may be distinguished by means of the key given below. Of them, no representative of the Stemmiulidea has yet been found within our limits.

KEY TO THE SUBORDERS OF CHORDEUMIDA

1. Body segments of adults 39 or more; repugnatorial pores present 2
   Body segments not more than 32; no repugnatorial pores 3
2. Only 1 or 2 ocelli on each side; body dorsoventrally compressed; segments with fine striae . . . . STEMMIULIDEA
   Ocelli numerous, in a triangular patch; body rounded; segments with pronounced longitudinal crests and enlarged poriferous knobs . . . LYSIOPETALIDEA (p. 108)
3. Metazonites with high carinae over middorsal region; collum large, hoodlike, partly concealing the head; anal segment trilobed . . . . . . STRIARIIDEA (p. 115)
   Metazonites without longitudinal carinae or ridges; collum smaller, never hoodlike, head usually exposed; anal segment entire . . . . . CHORDEUMIDEA (p. 85)

Suborder CHORDEUMIDEA

Chordeumidae (in part) Koch, 1847, *in* Krit. Rev. Insect. Deutschlands, vol. 3, p. 49.

Chordeumoidea Cook, 1899, Proc. U. S. Nat. Mus., vol. 21, p. 669.—Attems, 1926, *in* Kükenthal-Krumbach, Handbuch der Zoologie, vol. 4, p. 154.

Ascospermophora Verhoeff, 1913, Zool. Anz., vol. 43, p. 53.

KEY TO NORTH AMERICAN FAMILIES OF CHORDEUMIDEA

1. Body composed of 20 or 26 segments 2
   Body composed of 28, 30, or 32 segments 3
2. Segments 20; tergites not produced laterally into paranota (lateral carinae of older authors) . . . . ERGETHIDAE (p. 105)
   Segments 26; tergites with numerous short dorsal crests and prominent paranota.
   BRANNERIIDAE (p. 86)
3. Telopodite of second pair of legs of the seventh segment of males much thickened, often clavate, the second joint often forming a distinct angle with the coxa, the latter with a conspicuous inner process 4
   Second legpair of seventh segment in males never clavately thickened as described above, and not forming a distinct angle with the coxa, which has no inner process . 6
4. Gnathochilarium undivided, no promentum set off . . . . CONOTYLIDAE (p. 97)
   Gnathochilarium with a promentum 5
5. Tergites with setigerous keels, the sides of segments at most vaguely striate.
   UNDERWOODIIDAE (p. 107)
   Tergites without setigerous keels, the sides with pronounced lateral striae
   CASEYIDAE (p. 87)

6. Last tergite prolonged into a projection which surpasses the anal valves.

UROCHORDEUMIDAE (p. 107)

Last tergite not thus prolonged 7

7. Collum enlarged, partly covering the head . . . . . . RHISCOSOMIDIDAE (p. 105)

Collum not enlarged, head entirely exposed 8

8. Gnathochilarium with mentum divided, the promentum distinctly set off; second legs of seventh segment of male hamate, the second joint robust; male gonopods with a distinct pair of coxal processes . . . . CLEIDOGONIDAE (p. 89)

Gnathochilarium undivided, promentum not set off; second legs of seventh segment of male clavate, the second joint slender; gonopods without coxal processes.

BACTROPIDAE (p. 86)

Family BACTROPIDAE Chamberlin and Hoffman

Bactropidae Chamberlin and Hoffman, 1950, Chicago Acad. Sci. Nat. Hist. Misc. No. 71, p. 6.

Genus BACTROPUS Cook and Collins

Bactropus Cook and Collins, 1895, Ann. New York Acad. Sci., vol. 9, p. 53.

GENEROTYPE: *Bactropus conifer* Cook and Collins, by monotypy.

RANGE: Indiana.

SPECIES: One.

Bactropus conifer Cook and Collins

Bactropus conifer Cook and Collins, 1895, Ann. New York Acad. Sci., vol. 9, p. 54, figs. 172–176.

TYPE: U. S. Nat. Mus. (No. 43).

TYPE LOCALITY: Bloomington, Monroe County, Indiana.

RANGE: Known only from type locality.

Family BRANNERIIDAE Cook

Branneriidae Cook, 1896, Brandtia, No. 2, p. 8.

Genus BRANNERIA Bollman

Branneria Bollman, 1893, U. S. Nat. Mus. Bull. 46, p. 158.

GENEROTYPE: *Craspedosoma carinatum* Bollman, by original designation.

RANGE: Central United States.

SPECIES: One.

Branneria carinata (Bollman)

Craspedosoma carinatum Bollman, 1888, Ann. New York Acad. Sci., vol. 4, p. 109.

Branneria carinata Cook and Collins, 1895, Ann. New York Acad. Sci., vol. 9, p. 33 (redescription).

TYPE: Present location unknown.

TYPE LOCALITY: Beaver Creek, Jefferson County, Tennessee.

RANGE: Known definitely only from the type locality. The records for Arkansas by Bollman and Michigan by Chamberlin probably pertain to other, undescribed, forms.

Family CASEYIDAE Verhoeff

Caseyidae Verhoeff, 1909, Zool. Anz., vol. 34, p. 567.

Genus CASEYA Cook and Collins

Caseya Cook and Collins, 1895, Ann. New York Acad. Sci., vol. 9, p. 84.
GENEROTYPE: Caseya heteropus Cook and Collins, by original designation.
RANGE: California and Oregon.
SPECIES: Six.

Caseya bentona Chamberlin

Caseya bentona Chamberlin, 1952, Chicago Acad. Sci. Nat. Hist. Misc. No. 113, p. 2, figs. 3–6.
TYPE: Collection of R. V. Chamberlin.
TYPE LOCALITY: Mary's Peak, Benton County, Oregon.
RANGE: Known only from type locality.

Caseya dynopta Chamberlin

Caseya dynopta Chamberlin, 1947, Proc. Biol. Soc. Washington, vol. 60, p. 9.
TYPE: Collection of R. V. Chamberlin.
TYPE LOCALITY: Hastings Reservation, Monterey County, California.
RANGE: Known only from type locality.

Caseya heteropus Cook and Collins

Caseya heteropus Cook and Collins, 1895, Ann. New York Acad. Sci., vol. 9, p. 85, figs. 191–219.
TYPE: U. S. Nat. Mus.
TYPE LOCALITY: California, probably vicinity of San Francisco.
RANGE: No precise localities are known for this species.

Caseya irritans Chamberlin

Caseya irritans Chamberlin, 1910, Ann. Ent. Soc. Amer., vol. 3, p. 241, pl. 34, figs. 6–9, pl. 35, fig. 1.
TYPE: Present location unknown.
TYPE LOCALITY: Portland, Multnomah County, Oregon.
RANGE: Known only from type locality.

Caseya sequoia Chamberlin

Caseya sequoia Chamberlin, 1941, Bull. Univ. Utah, biol. ser., vol. 6, No. 8, p. 10, figs. 17, 18.
TYPE: Collection of R. V. Chamberlin.

TYPE LOCALITY: Sequoia National Park, Tulare County, California.
RANGE: Known only from type locality.

Caseya similis Causey

Caseya similis Causey, 1952, Proc. Biol. Soc. Washington, vol. 65, p. 113, figs. 6, 7.
TYPE: U. S. Nat. Mus.
TYPE LOCALITY: Telachapi Pass, Kern County, California.
RANGE: Known only from type locality.

Genus OPIONA Chamberlin

Opiona Chamberlin, 1951, Chicago Acad. Sci. Nat. Hist. Misc. No. 87, p. 8.
GENEROTYPE: *Opiona columbiana* Chamberlin, by original designation.
RANGE: Washington and British Columbia.
SPECIES: Two.

Opiona columbiana Chamberlin

Opiona columbiana Chamberlin, 1951, Chicago Acad. Sci. Nat. Hist. Misc. No. 87, p. 8, figs. 15–19.
TYPE: Provincial Museum, British Columbia.
TYPE LOCALITY: Victoria, British Columbia.
RANGE: Known only from type locality.

Opiona hatchi Causey

Opiona hatchi Causey, 1954, Ann. Ent. Soc. America, vol. 47, p. 81, figs. 1–3.
TYPE: Amer. Mus. Nat. Hist.
TYPE LOCALITY: Carkeek Park, Seattle, King County, Washington.
RANGE: Known only from type locality.

Genus PLACERNA Chamberlin

Placerna Chamberlin, 1941, Bull. Univ. Utah, biol. ser., vol. 6, No. 5, p. 10.
GENEROTYPE: *Placerna dorada* Chamberlin, by original designation.
RANGE: California.
SPECIES: One.

Placerna dorada Chamberlin

Placerna dorada Chamberlin, 1941, Bull. Univ. Utah, biol. ser., vol. 6, No. 5, p. 10, figs. 19–21.
TYPE: Collection of R. V. Chamberlin.
TYPE LOCALITY: 9 miles north of Placerville, Eldorado County, California.
RANGE: Known only from type locality.

Genus VASINGTONA Chamberlin

Vasingtona Chamberlin, 1941, Bull. Univ. Utah, biol. ser., vol. 6, No. 5, p. 12.
GENEROTYPE: *Caseya fasciata* Chamberlin, by original designation.
RANGE: Washington.
SPECIES: One.

Vasingtona fasciata (Chamberlin)

Caseya fasciata Chamberlin, 1941, Bull. Univ. Utah, biol. ser., vol. 6, No. 4, p. 22.
TYPE: Collection of R. V. Chamberlin.
TYPE LOCALITY: Arlington, Snohomish County, Washington.
RANGE: Known only from type locality.

Genus ZANTONA Chamberlin

Zantona Chamberlin, 1941, Bull. Univ. Utah, biol. ser., vol. 6, No. 5, p. 11.
GENEROTYPE: *Zantona douglasi* Chamberlin, by original designation.
RANGE: Oregon.
SPECIES: One.

Zantona douglasi Chamberlin

Zantona douglasi Chamberlin, 1941, Bull. Univ. Utah, biol. ser., vol. 6, No. 5, p. 11, figs. 22–24.
TYPE: Collection of R. V. Chamberlin.
TYPE LOCALITY: John Day Creek, Douglas County, Oregon.
RANGE: Known only from type locality.

Family CLEIDOGONIDAE Cook

Cleidogonidae Cook, 1896, Brandtia, No. 2, p. 8.—Hoffman, 1950, Journ. Washington Acad. Sci., vol. 40, p. 87.
Pseudocleididae Attems, 1926, *in* Kükenthal-Krumbach, Handbuch der Zoologie, vol. 4, p. 170 (in part).
Entomobielziinae Verhoeff, 1909, Zool. Anz., vol. 34, p. 570.
Mexiceumidae Verhoeff, 1926, Zool. Anz., vol. 68, p. 110.

Genus CLEIDOGONA Cook and Collins

Cryptotrichus Packard, 1883, Proc. Amer. Philos. Soc., vol. 21, p. 189 (preoccupied by *Cryptotrichus* Schaufuss 1865).
Campodes (not C. L. Koch) Bollman, 1893, U. S. Nat. Mus. Bull. 46, p. 120.
Cleidogona Cook and Collins, 1895, Ann. New York Acad. Sci., vol. 9, p. 41.
GENEROTYPE: *Cleidogona major* Cook and Collins, by subsequent designation of Hoffman, 1950.

RANGE: Eastern United States; Texas; Mexico; Guatemala?

SPECIES: About 25, of which 17 occur in the United States. Some of these should be removed to other genera.

Cleidogona arkansana Causey

Cleidogona arkansana Causey, 1954, Tulane Stud. Zool., vol. 2, No. 4, p. 66, figs. 6–9.

TYPE: Amer. Mus. Nat. Hist.

TYPE LOCALITY: 4 miles east of Princeton, Dallas County, Arkansas.

RANGE: Known only from the type locality.

Cleidogona aspera Causey

Cleidogona aspera Causey, 1951, Journ. Washington Acad. Sci., vol. 41, p. 78, figs. 1–4.

TYPE: Acad. Nat. Sci. Philadelphia.

TYPE LOCALITY: 6 miles east of Imboden, Lawrence County, Arkansas.

RANGE: Lawrence, Randolph, and Dallas Counties, Arkansas.

Cleidogona caesioannulata (Wood)

Spirostrephon caesioannulatus Wood, 1865, Trans. Amer. Philos. Soc., vol. 13, p. 194.

TYPE: Acad. Nat. Nat. Sci. Philadelphia (No. 11202).

TYPE LOCALITY: Allegheny County, Pennsylvania.

RANGE: Western Pennsylvania (Allegheny and Westmoreland Counties), south through the Appalachian Plateaus Province to extreme southwestern Virginia (Buchanan County) and eastern Kentucky (Bell County).

This statement of range is based on unpublished studies, which include an examination of the original type specimen of Wood. None of the numerous published references to "*caesioannulata*" actually apply to this species. *C. fustis* Cook and Collins was incorrectly placed in the synonymy of *caesioannulata* by Williams and Hefner (1928, Bull. Ohio Biol. Surv., No. 18, p. 116).

Cleidogona celerita Williams and Hefner

Cleidogona celerita Williams and Hefner, 1928, Bull. Ohio Biol. Surv., No. 18, p. 117, fig. 14c.

TYPE: U. S. Nat. Mus. (No. 2271).

TYPE LOCALITY: "Ohio," without further locality.

RANGE: "General throughout Ohio" (Williams and Hefner).

Cleidogona exaspera Williams and Hefner

Cleidogona exaspera Williams and Hefner, 1928, Bull. Ohio Biol. Surv., No. 18, p. 117, fig. 14b.

TYPE: U. S. Nat. Mus. (No. 2270).

TYPE LOCALITY: Delaware County, Ohio.

RANGE: Known only from type locality.

Cleidogona forceps Cook and Collins

Cleidogona forceps Cook and Collins, 1895, Ann. New York Acad. Sci., vol. 9, p. 49, figs. 159–163.

TYPE: U. S. Nat. Mus.

TYPE LOCALITY: Probably somewhere in Indiana.

RANGE: No definite localities known for this species.

Cleidogona fustis Cook and Collins

Cleidogona fustis Cook and Collins, 1895, Ann. New York Acad. Sci., vol. 9, p. 50, figs. 151–153.

TYPE: U. S. Nat. Mus. (No. 446).

TYPE LOCALITY: Indiana, without precise locality.

RANGE: Recorded only from Montgomery County, Indiana.

Cleidogona inexpectata Hoffman

Cleidogona inexpectata Hoffman, 1950, Journ. Elisha Mitchell Sci. Soc., vol. 66, p. 22, figs. 23–25.

TYPE: U. S. Nat. Mus. (No. 1878).

TYPE LOCALITY: Chimneys Camp Ground, Sevier County, Tennessee.

RANGE: Known only from type locality.

Cleidogona inflata Causey

Cleidogona inflata Causey, 1951, Journ. Washington Acad. Sci., vol. 41, p. 80, figs. 14–19.

TYPE: Illinois Nat. Hist. Surv.

TYPE LOCALITY: Starved Rock State Park, Putnam County, Illinois.

RANGE: Known only from type locality.

Cleidogona jocassee Hoffman

Cleidogona jocassee Hoffman, 1950, Journ. Elisha Mitchell Sci. Soc., vol. 66, p. 19, figs. 15–18.

TYPE: U. S. Nat. Mus. (No. 1876).

TYPE LOCALITY: Jocassee, Oconee County, South Carolina.

RANGE: Western South Carolina, northern Georgia, and western North Carolina (Macon, Jackson, Transylvania, Swain Counties).

Cleidogona laminata Cook and Collins

Cleidogona laminata Cook and Collins, 1895, Ann. New York Acad. Sci., vol. 9, p. 48, figs. 164–171.

TYPE: U. S. Nat. Mus. (No. 427).

TYPE LOCALITY: Probably somewhere in Indiana.

RANGE: No definite localities known for this species.

Cleidogona major Cook and Collins

Cleidogona major Cook and Collins, 1895, Ann. New York Acad. Sci., vol. 9, p. 47, figs. 110–137.

Type: U. S. Nat. Mus.
Type Locality: Washington, D. C.
Range: Maryland, District of Columbia, and north-central Virginia.

Cleidogona margarita Hoffman

Cleidogona margarita Hoffman, 1950, Journ. Elisha Mitchell Sci. Soc., vol. 66, p. 21, figs. 19–22.
Type: U. S. Nat. Mus. (No. 1877).
Type Locality: Chimneys Camp Ground, Sevier County, Tennessee.
Range: Known only from type locality.

Cleidogona minima Causey

Cleidogona minima Causey, 1951, Journ. Washington Acad. Sci., vol. 41, p. 80, figs. 10–13.
Type: Acad. Nat. Sci. Philadelphia.
Type Locality: Tuscaloosa, Tuscaloosa County, Alabama.
Range: Known only from type locality.

Cleidogona mississippiana Chamberlin

Cleidogona mississippiana Chamberlin, 1942, Bull. Univ. Utah, biol. ser., vol. 6, No. 8, p. 3, figs. 4–6.
Type: Collection of R. V. Chamberlin.
Type Locality: Eight miles east of Vicksburg, Warren County, Mississippi.
Range: Known from three localities in central Mississippi.

Cleidogona sublettei Causey

Cleidogona sublettei Causey, 1954, Tulane Stud. Zool., vol. 2, No. 4, p. 66, figs. 4, 5.
Type: Amer. Mus. Nat. Hist.
Type Locality: Grand Ecore, Natchitoches Parish, Louisiana.
Range: Known only from type locality.

Cleidogona unita Causey

Cleidogona unita Causey, 1951, Journ. Washington Acad. Sci., vol. 41, p. 78, figs. 5–9.
Type: Illinois Nat. Hist. Surv.
Type Locality: Giant City State Park, Union County, Illinois.
Range: Also known from Dixon, Lee County, Illinois.

Genus DEAROLFIA Loomis

Dearolfia Loomis, 1939, Bull. Mus. Comp. Zool., vol. 86, p. 177.
Generotype: *Dearolfia lusciosa* Loomis, by original designation.
Range: Northeastern West Virginia.
Species: One.

Dearolfia lusciosa Loomis

Dearolfia lusciosa Loomis, 1939, Bull. Mus. Comp. Zool., vol. 86, p. 178, figs. 7a–f.

TYPE: Mus. Comp. Zool.

TYPE LOCALITY: Seneca Caverns, Pendleton County, West Virginia.

RANGE: Caves in Pendleton County, West Virginia.

Genus OFCOOKOGONA Causey

Ofcookogona Causey, 1951, Proc. Biol. Soc. Washington, vol. 64, p. 120.

GENEROTYPE: *Ofcookogona steuartae* Causey, by original designation.

RANGE: Arkansas.

SPECIES: Two.

Ofcookogona alia Causey

Ofcookogona alia Causey, 1951, Proc. Biol. Soc. Washington, vol. 64, p. 121, figs. 14–16.

TYPE: Acad. Nat. Sci. Philadelphia.

TYPE LOCALITY: Junction City, Union County, Arkansas.

RANGE: Known only from type locality.

Ofcookogona steuartae Causey

Ofcookogona steuartae Causey, 1951, Proc. Biol. Soc. Washington, vol. 64, p. 121, fig. 13.

TYPE: Acad. Nat. Sci. Philadelphia.

TYPE LOCALITY: Greenwood, Sebastian County, Arkansas.

RANGE: Known only from type locality.

Genus OZARKOGONA Causey

Ozarkogona Causey, 1951, Journ. Washington Acad. Sci., vol. 41, p. 80.

GENEROTYPE: *Ozarkogona glebosa* Causey, by original designation.

RANGE: Arkansas.

SPECIES: Two.

Ozarkogona glebosa Causey

Ozarkogona glebosa Causey, 1951, Journ. Washington Acad. Sci., vol. 41, p. 82, figs. 20, 21.

TYPE: Acad. Nat. Sci. Philadelphia.

TYPE LOCALITY: Fayetteville, Washington County, Arkansas.

RANGE: Known only from Washington, Benton, and Johnston Counties, Arkansas.

Ozarkogona ladymani Causey

Ozarkogona ladymani Causey, 1952, Proc. Biol. Soc. Washington, vol. 65, p. 114, figs. 8, 9.

TYPE: U. S. Nat. Mus.

TYPE LOCALITY: Rector, Clay County, Arkansas.

RANGE: Known only from type locality.

Genus PSEUDOTREMIA Cope

Pseudotremia Cope, 1869, Proc. Amer. Philos. Soc., vol. 11, p. 179.—
Cook and Collins, 1895, Ann. New York Acad. Sci., vol. 9, p. 34.
GENEROTYPE: *Pseudotremia cavernarum* Cope, by monotypy.
RANGE: Appalachian region from northwest Georgia to West Virginia, and
west into Kentucky and Indiana.
SPECIES: Fourteen.

Pseudotremia carterensis Packard

Pseudotremia cavernarum var. *carterensis* Packard, 1883, Proc. Amer.
Philos. Soc., vol. 21, p. 186.
Pseudotremia carterensis Cook and Collins, 1895, Ann. New York Acad.
Sci., vol. 9, p. 40, figs. 8–10.
TYPE: Not known to exist.
TYPE LOCALITY: Carter Caves, Carter County, Kentucky.
RANGE: Northeastern Kentucky, also reported from Wyandotte Cave, In-
diana, and Marietta, Ohio.   Confirmation of the last locality is desirable.

Pseudotremia cavernarum Cope

Pseudotremia cavernarum Cope, 1869, Proc. Amer. Philos. Soc., vol. 11,
p. 179.
Pseudotremia sublevis Loomis, 1944, Psyche, vol. 51, p. 167, fig. 1. (type
locality: Tony's Cave, near Newport, Giles County, Virginia; type:
Mus. Comp. Zool.).
TYPE: Not known to exist.
TYPE LOCALITY: Erhart's Cave, near Radford, Montgomery County, Vir-
ginia.
RANGE: Known only from Giles and Montgomery Counties, Virginia.

Pseudotremia eburnea Loomis

Pseudotremia eburnea Loomis, 1939, Bull. Mus. Comp. Zool., vol. 86, No.
4, p. 174, figs. 5a–c.
TYPE: Mus. Comp. Zool.
TYPE LOCALITY: Cricket Cave, Rising Fawn, Walker County, Georgia.
RANGE: Known only from type locality.

Pseudotremia fracta Chamberlin

Pseudotremia fracta Chamberlin, 1951, Great Basin Nat., vol. 11, p. 25.
TYPE: Collection of R. V. Chamberlin.
TYPE LOCALITY: Gatlinburg Cove, Sevier County, Tennessee.
RANGE: Known only from type locality.

Pseudotremia fulgida Loomis

Pseudotremia fulgida Loomis, 1943, Bull. Mus. Comp. Zool., vol. 92, p.
378, figs. 3a–d.
TYPE: Mus. Comp. Zool.

TYPE LOCALITY: Higginbotham Cave, 1.5 miles northwest of Frankfort, Greenbrier County, West Virginia.

RANGE: Caves in Greenbrier County, West Virginia.

Pseudotremia hansoni Chamberlin

Pseudotremia hansoni Chamberlin, 1951, Great Basin Nat., vol. 11, p. 25.

TYPE: Collection of R. V. Chamberlin.

TYPE LOCALITY: Pineville, Bell County, Kentucky.

RANGE: Known only from type locality.

Pseudotremia hobbsi Hoffman

Pseudotremia hobbsi Hoffman, 1950, Journ. Washington Acad. Sci., vol. 40, p. 90, figs. 4, 5.

TYPE: U. S. Nat. Mus. (No. 1783).

TYPE LOCALITY: Chestnut Ridge Cave, 2.5 miles northwest of Clifton Forge, Alleghany County, Virginia.

RANGE: Known only from caves in the upper James River system, in Alleghany and Bath Counties, Virginia.

Pseudotremia indianae, new species

Pseudotremia cavernarum (not Cope) Cook and Collins, 1895, Ann. New York Acad. Sci., vol. 9, p. 36, figs. 2–7, 11.

TYPE: U. S. Nat. Mus.

TYPE LOCALITY: Wyandotte Cave, Crawford County, Indiana.

RANGE: Caves in southern Indiana.

Pseudotremia nodosa Loomis

Pseudotremia nodosa Loomis, 1939, Bull. Mus. Comp. Zool., vol. 86, p. 175, figs. 6a–d.

TYPE: Mus. Comp. Zool.

TYPE LOCALITY: English Cave near Harrowgate, Clairborne County, Tennessee.

RANGE: Known only from type locality.

Pseudotremia princeps Loomis

Pseudotremia princeps Loomis, 1939, Bull. Mus. Comp. Zool., vol. 86, p. 168, figs. 1a–c.

TYPE: Mus. Comp. Zool.

TYPE LOCALITY: Eagle Cave, Pendleton County, West Virginia.

RANGE: Caves in Pendleton and Grant Counties, West Virginia.

Pseudotremia simulans Loomis

Pseudotremia simulans Loomis, 1939, Bull. Mus. Comp. Zool., vol. 86, p. 170, figs. 2a, b.

TYPE: Mus. Comp. Zool.

TYPE LOCALITY: Cave, Pendleton County, West Virginia.

RANGE: Known only from type locality.

Pseudotremia sodalis Loomis

Pseudotremia sodalis Loomis, 1939, Bull. Mus. Comp. Zool., vol. 86, No. 4, p. 173, figs. 4a–d.

TYPE: Mus. Comp. Zool.

TYPE LOCALITY: Bat Cave, Carter County, Kentucky.

RANGE: Known only from type locality.

Pseudotremia tuberculata Loomis

Pseudotremia tuberculata Loomis, 1939, Bull. Mus. Comp. Zool., vol. 86, p. 171, figs. 3a, b.

TYPE: Mus. Comp. Zool.

TYPE LOCALITY: Cassell's Cave, Burkes Garden, Tazewell County, Virginia.

RANGE: Caves in vicinity of type locality.

Pseudotremia valga Loomis

Pseudotremia valga Loomis, 1943, Bull. Mus. Comp. Zool., vol. 92, p. 377, figs. 2a–c.

TYPE: Mus. Comp. Zool.

TYPE LOCALITY: King Solomon's Cave (now called Cudjo's Cave), Cumberland Gap, Lee County, Virginia.

RANGE: Known only from type locality.

Genus RHABDARONA Chamberlin and Mulaik

Rhabdarona Chamberlin and Mulaik, 1941, Journ. New York Ent. Soc., vol. 49, p. 60.

GENEROTYPE: *Rhabdarona bacillipus* Chamberlin and Mulaik, by original designation.

RANGE: Southwestern Texas.

SPECIES: One.

Rhabdarona bacillipus Chamberlin and Mulaik

Rhabdarona bacillipus Chamberlin and Mulaik, 1941, Journ. New York Ent. Soc., vol. 49, p. 60.

TYPE: Collection of R. V. Chamberlin.

TYPE LOCALITY: Raven Ranch, Kerr County, Texas.

RANGE: Known only from type locality.

Genus TIGANOGONA Chamberlin

Tiganogona Chamberlin, 1928, Ent. News, vol. 39, p. 154—Causey, 1951, Journ. Washington Acad., Sci., vol. 41, p. 82.

GENEROTYPE: *Tiganogona brownae* Chamberlin, by original designation.

RANGE: Missouri, Arkansas.

SPECIES: Two.

Tiganogona brownae Chamberlin

Tiganogona brownae Chamberlin, 1928, Ent. News, vol. 39, p. 154.—
   Causey, 1951, Proc. Biol. Soc. Washington, vol. 64, p. 124, figs. 17–18.
TYPE: Collection of R. V. Chamberlin.
TYPE LOCALITY: St. Charles, St. Louis County, Missouri.
RANGE: Known only from type locality.

Tiganogona moesta Causey

Tiganogona moesta Causey, 1951, Journ. Washington Acad. Sci., vol. 41,
   p. 82, figs. 22, 23.
TYPE: Acad. Nat. Sci. Philadelphia.
TYPE LOCALITY: Blue Spring, Carroll County, Arkansas.
RANGE: Known from Carroll and Washington Counties, Arkansas.

Cleidogonidae of uncertain generic position

Pseudotremia vudii Cope

Pseudotremia vudii Cope, 1869, Proc. Amer. Philos, Soc. vol. 11, p. 180.
TYPE: Not known to exist.
TYPE LOCALITY: Montgomery County, Virginia.
Probably a species of *Cleidogona*.

Family CONOTYLIDAE Cook

Conotylidae Cook, 1896, Brandtia, No. 2, p. 8.

Genus BOLLMANELLA Chamberlin

Bollmanella Chamberlin, 1941, Bull. Univ. Utah, biol. ser., vol. 6, No. 3,
   p. 12.
GENEROTYPE: *Bollmanella oregona* Chamberlin, by original designation.
RANGE: Oregon.
SPECIES: One

Bollmanella oregona Chamberlin

Bollmanella oregona Chamberlin, 1941, Bull. Univ. Utah, biol. ser.,
   vol. 6, No. 5, p. 12.
TYPE: Collection of R. V. Chamberlin.
TYPE LOCALITY: Douglas County, Oregon.
RANGE: Known only from type locality.

Genus CONOTYLA Cook and Collins

Conotyla Cook and Collins, 1895, Ann. New York Acad. Sci., vol. 9,
   p. 70.—Loomis, 1943, Bull. Mus. Comp. Zool., vol. 92, p. 381.
GENEROTYPE: *Conotyla fischeri* Cook and Collins, by original designation.

RANGE: Western North America from New Mexico and California north to British Columbia; eastern United States from Ontario and New York west to Minnesota and Indiana, south to Maryland.

SPECIES: Thirteen.

Conotyla albertana Chamberlin

Conotyla albertana Chamberlin, 1920, Canadian Ent., vol. 52, p. 167.

TYPE: Mus. Comp. Zool.

TYPE LOCALITY: Bow River, Alberta.

RANGE: Known only from type locality.

Conotyla atrolineata (Bollman)

Craspedosoma atrolineatum Bollman, 1888, Proc. U. S. Nat. Mus., vol. 10, p. 618.

Conotyla atrolineata Cook and Collins, 1895, Ann. New York Acad. Sci., vol. 9, p. 75, figs. 95–100.—Loomis, 1943, Bull. Mus. Comp. Zool., vol. 92, p. 382 (key).

TYPE: U. S. Nat. Mus. (No. 439).

TYPE LOCALITY: Glacier, British Columbia.

RANGE: Known only from type locality.

Conotyla bollmani (McNeill)

Trichopetalum bollmani McNeill, 1887, Proc. U. S. Nat. Mus., vol. 10, p. 330.

Conotyla bollmani Cook and Collins, 1895, Ann. New York Acad. Sci., vol. 9, p. 76, figs. 79–94.

TYPE: U. S. Nat. Mus.

TYPE LOCALITY: Mayfield's Cave, Bloomington, Monroe County, Indiana.

RANGE: Southern and central Indiana.

Conotyla coloradensis Chamberlin

Conotyla coloradensis Chamberlin, 1910, Ann. Ent. Soc. Amer., vol. 3, p. 237, pl. 32, figs. 8, 9; pl. 33, figs. 1–3.

TYPE: Present location unknown.

TYPE LOCALITY: Colorado, without further locality.

RANGE: No definite localities known for this species.

Conotyla deseretae Chamberlin

Conotyla deseretae Chamberlin, 1910, Ann. Ent. Soc. Amer., vol. 3, p. 235, pl. 31, figs. 3–8; pl. 32, figs. 1–7.

TYPE: Present location unknown.

TYPE LOCALITY: Wasatch Mountains, Utah.

RANGE: The Wasatch Range in central and northern Utah.

Conotyla fischeri Cook and Collins

Conotyla fischeri Cook and Collins, 1895, Ann. New York Acad. Sci., vol. 9, p. 71, figs. 55–78.

TYPE: U. S. Nat. Mus.
TYPE LOCALITY: Here restricted to Syracuse, Onandaga County, New York.
RANGE: Central portion of New York State.

Conotyla humerosa Loomis

Conotyla humerosa Loomis, 1943, Bull. Mus. Comp. Zool., vol. 92, p. 384,
  figs. 5a–d.
TYPE: U. S. Nat. Mus. (No. 1443).
TYPE LOCALITY: Sunnyside Mine, 3 miles southwest of Seneca, Plumas
County, California.
RANGE: Known only from type locality.

Conotyla jonesi Chamberlin

Conotyla jonesi Chamberlin, 1951, Chicago Acad. Sci. Nat. Hist. Misc.
  No. 87, p. 6, figs. 12, 13.
TYPE: Collection of R. V. Chamberlin.
TYPE LOCALITY: Eugene, Layne County, Oregon.
RANGE: Known only from type locality.

Conotyla montivaga Loomis

Conotyla montivaga Loomis, 1943, Bull. Mus. Comp. Zool., vol. 92, p.
  383, figs. 4a–d.
TYPE: Mus. Comp. Zool.
TYPE LOCALITY: Santa Rita Mountains, Arizona.
RANGE: Pima and Santa Cruz Counties, southwestern Arizona, and Otero
County, New Mexico.

Conotyla pectinata Causey

Conotyla pectinata Causey, 1952, Proc. Biol. Soc. Washington, vol. 65,
  p. 112, figs. 4, 5.
TYPE: Illinois Nat. Hist. Survey.
TYPE LOCALITY: Mount Carroll, Carroll County, Illinois.
RANGE: Known only from type locality.

Conotyla specus Loomis

Conotyla specus Loomis, 1939, Bull. Mus. Comp. Zool., vol. 86, p. 184,
  figs. 11a–c.
TYPE: Mus. Comp. Zool.
TYPE LOCALITY: Rice's Cave, 3 miles northeast of Goldman, Jefferson
County, Missouri.
RANGE: Eastern Missouri and adjacent western Illinois.

Conotyla vaga Loomis

Conotyla vaga Loomis, 1939, Bull. Mus. Comp. Zool., vol. 86, p. 182,
  fig. 10.
TYPE: Mus. Comp. Zool.

TYPE LOCALITY: South Temple Cave, Berks County, Pennsylvania.
RANGE: Eastern Pennsylvania south as far as western Maryland.

Conotyla wyandotte (Bollman)

Scotherpes wyandotte Bollman, 1889, Proc. U. S. Nat. Mus., vol. 11, p. 405.
Conotyla wyandotte Cook and Collins, 1895, Ann. New York Acad.
Sci., vol. 9, p. 78, fig. 101.
TYPE: U. S. Nat. Mus. (No. 440).
TYPE LOCALITY: "A few miles north of Wyandotte Cave, Crawford Co.,
Indiana" (Bollman).
RANGE: Known only from type locality.

Genus COOKELLA Chamberlin

Cookella Chamberlin, 1941, Bull. Univ. Utah, biol. ser., vol. 6, No. 5,
p. 13.
GENEROTYPE: *Conotyla leibergi* Cook and Collins, by original designa-
tion.
RANGE: Northern Idaho.
SPECIES: One.

Cookella leibergi (Cook and Collins)

Conotyla leibergi Cook and Collins, 1895, Ann. New York Acad. Sci.,
vol. 9, p. 77, figs. 102–104.
TYPE: U. S. Nat. Mus.
TYPE LOCALITY: Lake Pend d'Oreille, Kootenai County, Idaho.
RANGE: Known only from type locality.

Genus FLAGELLOPETALUM Causey

Flagellopetalum Causey, 1951, Proc. Biol. Soc. Washington, vol. 64, p. 119.
GENEROTYPE: *Flagellopetalum stannardi* Causey, by original designation.
RANGE: Illinois.
SPECIES: One.

Flagellopetalum stannardi Causey

Flagellopetalum stannardi Causey, 1951, Proc. Biol. Soc. Washington,
vol. 64, p. 120, figs. 9–12.
TYPE: Illinois Nat. Hist. Surv.
TYPE LOCALITY: Rocky Branch, Clark County, Illinois.
RANGE: Known only from type locality.

Genus PROCONOTYLA Verhoeff

Proconotyla Verhoeff, 1932, Zool. Jahrb., Abt. Syst., vol. 62, p. 501.
GENEROTYPE: *Proconotyla blakei* Verhoeff, by monotypy.
RANGE: Eastern New York.
SPECIES: One.

Proconotyla blakei Verhoeff

Proconotyla blakei Verhoeff, 1932, Zool. Jahrb., Abt. Syst., vol. 62, p. 501, pl. 5, figs. 33–37, pl. 6, fig. 38.

TYPE: Verhoeff collection.

TYPE LOCALITY: Mount Adams, Essex County, New York.

RANGE: Known only from type locality.

Genus SCOTERPES Cope

Scoterpes Cope, 1872, Amer. Nat., vol. 6, p. 414.—Bollman, 1893, U. S. Nat. Mus. Bull. 46, p. 121.—Cook and Collins, 1895, Ann. New York Acad. Sci., vol. 9, p. 55.

GENEROTYPE: *Spirostrephon copei* Packard, by original designation.

RANGE: Central eastern United States, Missouri and Kentucky south into northern Georgia and Alabama.

SPECIES: Three, one with two subspecies.

Scoterpes austrinus austrinus Loomis

Scoterpes austrinus Loomis, 1943, Bull. Mus. Comp. Zool., vol. 92, p. 386, fig. 6, pl. 1, figs. 1, 2.

TYPE: Mus. Comp. Zool.

TYPE LOCALITY: Manitou Cave, 1 mile south of Fort Payne, De Kalb County, Alabama.

RANGE: Known only from type locality.

Scoterpes austrinus nudus Chamberlin

Scoterpes austrinus nudus Chamberlin, 1946, Ent. News. vol. 57, p. 152.

TYPE: Collection of R. V. Chamberlin.

TYPE LOCALITY: 4 miles north of Kingston, Bartow County, Georgia (Saltpeter Cave).

RANGE: Known only from type locality.

Scoterpes copei (Packard)

Spirostrephon (Pseudotremia) copei Packard, 1871, Amer. Nat., vol. 5, p. 748.

Scoterpes copei Cope, 1872, Amer. Nat., vol. 6, p. 414.—Cook and Collins, 1895, Ann. New York Acad. Sci., vol. 9, p. 55, figs. 12, 13.

TYPE: Present location unknown.

TYPE LOCALITY: Mammoth Cave, Edmonson County, Kentucky.

RANGE: Central Kentucky, southeast to northern Georgia and eastern Tennessee.

Scoterpes dendropus Loomis

Scoterpes dendropus Loomis, 1939, Bull. Mus. Comp. Zool., vol. 86, p. 181, figs. 9a–c.

TYPE: Mus. Comp. Zool.

TYPE LOCALITY: Marvel Cave, Stone County, Missouri.
RANGE: Also known from near Galena, Stone County, Missouri.

Genus TAIYUTYLA Chamberlin

Taiyutyla Chamberlin, 1952, Chicago Acad. Sci. Nat. Hist. Misc. No. 113, p. 1.
GENEROTYPE: *Taiyutyla corvallis* Chamberlin, by original designation.
RANGE: Oregon.
SPECIES: One.

Taiyutyla corvallis Chamberlin

Taiyutyla corvallis Chamberlin, 1952, Chicago Acad. Sci. Nat. Hist. Misc. No. 113, p. 1, figs. 1, 2.
TYPE: Collection of R. V. Chamberlin.
TYPE LOCALITY: Corvallis, Benton County, Oregon.
RANGE: Known only from type locality.

Genus TRICHOPETALUM Harger

Trichopetalum Harger, 1872, Amer. Journ. Sci. Arts, vol. 4, p. 117.—Cook and Collins, 1895, Ann. New York Acad. Sci., vol. 9, p. 62.
GENEROTYPE: *Trichopetalum lunatum* Harger, by subsequent designation of Cook and Collins, 1895.
RANGE: Northeastern United States, from New York and Connecticut south to Tennessee and west through Illinois and Indiana to Arkansas.
SPECIES: Five.

Trichopetalum album Cook and Collins

Trichopetalum album Cook and Collins, 1895, Ann. New York Acad. Sci., vol. 9, p. 64, figs. 22–29, 36–45.
TYPE: U. S. Nat. Mus.
TYPE LOCALITY: Here restricted to Syracuse, Onondaga County, New York.
RANGE: Central New York, southern Ontario.

Trichopetalum cornutum Cook and Collins

Trichopetalum cornutum Cook and Collins, 1895, Ann. New York Acad. Sci., vol. 9, p. 66, figs. 46–49.
TYPE: U. S. Nat Mus.
TYPE LOCALITY: Bloomington, Monroe County, Indiana.
RANGE: Indiana and Illinois.

Trichopetalum lunatum Harger

Trichopetalum lunatum Harger, 1872, Amer. Journ. Sci. Arts, vol. 4, p. 118.—Cook and Collins, 1895, Ann. New York Acad. Sci., vol. 9, p. 63, figs. 52, 53.

TYPE: Present location unknown.
TYPE LOCALITY: New Haven, Orange County, Connecticut.
RANGE: Known definitely only from type locality.

Trichopetalum montis Chamberlin

Trichopetalum montis Chamberlin, 1951, Great Basin Nat., vol. 11, p. 24, figs. 13, 14.
TYPE: Collection of R. V. Chamberlin.
TYPE LOCALITY: Gatlinburg, Sevier County, Tennessee.
RANGE: Known only from type locality.

Trichopetalum uncum Cook and Collins

Trichopetalum uncum Cook and Collins, 1895, Ann. New York Acad. Sci., vol. 9, p. 66, fig. 51.
TYPE: U. S. Nat. Mus.
TYPE LOCALITY: Bloomington, Monroe County, Indiana.
RANGE: Indiana and Illinois, south to Arkansas.

Genus TRIGENOTYLA Causey

Trigenotyla Causey, 1951, Proc. Biol. Soc. Washington, vol. 64, p. 118.
GENEROTYPE: *Trigenotyla parca* Causey, by original designation.
RANGE: Arkansas.
SPECIES: One.

Trigenotyla parca Causey

Trigenotyla parca Causey, 1951, Proc. Biol. Soc. Washington, vol. 64, p. 118, figs. 1–5.
TYPE: Acad. Nat. Sci. Philadelphia.
TYPE LOCALITY: Carroll County, Arkansas.
RANGE: Known only from Carroll and Washington Counties, Arkansas.

Genus TYNOPUS Chamberlin

Tynopus Chamberlin, 1940, Canadian Ent., vol. 72, p. 57.
GENEROTYPE: *Tynopus dux* Chamberlin, by original designation.
RANGE: North Carolina.
SPECIES: One.

Tynopus dux Chamberlin

Tynopus dux Chamberlin, 1940, Canadian Ent., vol. 72, p. 57.
TYPE: Collection of R. V. Chamberlin.
TYPE LOCALITY: Duke Forest, Orange County, North Carolina.
RANGE: Known only from type locality.

Genus ZYGONOPUS Ryder

Zygonopus Ryder, 1881, Proc. U. S. Nat. Mus., vol. 3, p. 527.—Cook and Collins, 1895, Ann. New York Acad. Sci., vol. 9, p. 59.

GENEROTYPE: *Zygonopus whitei* Ryder, by monotypy.
RANGE: Western Virginia, in caves.
SPECIES: One.

Zygonopus whitei Ryder

Zygonopus whitei Ryder, 1881, Proc. U. S. Nat. Mus., vol. 3, p. 527.—
    Cook and Collins, 1895, Ann. New York Acad. Sci., vol. 9, p. 60,
    figs. 14–21.
TYPE: Present location unknown.
TYPE LOCALITY: Luray Caverns, Page County, Virginia.
RANGE: Caves in Roanoke, Montgomery, Alleghany, Bath, and Page Counties, Virginia, and in Pendleton County, West Virginia.

Genus ZYGOTELA Chamberlin

Zygotela Chamberlin, 1951, Chicago Acad. Sci. Nat. Hist. Misc., No. 87,
    p. 6.
GENEROTYPE: *Zygotela phana* Chamberlin, by original designation.
RANGE: British Columbia.
SPECIES: One.

Zygotela phana Chamberlin

Zygotela phana Chamberlin, 1951, Chicago Acad. Sci. Nat. Hist. Misc.
    No. 87, p. 7, fig. 14.
TYPE: Provincial Mus., British Columbia.
TYPE LOCALITY: Blue River, British Columbia.
RANGE: Known only from type locality.

Conotylidae of uncertain generic position

Craspedosoma flavidum Bollman

Craspedosoma flavidum Bollman, 1888, Ent. Amer., vol. 4, p. 2.
Trichopetalum flavidum Cook and Collins, 1895, Ann. New York Acad.
    Sci. vol. 9, p. 67, fig. 50.
TYPE: U. S. Nat. Mus.
TYPE LOCALITY: Okolona, Clark County, Arkansas.
The male of Bollman's original pair of types was lost after his demise, and could not be found in 1894 nor during recent renovation of the collection at Washington.   Until such a time as male topotypes are studied, the position of this species must remain unsettled.

Polydesmus ocellatus Packard

Polydesmus ocellatus Packard, 1883, Amer. Nat., vol. 17, p. 428.
Craspedosoma packardi Stuxberg, 1885, Amer. Nat., vol. 19, p. 400.
Trichopetalum ocellatum Cook and Collins, 1895, Ann. New York Acad.
    Sci., vol. 9, p. 68, figs. 30–35.

TYPE: Probably lost.

TYPE LOCALITY: "Oregon."

This poorly described form presents an extremely difficult problem, and the name may never be placed except by some empirical action.

Trichopetalum glomeratum Harger

Trichopetalum glomeratum Harger, 1872, Amer. Journ. Sci. Arts, vol. 4, p. 118.

TYPE: Present location unknown.

TYPE LOCALITY: John Day Valley, Oregon.

Possibly a species of *Conotyla*, but, as observed by Cook and Collins, "The original description of this species is so brief that the generic position must remain in doubt."

Family ERGETHIDAE Chamberlin

Ergethidae Chamberlin, 1949, Proc. Biol. Soc. Washington, vol. 62, p. 7.

Genus ERGETHUS Chamberlin

Ergethus Chamberlin, 1949, Proc. Biol. Soc. Washington, vol. 62, p. 7.

GENEROTYPE: *Ergethus perditus* Chamberlin, by original designation.

RANGE: Texas.

SPECIES: Onc.

Ergethus perditus Chamberlin

Ergethus perditus Chamberlin, 1949, Proc. Biol. Soc. Washington, vol. 62, p. 7, figs. 1, 2.

TYPE: Collection of R. V. Chamberlin.

TYPE LOCALITY: Near Kerrville, Kerr County, Texas.

RANGE: Known only from type locality.

Family RHISCOSOMIDIDAE Silvestri

Rhiscosomididae Silvestri, 1909, Atti Accad. Lincei, Rendic., vol. 18, p. 232.

Genus RHISCOSOMIDES Silvestri

Rhiscosomides Silvestri, 1909, Atti Acad. Lincei, Rendic., vol. 18, p. 232.

GENEROTYPE: *Rhiscosomides meineri* Silvestri, by monotypy.

RANGE: Oregon.

SPECIES: Two.

Rhiscosomides josephi Chamberlin

Rhiscosomides josephi Chamberlin, 1941, Bull. Univ. Utah, biol. ser., vol. 6, No. 5, p. 16.

TYPE: Collection of R. V. Chamberlin.

TYPE LOCALITY: John Day Creek, Douglas County, Oregon.
RANGE: Known only from type locality.

Rhiscosomides meineri Silvestri

Rhiscosomides meineri Silvestri, 1909, Atti Acad. Lincei, Rendic., vol. 18, p. 232.
TYPE: Present location unknown.
TYPE LOCALITY: Lebanon, Linn County, Oregon.
RANGE: Known only from type locality.

Genus TINGUPA Chamberlin

Tingupa Chamberlin, 1910, Ann. Ent. Soc. Amer., vol. 3, No. 4, p. 238.
GENEROTYPE: *Tingupa utahensis* Chamberlin, by original designation.
RANGE: California, Utah, Missouri.
SPECIES: Three, one having two subspecies.

Tingupa monterea Chamberlin

Tingupa monterea Chamberlin, 1910, Ann. Ent. Soc. Amer., vol. 3, p. 240, pl. 34, figs. 3–5.
TYPE: Present location unknown.
TYPE LOCALITY: Pacific Grove, Monterey County, California.
RANGE: Known only from type locality.

Tingupa pallida Loomis

Tingupa pallida Loomis, 1939, Bull. Mus. Comp. Zool., vol. 86, No. 4, p. 185, figs. 12a–c.
TYPE: Mus. Comp. Zool.
TYPE LOCALITY: River Cave at Hahatunka, Camden County, Missouri.
RANGE: Extreme eastern Missouri and adjacent western Illinois, in caves.

Tingupa utahensis utahensis Chamberlin

Tingupa utahensis Chamberlin, 1910, Ann. Ent. Soc. Amer., vol. 3, p. 238, pl. 33, figs. 4–8; pl. 34, figs. 1, 2.
TYPE: Present location unknown.
TYPE LOCALITY: Mill Creek Canyon, Salt Lake County, Utah.
RANGE: Canyons of the northern Wasatch Mountains, in Utah.

Tingupa utahensis australis Chamberlin

Tingupa utahensis australis Chamberlin, 1925, Pan-Pacific Ent., vol. 2, No. 2, p. 62.
TYPE: Collection of R. V. Chamberlin.
TYPE LOCALITY: Cedar City, Iron County, Utah.
RANGE: Known only from type locality.

Family UNDERWOODIIDAE Verhoeff

Underwoodiidae Verhoeff, 1909, Zool. Anz., vol. 34, p. 568.

Genus UNDERWOODIA Cook and Collins

Underwoodia Cook and Collins, 1895, Ann. New York Acad. Sci., vol. 9, p. 79.

GENEROTYPE: *Underwoodia polygama* Cook and Collins, by present designation.

RANGE: Northeastern North America; Utah.

SPECIES: Four.

Underwoodia hespera Chamberlin

Underwoodia hespera Chamberlin, 1925, Pan-Pacific Ent., vol. 2, No. 2, p. 63.

TYPE: Collection of R. V. Chamberlin.

TYPE LOCALITY: Mill Creek Canyon, Salt Lake County, Utah.

RANGE: Canyons of the Wasatch Mountains, Utah.

Underwoodia iuloides (Harger)

Trichopetalum iuloides Harger, 1872, Amer. Journ. Sci. Arts, vol. 4, p. 118.

Underwoodia iuloides Cook and Collins, 1895, Ann. New York Acad. Sci., vol. 9, p. 83, figs. 177–179.

TYPE: Present location unknown.

TYPE LOCALITY: Simmon's Harbor, Ontario.

RANGE: Recorded from Ontario, Michigan, and central New York.

Underwoodia polygama Cook and Collins

Underwoodia polygama Cook and Collins, 1895, Ann. New York Acad. Sci. vol. 9, p. 80, figs. 180–190.—Palmén, 1952, Ann. Zool. Soc. 'Vanamo', vol. 15, No. 1, p. 2, figs. 1–9.

TYPE: U. S. Nat. Mus.

TYPE LOCALITY: Centerport (Long Island), Suffolk County, New York.

RANGE: Recorded only from Long Island and from Newfoundland.

Underwoodia tida Chamberlin

Underwoodia tida Chamberlin, 1925, Pan-Pacific Ent., vol. 2, No. 2, p. 62.

TYPE: Collection of R. V. Chamberlin.

TYPE LOCALITY: Logan Canyon, Cache County, Utah.

RANGE: Known only from type locality.

Family UROCHORDEUMIDAE Silvestri

Urochordeumidae Silvestri, 1909, Atti Accad. Lincei, Rendic., vol. 18, p. 230.

Genus UROCHORDEUMA Silvestri

Urochordeuma Silvestri, 1909, Atti Accad. Lincei, Rendic., vol. 18, p. 230.
GENEROTYPE: *Urochordeuma bumpusi* Silvestri, by monotypy.
RANGE: Washington.
SPECIES: Two.

Urochordeuma bumpusi Silvestri

Urochordeuma bumpusi Silvestri, 1909, Atti Accad. Lincei, Rendic., vol. 18, p. 230.
TYPE: Present location unknown.
TYPE LOCALITY: Longmire Springs, near Tacoma, Pierce County, Washington.
RANGE: Known only from type locality.

Urochordeuma porona Chamberlin

Urochordeuma porona Chamberlin, 1941, Bull. Univ. Utah, biol. ser., vol. 6, No. 4, p. 23, figs. 45, 46.
TYPE: Collection of R. V. Chamberlin.
TYPE LOCALITY: Snoqualmie Pass, King County, Washington.
RANGE: Known only from type locality.

Suborder LYSIOPETALIDEA

Lysiopetalidae Wood, 1865, Trans. Amer. Philos. Soc., new ser., vol. 13, p. 191.—Ryder, 1881, Proc. U. S. Nat. Mus., vol. 3, p. 524.
Monozonia (in part) Brandt, 1833, Bull. Soc. Nat. Moscou, vol. 6, p. 205.
Craspedosomidae (in part) Gray, 1842, *in* Todd, Cyclop. Anat. and Physiol., vol. 3, p. 546.—Saussure and Humbert, 1872, Études sur les myriapodes, *in* Miss. Sci. Mexique, Zool., pt. 6, sect. 2, p. 56.
Callipodoidae Bollman, 1893, U. S. Nat. Mus. Bull. 46, p. 155.
Lysiopetaloidea Cook, 1895, Ann. New York Acad. Sci., vol. 9, p. 3.—Attems, 1926, *in* Kükenthal-Krumbach, Handbuch der Zoologie, vol. 4, p. 177.

Family LYSIOPETALIDAE Wood

Lysiopetalidae Wood, 1865, Trans. Amer. Philos. Soc., vol. 13, p. 191.—Cook, 1895, Ann. New York Acad. Sci., vol. 9, p. 3.—Loomis, 1937, Proc. U. S. Nat. Mus., vol. 84, No. 3006, p. 97 (monograph of North American species).

Genus ABACION Rafinesque [5]

Abacion Rafinesque, 1820, Annals of nature, p. 9.—Hoffman and Crabill, 1953, Florida Ent., vol. 36, p. 81.

---

[5] The arrangement of species in this genus is based on unpublished work by the junior author.

Spirostrephon Brandt, 1841 Bull. Sci. Acad. Sci. Saint-Pétersbourg, vol. 8,
    p. 105.—Cook, 1895, Amer. Nat., vol. 29, p. 1017.—Loomis, 1937,
    Proc. U. S. Nat. Mus., vol. 84, p. 105 (generotype, *Julus lactarius*
    Say, by monotypy).

Platops Newport, 1844, Ann. Mag. Nat. Hist., vol. 13, p. 267 (generotype,
    P. rugulosa Newport, by present designation).

GENEROTYPE: *Abacion tesselatum* Rafinesque, by monotypy.

RANGE: Eastern United States, east of the 100th Meridian.

SPECIES: Four, of which two have one subspecies each.

Abacion lactarium (Say)

Julus lactarius Say, 1821, Journ. Acad. Nat. Sci. Philadelphia, vol. 2,
    p. 104.

Spirostrephon lactarium Brandt, 1841, Bull. Sci. Acad. Sci. Saint-Péters-
    bourg, vol. 8, p. 105.—Loomis, 1937, Proc. U. S. Nat. Mus., vol. 84,
    p. 108, fig. 16 l–m.

Platops lineata Newport, 1844, Ann. Mag. Nat. Hist., vol. 13, p. 267 (type
    locality: "North America"; type: British Museum, probably the orig-
    inal Say type of *lactarius*).

TYPE: Location not known with certainty (see note above in entry for
Platops lineata).

TYPE LOCALITY: Here restricted to the vicinity of Philadelphia,
Pennsylvania.

RANGE: Coastal Plain and Piedmont of the Atlantic States, from northern New Jersey south into peninsular Florida. Exact limits of range still
very poorly known.

Abacion magnum magnum (Loomis)

Spirostrephon magnum Loomis, 1943, Bull. Mus. Comp. Zool., vol. 92,
    p. 388, fig. 8a, b.

TYPE: Mus. Comp. Zool.

TYPE LOCALITY: Monte Sano State Park, Madison County, Alabama.

RANGE: Extreme northeastern Alabama, probably also adjacent parts of
Tennessee and Georgia.

Abacion magnum highlandense (Hoffman)

Spirostrephon highlandensis Hoffman, 1950, Journ. Elisha Mitchell Sci.
    Soc., vol. 66, p. 17, figs. 5, 6.

TYPE: U. S. Nat. Mus. (No. 1875).

TYPE LOCALITY: Highlands, Macon County, North Carolina.

RANGE: Most of the Appalachian Mountains. Peripheral localities include St. Clair and Lee Counties, Alabama; Stephens County, Georgia;
Greenville County, South Carolina; Harlan County, Kentucky; Upshur

County, West Virginia; Tompkins and Greene Counties, New York. Merges with *A. m. magnum* in northeastern Alabama.

Abacion tesselatum tesselatum Rafinesque

Abacion tesselatum Rafinesque, 1820, Annals of nature, p. 9.—Hoffman and Crabill, 1953, Florida Ent., vol. 36, p. 81.

Platops rugulosa Newport, 1844, Ann. Mag. Nat. Hist., vol. 13, p. 267 (type locality unknown, probably Ohio River Valley; type: British Museum).

Reasia spinosa Sager, 1856, Proc. Acad. Nat Sci. Philadelphia, p. 109 (type locality here designated: vicinity of Detroit, Michigan; type: not known to exist).

Lysiopetalum eudasym McNeill, 1887, Proc. U. S. Nat. Mus., vol. 10, p. 330 (type locality: Bloomington, Indiana; types: U. S. Nat. Mus.).

TYPE: Not known to exist.

TYPE LOCALITY: Estill County, Kentucky.

RANGE: Centered in the Interior Lowlands; peripheral localities include St. Louis, Missouri; Winnebago County, Illinois (the species surely occurs in Wisconsin); Estill County, Kentucky; Washington County, Pennsylvania; Alleghany and Montgomery Counties, Virginia. Intergradation with the following race takes place in southern Missouri and probably also through much of Tennessee.

Abacion tesselatum creolum (Chamberlin)

Spirostrephon creolum Chamberlin, 1942, Bull. Univ. Utah, biol. ser., vol. 6, No. 8, p. 9, figs. 24, 25.

TYPE: Collection of R. V. Chamberlin.

TYPE LOCALITY: Covington, St. Tammany Parish, Louisiana.

RANGE: From Lee County, Alabama (doubtless also the western Panhandle of Florida), west through Mississippi and Louisiana to the northwestern corner of Arkansas.

Abacion texense (Loomis)

Spirostrephon texensis Loomis, 1937, Proc. U. S. Nat. Mus., vol. 84, p. 109, fig. 16n.

Spirostrephon jonesi Chamberlin, 1942, Canadian Ent., vol. 74, p. 17, fig 1 (type locality: Ames, Story County, Iowa; type: collection of R. V. Chamberlin).

TYPE: U. S. Nat Mus. (No. 1237).

TYPE LOCALITY: Pierce, Wharton County, Texas.

RANGE: Great Plains from Ames, Iowa, and Lincoln, Nebraska, through Kansas, Oklahoma, and western Missouri, south as far as Kerr, Bandera, and Wharton Counties, Texas, east through Arkansas and Louisiana to Rankin County, Mississippi. The exact limits of distribution remain to be determined.

Genus COLACTIS Loomis

Colactis Loomis, 1937, Proc. U. S. Nat. Mus., vol. 84, p. 120.
GENEROTYPE: *Colactis saxetana* Loomis, by original designation.
RANGE: Arizona and Utah, south into the Mexican Plateau.
SPECIES: Six, of which five occur in our limits.

Colactis baboquivari Loomis

Colactis baboquivari Loomis, 1937, Proc. U. S. Nat. Mus., vol. 84, p. 123,
figs. 16c, d, pl. 3, fig. 4.
TYPE: U. S. Nat. Mus. (No. 1244).
TYPE LOCALITY: Baboquivari Canyon, Pima County, Arizona.
RANGE: Known only from type locality.

Colactis quadrata Loomis

Colactic quadrata Loomis, 1937, Proc. U. S. Nat. Mus., vol. 84, p. 128,
figs. 16e, f, pl. 3, fig. 5.
TYPE: U. S. Nat. Mus. (No. 1247).
TYPE LOCALITY: Cave Creek Canyon, Chiricahua Mountains, Cochise
County, Arizona.
RANGE: Known only from type locality.

Colactis saxetana Loomis

Colactis saxetana Loomis, 1937, Proc. U. S. Nat. Mus., vol. 84, p. 122,
figs. 16a, b, pl. 3, fig. 2.
TYPE: U. S. Nat. Mus. (No. 1243).
TYPE LOCALITY: Piacacho Mountain, between Tucson and Casa Grande,
Pinal County, Arizona.
RANGE: Also recorded with a doubt (female material) from near Sacaton,
Arizona.

Colactis sideralis Loomis

Colactis sideralis Loomis, 1937, Proc. U. S. Nat. Mus., vol. 84, p. 125,
figs. 16j, k, pl. 4, figs. 1, 2.
TYPE: U. S. Nat. Mus. (No. 1245).
TYPE LOCALITY: Estrella Mountains, Maricopa County, Arizona.
RANGE: Reported from Maricopa, Pinal, and Yuma Counties, Arizona.

Colactis utorum (Chamberlin)

Spirostrephon utorum Chamberlin, 1925, Pan-Pacific Ent., vol. 2, No. 2,
p. 61.
Colactis utorum Loomis, 1937, Proc. U. S. Nat. Mus., vol. 84, p. 130.
TYPE: Collection of R. V. Chamberlin.
TYPE LOCALITY: Green River, Emery County, Utah.
RANGE: Known only from type locality.

Genus DELOPHON Chamberlin [6]

Delophon Chamberlin, 1943, Bull. Univ. Utah, biol. ser., vol. 8, No. 2, p. 13.—Causey, 1954, Tulane Stud. Zool., vol. 2, No. 4, p. 63 (key to species).
GENEROTYPE: *Delophon georgianum* Chamberlin, by original designation.
RANGE: Southern end of the Appalachian Mountains.
SPECIES: Three.

Delophon carolinum Hoffman

Delophon carolinum Hoffman, 1950, Journ. Elisha Mitchell Sci. Soc., vol. 66, p. 18, fig. 5.
TYPE: U. S. Nat. Mus. (No. 1874).
TYPE LOCALITY: Highlands, Macon County, North Carolina.
RANGE: Known from Macon, Transylvania, and Swain Counties, North Carolina, and Rabun County, Georgia.

Delophon georgianum Chamberlin

Delophon georgianum Chamberlin, 1943, Bull. Univ. Utah, biol. ser., vol. 8, No. 2, p. 13, figs. 28–30.
TYPE: Collection of R. V. Chamberlin.
TYPE LOCALITY: Gainesville, Hall County, Georgia.
RANGE: Known only from type locality.

Delophon serrulatum Causey

Delophon serrulatum Causey, 1954, Tulane Stud. Zool., vol. 2, No. 4, p. 64, figs. 1–3.
TYPE: Amer. Mus. Nat. Hist.
TYPE LOCALITY: Nine miles west of Loxley, Baldwin County, Alabama (stated to be Mississippi in the original description).
RANGE: Known only from type locality.

Genus DIACTIS Loomis

Diactis Loomis, 1937, Proc. U. S. Nat. Mus., vol. 84, p. 110.
GENEROTYPE: *Diactis soleata* Loomis, by original designation.
RANGE: Southern California.
SPECIES: Three.

Diactis frondifera Loomis

Diactis frondifera Loomis, 1937, Proc. U. S. Nat. Mus., vol. 84, p. 116, fig. 17f.
TYPE: U. S. Nat. Mus. (No. 1240).
TYPE LOCALITY: Torrey Pines, La Jolla, San Diego County, California.
RANGE: Known only from type locality.

---

[6] Assigned to the European family Dorypetalidae by Causey (1954), but without, as far as we can see, adequate justification.

Diactis soleata Loomis

Diactis soleata Loomis, 1937, Proc. U. S. Nat. Mus., vol. 84, p. 113, figs. 17b–e, pl. 3, fig. 1.

TYPE: U. S. Nat. Mus. (No. 1238).

TYPE LOCALITY: Temescal Canyon Road, near Corona, Riverside County, California.

RANGE: Known only from type locality.

Diactis triangula Loomis

Diactis triangula Loomis, 1937, Proc. U. S. Nat. Mus., vol. 84, p. 114, fig. 17a.

TYPE: U. S. Nat. Mus. (No. 1239).

TYPE LOCALITY: Cottonwood Creek, 46 miles east of San Diego, on the road to El Centro, San Diego County, California.

RANGE: Known only from type locality.

Genus ETIRON Chamberlin

Etiron Chamberlin, 1941, Bull. Univ. Utah, biol. ser., vol. 6, No. 4, p. 21.

GENEROTYPE: *Etiron paroicum* Chamberlin, by original designation.

RANGE: Southern California.

SPECIES: Two.

Etiron paroicum Chamberlin

Etiron paroicum Chamberlin, 1941, Bull. Univ. Utah, biol. ser., vol. 6, No. 4, p. 21, figs. 37–41.

TYPE: Collection of R. V. Chamberlin.

TYPE LOCALITY: Mountain Spring, Riverside County, California.

RANGE: Known only from type locality.

Etiron pearcei Chamberlin

Etiron pearcei Chamberlin, 1941, Bull. Univ. Utah, biol. ser., vol. 6, No. 4, p. 22.

TYPE: Collection of R. V. Chamberlin.

TYPE LOCALITY: Castro Valley, Alameda County, California.

RANGE: Known only from type locality.

Genus HEPTIUM Loomis

Heptium Loomis, 1937, Proc. U. S. Nat. Mus., vol. 84, p. 130.

GENEROTYPE: *Heptium carinellum* Loomis, by original designation.

RANGE: Southern California.

SPECIES: Three.

Heptium canum Chamberlin

Heptium canum Chamberlin, 1941, Bull. Univ. Utah, biol. ser., vol. 6, No. 4, p. 22, figs. 42–44.

TYPE: Collection of R. V. Chamberlin.

TYPE LOCALITY: Coyote Wells, Riverside County, California.
RANGE: Known only from type locality.

Heptium carinellum Loomis

Heptium carinellum Loomis, 1937, Proc. U. S. Nat. Mus., vol. 84, p. 132, figs. 18f–j, pl. 4, figs. 3, 4.
TYPE: U. S. Nat. Mus. (No. 1248).
TYPE LOCALITY: 2 miles east of "Indian Head" on the Indio-El Centro road, Imperial County, California.
RANGE: Imperial and Riverside Counties, California.

Heptium scamillatum Loomis

Heptium scamillatum Loomis, 1937, Proc. U. S. Nat. Mus., vol. 84, p. 134, figs. 18a–e, pl. 4, figs. 5, 6.
TYPE: U. S. Nat. Mus. (No. 1249).
TYPE LOCALITY: Between Perris and Elsinore, Riverside County, California.
RANGE: Known only from type locality.

Genus TEXOPHON Chamberlin

Texophon Chamberlin, 1946, Ent. News, vol. 57, p. 97.
GENEROTYPE: *Texophon nessius* Chamberlin, by original designation.
RANGE: Southern Texas.
SPECIES: One.

Texophon nessius Chamberlin

Texophon nessius Chamberlin, 1946, Ent. News, vol. 57, p. 97, figs. 1, 2.
TYPE: Collection of R. V. Chamberlin.
TYPE LOCALITY: Laguna Madre, 23 miles southeast of Harlingen, Cameron County, Texas.
RANGE: Known only from several localities in Cameron County, Texas.

Genus TYNOMMA Loomis

Tynomma Loomis, 1937, Proc. U. S. Nat. Mus., vol. 84, p. 117.
GENEROTYPE: *Tynomma sedecimum* Loomis, by original designation.
RANGE: Central California.
SPECIES: Three.

Tynomma consanguineum Loomis

Tynomma consanguineum Loomis, 1937, Proc. U. S. Nat. Mus., vol. 84, p. 119, figs. 17g–i.
TYPE: U. S. Nat. Mus. (No. 1242).
TYPE LOCALITY: Santa Cruz Mountains, between Santa Cruz and Holy City, Santa Cruz County, California.
RANGE: Known only from type locality.

Tynomma mutans (Chamberlin)

Lysiopetalum mutans Chamberlin, 1910, Ann. Ent. Soc. America, vol. 3, p. 233, pl. 30, figs. 1–10, pl. 31, figs. 1, 2.
Tynomma mutans Loomis, 1937, Proc. U. S. Nat. Mus., vol. 84, p. 120.
TYPE: Present location unknown.
TYPE LOCALITY: Stanford, Santa Clara County, California.
RANGE: Known only from type locality.

Tynomma sedecimum Loomis

Tynomma sedecimum Loomis, 1937, Proc. U. S. Nat. Mus., vol. 84, p. 118, figs. 17j–l, pl. 3, fig. 6.
TYPE: U. S. Nat. Mus. (No. 1241).
TYPE LOCALITY: Between Vallejo and Cordelia, Solano County, California.
RANGE: Known only from the vicinity of the type locality.

Suborder STRIARIDEA

Striaroidea Cook, 1896, Brandtia, No. 2, p. 8; 1899, Proc. U. S. Nat. Mus., vol. 21, p. 670.—Attems, 1926, *in* Kükenthal-Krumbach, Handbuch der Zoologie, vol. 4, p. 177.

Family STRIARIIDAE Bollman

Striariinae Bollman, 1893, U. S. Nat. Mus. Bull. 46, p. 158.
Striariidae Cook, 1895, Ann. New York Acad. Sci., vol. 9, p. 4; 1899, Proc. U. S. Nat. Mus., vol. 21, p. 670.—Loomis, 1936, Journ. Washington Acad. Sci., vol. 26, p. 404.

Genus AMPLARIA Chamberlin

Amplaria Chamberlin, 1941, Bull. Univ. Utah, biol. ser., vol. 6, No. 5, p. 9.
GENEROTYPE: *Amplaria eutypa* Chamberlin, by original designation.
RANGE: California and Oregon; North Carolina.
SPECIES: Three.

Amplaria causeyae (Chamberlin)

Striaria causeyae Chamberlin, 1940, Canadian Ent., vol. 72, p. 58.
TYPE: Collection of R. V. Chamberlin.
TYPE LOCALITY: Duke Forest, Orange County, North Carolina.
RANGE: Known only from type locality.

Amplaria eutypa Chamberlin

Amplaria eutypa Chamberlin, 1941, Bull. Univ. Utah., biol. ser., vol. 6, No. 5, p. 9.
TYPE: Collection of R. V. Chamberlin.
TYPE LOCALITY: 9 miles north of Placerville, Eldorado County, California.
RANGE: Known only from type locality.

Amplaria nazinta (Chamberlin)

Striaria nazinta Chamberlin, 1910, Ann. Ent. Soc. Amer., vol. 3, p. 242, pl. 35, figs. 2–6.

TYPE: Present location unknown.

TYPE LOCALITY: Portland, Multnomah County, Oregon.

RANGE: Known only from type locality.

Genus STRIARIA Bollman

Striaria Bollman, 1888, Ann. New York Acad. Sci., vol. 4, p. 108.—Cook, 1899, Proc. U. S. Nat. Mus., vol. 21, p. 671.—Loomis, 1936, Journ. Washington Acad. Sci., vol. 26, p. 409 (key to species).

GENEROTYPE: *Striaria granulosa* Bollman, by original description.

RANGE: Appalachian region; Illinois; California.

SPECIES: Nine.

Striaria antica Causey

Striaria antica Causey, 1952, Proc. Biol. Soc. Washington, vol. 65, p. 112, figs. 1–3.

TYPE: Illinois Nat. Hist. Surv.

TYPE LOCALITY: Turkey Run State Park, Montgomery County, Indiana.

RANGE: Known only from type locality.

Striaria californica Cook

Striaria californica Cook, 1899, Proc. U. S. Nat. Mus., vol. 21, p. 675, pl. 53, fig. 2a.—Loomis, 1936, Journ. Washington Acad. Sci., vol. 26, p. 409, fig. 1f.

TYPE: U. S. Nat. Mus. (No. 776).

TYPE LOCALITY: California, probably near Sausalito, Marin County.

RANGE: Reported from three localities in southern California.

Striaria carmela Chamberlin

Striaria carmela Chamberlin, 1947, Proc. Biol. Soc. Washington, vol. 60, p. 9, figs. 1, 2.

TYPE: Collection of R. V. Chamberlin.

TYPE LOCALITY: Hastings Reservation, Monterey County, California.

RANGE: Known only from type locality.

Striaria columbiana Cook

Striaria columbiana Cook, 1899, Proc. U. S. Nat. Mus., vol. 21, p. 674, pl. 53, fig. 3a, pl. 54, figs. 1a–m.

TYPE: U. S. Nat. Mus. (No. 775).

TYPE LOCALITY: Washington, D. C.

RANGE: Known from the District of Columbia, adjacent Maryland, and southwest to Front Royal and Charlottesville, Virginia.

Striaria eldora Chamberlin

Striaria eldora Chamberlin, 1953, Ent. News, vol. 64, p. 95.

TYPE: Collection of R. V. Chamberlin.

TYPE LOCALITY: Crystal Cosumnes Cave, Eldorado County, California.

RANGE: Known only from type locality.

Striaria granulosa Bollman

Striaria granulosa Bollman, 1888, Ann. New York Acad. Sci., vol. 4, p.
   108.—Cook, 1899, Proc. U. S. Nat. Mus., vol. 21, p. 672, pl. 53,
   figs. 1a–j.

TYPE: U. S. Nat Mus. (No. 230).

TYPE LOCALITY: Beaver Creek, Jefferson County, Tennessee.

RANGE: Eastern Tennessee, southwestern Virginia; exact limits of range
not yet established.

Striaria imberbis Loomis

Striaria imberbis Loomis, 1936, Journ. Washington Acad. Sci., vol. 26,
   p. 408, fig. 1d.

TYPE: U. S. Nat. Mus.

TYPE LOCALITY: South of Atascadero, San Luis Obispo County,
California.

RANGE: Known only from type locality.

Striaria nana Loomis

Striaria nana Loomis, 1936, Journ. Washington Acad. Sci., vol. 26, p. 407,
   figs. 1a–c.

TYPE: U. S. Nat. Mus.

TYPE LOCALITY: Altamont Pass, above Miles, Alameda County, California.

RANGE: Also recorded from Pescadero, Santa Cruz County, California.

Striaria zygoleuca Hoffman

Striaria zygoleuca Hoffman, 1950, Journ. Elisha Mitchell Sci. Soc., vol. 66,
   p. 16, fig. 4.

TYPE: U. S. Nat. Mus. (No. 1873).

TYPE LOCALITY: Highlands, Macon County, North Carolina.

RANGE: Known from several localities in western North Carolina and
adjacent eastern Tennessee.

Order JULIDA

Julidea Brandt, 1833, Bull. Soc. Nat. Moscou, vol. 6, p. 201.

Julidae Meinert, 1868, Naturh. Tidsskr., ser. 3, vol. 5, p. 6.—Latzel, 1884,
   Myr. Öst.-Ung. Monarch., vol. 2, p. 238.

Juloidea Cook, 1895, Ann. New York Acad. Sci., vol. 9, p. 6.—Silvestri,
   1897, Ann. Mus. Civ. Stor. Nat. Genova, ser. 2, vol. 18, p. 650.

Zygocheta Cook, 1896, Brandtia, No. 2, p. 8.
Diplocheta (in part) Cook, 1895, Ann. New York Acad. Sci., vol. 9, p. 5.—
    Silvestri, 1897, Ann. Mus. Civ. Stor. Nat. Genova, ser. 2, vol. 18, p. 650.
Symphyognatha Verhoeff, 1909, Zool. Anz., vol. 34, p. 542.
Juliformia (in part) Attems, 1926, in Kükenthal-Krumbach, Handbuch
    der Zoologie, vol. 4, p. 181.
Julida Chamberlin, 1938, Publ. Carnegie Inst. Washington, No. 491,
    p. 166; 1943, Bull. Univ. Utah, biol. ser., vol. 8, No. 3, p. 29.

KEY TO THE SUBORDERS OF JULIDA

1. Telopodite of anterior gonopods mostly absent or rudimentary, when present not
moveable by muscles; gonopods sunk in a pocket and more or less concealed;
grinding plate of mandibles with a pitted area and adjacent fluted band or file,
or if this development is absent, the cutting teeth are also aborted or weak;
labroclypeal processes absent . . . . JULIDEA (p. 118)
Telopodite of anterior gonopods strongly developed and always moveable by muscles;
gonopods not sunk in a pocket, freely exposed; grinding plate of mandibles
without pits and fluting; labroclypeal processes present . . PARAIULIDEA (p. 122)

Suborder JULIDEA

Julidae Attems, 1926, in Kükenthal-Krumbach, Handbuch der Zoologie,
    vol. 4, p. 186.
Oncophora Verhoeff, 1930, in Bronn, Klass. und Ordn. des Tier-Reichs,
    Band 5, Abt. 2, Lief. 10, p. 1643 (as superfamily).

Family JULIDAE Meinert

Julidae (in part) Meinert, 1868, Naturh. Tidsskr., ser. 3, vol. 5, p. 6.—
    Latzel., 1884, Myr. Öst.-Ung., Monarch., vol. 2, p. 238.—Wood, 1865,
    Trans. Amer. Philos. Soc., new ser., vol. 13, p. 194.
Julinae Bollman, 1893, U. S. Nat. Mus. Bull. 46, p. 157.

Genus BRACHYIULUS Berlese

Brachyiulus Berlese, 1884, Acari, Myriopoda, et scorpiones hucusque in
    Italia reperta, fasc. 12, p. 1 (as subgenus of Julus).
GENEROTYPE: Julus pusillus Leach.
RANGE: Europe, North Africa, and introduced in North America.
SPECIES: Eleven, of which one is established in North America.

Brachyiulus pusillus (Leach)

Julus pusillus Leach, 1815, Trans. Linnean Soc. London, vol. 11, p. 379.
Julus exiguus Brandt, 1841, Recueil, p. 85.
Julus virgatus Wood, 1864, Proc. Acad. Nat. Sci. Philadelphia, p. 14 (type
    locality: Philadelphia, Pennsylvania; type unknown).

Julus stuxbergi Fanzago, 1875, Atti. Accad. Sci. Veneto-Trentino-Istriana, vol. 4, p. 150.

Brachyiulus littoralis Verhoeff, 1898, Arch. Naturg., vol. 64, p. 154, pl. 6, fig. 29.

Microbrachyiulus littoralis Jawlowski, 1939, Frag. Faun. Mus. Zool. Polonici, vol. 4, p. 154.

TYPE: British Museum (Nat. Hist.).

TYPE LOCALITY: England.

RANGE: Throughout Europe and in the Azores; northern portion of North America in developed areas, south at least as far as Virginia. A synanthropic species doubtless introduced into this country from Europe.

Genus DIPLOIULUS Berlese

Diploiulus Berlese, 1884, Acari, Myriopoda, et scorpiones hucusque in Italia reperta, fasc. 12, p. 2 (as subgenus of *Julus*).—Chamberlin, 1922, Proc. Biol. Soc. Washington, vol. 35, p. 8.

Cylindroiulus Verhoeff, 1893, Zool. Anz., vol. 16, p. 480 nomen nudum; 1894, Verh. Zool.-Bot. Ges. Wien, vol. 44, Abt. 29, p. 151.

GENEROTYPE: *Julus boleti* Koch.

RANGE: Europe; introduced into North America.

SPECIES: About 70, of which 5 are known to be established in North America.

Diploiulus caeruleocinctus (Wood)

Julus caeruleocinctus Wood, 1864, Proc. Acad. Nat. Sci. Philadelphia, p. 14.

Iulus multistriatus Walsh, 1866, Practical Ent., vol. 2, pp. 34, 70.

Julus londinensis Porat, 1866, Bidrag t. K. Sver., Myr. Diplop., p. 28.— Meinert, 1868, Naturh. Tidsskr., ser. 3, vol. 5, p. 8.

Iulus teutonicus Pocock, 1900, Ann. Mag. Nat. Hist., ser. 7, vol. 6, p. 206.

Cylindroiulus londinensis teutonicus Jackson, 1915, Lancashire and Cheshire Nat., p. 433.

Diploiulus londinensis caeruleocinctus Chamberlin, 1922, Proc. Biol. Soc. Washington, vol. 35, p. 8.

TYPE: Present location unknown.

TYPE LOCALITY: Pennsylvania.

RANGE: Introduced from Europe and now occurring abundantly throughout the New England States and adjoining parts of Canada, southward to Pennsylvania and Maryland, westward to Indiana, Illinois, and Iowa.

Diploiulus latistriatus latistriatus (Curtis)

Julus latistriatus Curtis, 1845 (in part), Journ. Royal Agr. Soc. England, vol. 5, pt. 1, p. 229.

Julus hortensis Wood, 1864, Proc. Acad. Nat. Sci. Philadelphia, p. 14.— 1865, Trans. Amer. Philos. Soc., vol. 13, p. 205.

Julus oweni Bollman, 1887, Ent. Amer., vol. 2, p. 228 (type locality: New Harmony, Indiana; type: U. S. Nat. Mus.).

Iulus frisius Verhoeff, 1891, Berliner Ent. Zeitschr., vol. 36, p. 133.

Diploiulus luscus Chamberlin, 1921, Proc. Biol. Soc. Washington, vol. 34, p. 82.

Diploiulus hortensis Chamberlin, 1947, Proc. Acad. Nat. Sci. Philadelphia, vol. 99, p. 35.

Cylindroiulus latistriatus Blower, 1953, Ann. Mag. Nat. Hist., ser. 12, vol. 6, p. 306, fig. 4.

TYPE: British Museum (Nat. Hist.).

TYPE LOCALITY: England.

RANGE: A synanthropic species introduced from Europe and now abundant in cultivated areas of Canada and the United States as far west as Washington and British Columbia.

Diploiulus latistriatus hesperus (Chamberlin)

Julus hesperus Chamberlin, 1914, Canadian Ent., vol. 46, p. 314.

Cylindroiulus frisius oceanicus Verhoeff, 1924, *in* Skottsberg, The natural history of Juan Fernandez and Easter Island, vol. 3, p. 406; 1944, Bull. Southern California Acad. Sci., vol. 43, p. 67.

TYPE: Mus. Comp. Zool.

TYPE LOCALITY: Los Angeles, California.

RANGE: Occurring in California from Los Angeles northward in the central coastal area as far as San Francisco Bay, and on the Hawaiian, Easter, and Juan Fernandez Islands.

Diploiulus luscus (Meinert)[7]

Julus luscus Meinert, 1868, Naturh. Tidsskr., ser. 3, vol. 5, p. 9.

Iulus britannicus Verhoeff, 1891, Berliner Ent. Zeitschr., vol. 36, p. 147, pl. 8, figs. 41, 42, 42b.

Cylindroiulus britannicus Schubart, 1934, *in* Dahl, Die Tierwelt Deutschlands, Teil 28, p. 228, fig. 361.—Palmén, 1952, Ann. Zool. Soc. 'Vanamo', vol. 15, No. 1, p. 20.—Blower, 1953, Ann. Mag. Nat. Hist., ser. 12, vol. 6, p. 307.

TYPE: Mus. Hauniensis (Copenhagen).

TYPE LOCALITY: Denmark.

RANGE: Europe and North America, where introduced. The only definite American locality thus far is Newfoundland, but in all probability part of the records for *latistriatus* pertain to this species, the two being easily confused.

Diploiulus punctatus (Leach)

Julus punctatus Leach, 1817, The zoological miscellany, vol. 3, p. 34.

---

[7] Meinert's types embrace specimens of this species and of *latistriatus*. Since the latter species must bear the prior name given by Curtis, it seems entirely proper to restrict *luscus* to the second species as here done.

Julus silvarum Meinert, 1868, Naturh. Tidsskr., ser. 3, vol. 5, p. 13.

Cylindroiulus punctatus Brade-Birks, 1919, Bull. Soc. Zool. France, vol. 44, p. 65.

Cylindroiulus silvarum Jawlowski, 1939, Frag. Faun. Mus. Zool. Polonici, vol. 4, p. 156.

TYPE: Not known to exist.

TYPE LOCALITY: England.

RANGE: Western, central, and northern Europe. In North America known to be established in Newfoundland, where probably introduced. A typically forest species.

Diploiulus truncorum Silvestri

Diploiulus truncorum Silvestri, 1896, Naturalista Siciliano, new ser., vol. 1, p. 160, pl. 7, figs. 11–13.

Julus (Anoploiulus) africanus Brölemann, 1897, Ann. Sci. Nat., ser. 8, vol. 4, p. 271, pl. 4, figs. 39–41.—Chamberlin, 1923, Proc. Biol. Soc. Washington, vol. 36, p. 191.

Cylindroiulus truncorum Attems, 1908, Notes sur les myriapodes, *in* Voyage zoologique en Khroumirie, pp. 112–113, pl. 24, figs. 10–12.— Schubart, 1946, Comun. Zool. Mus. Hist. Nat. Montevideo, vol. 2, No. 29, p. 2.

TYPE: Present location unknown.

TYPE LOCALITY: North Africa.

RANGE: From its native habitat in French North Africa, this species has been carried by commerce over much of Europe and Russia, and has been more recently recorded from hothouses in Brasil and North America.

Genus OPHYIULUS Berlese

Ophyiulus Berlese, 1884, Acari, Myriopoda, et scorpiones hucusque in Italia reperta, fasc. 12, p. 2 (as subgenus of *Julus*).

GENEROTYPE: *Julus terrestris* Linnaeus.

RANGE: Europe; eastern North America.

SPECIES: Four, one of which occurs in North America.

Ophyiulus pilosus (Newport)

Julus pilosus Newport, 1843, Ann. Mag. Nat. Hist., ser. 1, vol. 11, p. 316.

Julus longabo Koch, 1847, *in* Krit. Rev. Insect. Deutschlands, vol. 3, p. 113.

Julus serpentinus Koch, 1863, Die Myriapoden, vol. 2, p. 106, fig. 228.

Julus ferreus Koch, 1863, Die Myriapoden, vol. 2, p. 107, fig. 229.

Julus canaliculatus Wood, 1864, Proc. Acad. Nat. Sci. Philadelphia, p. 12.

Julius laqueatus Wood, 1864, Proc. Acad. Nat. Sci. Philadelphia, p. 13.

Julus fallax Meinert, 1868, Naturh. Tidsskr., ser. 3, vol. 5, p. 15.

Ophyiulus fallax Jawlowski, 1939, Frag. Faun. Mus. Zool. Polonici, vol. 4, p. 153.

TYPE: British Mus. (Nat. Hist.).

TYPE LOCALITY: England.

RANGE: Europe, from where introduced into North America where it is known from Nova Scotia and Quebec south to Virginia and Tennessee. In many places it is well established in cultivated areas.

Suborder PARAIULIDEA

Paraiulidi Brölemann, 1923, Arch. Zool. Expér. Gén., vol. 61, No. 2, p. 103.

Blaniulidae Attems, 1926, *in* Kükenthal-Krumbach, Handbuch der Zoologie, vol. 4, p. 182.

Arthrophora Verhoeff, 1930, *in* Bronn, Klass. und Ordn. des Tier-Reichs, Band 5, Abt. 2, Lief. 10, p. 1643.

KEY TO THE FAMILIES OF PARAIULIDEA

1. Coxite and basal part of telopodites of anterior gonopods broadly articulated and connected at the median line; gonopods partially sunk in pockets; tergites strongly longitudinally striate . . . . PAEROMOPIDAE (p. 126)
   Anterior gonopods not articulated as described above 2
2. Anterior and posterior gonopods very unequal in size, the anterior pair long and exposed, the posterior pair short and concealed within the body.
                                                    ZOSTERACTIIDAE (p. 150)
   Anterior and posterior gonopods not especially unequal in size, both visible externally 3
3. Mandible with 4 pectinate lamellae; gnathochilarium of similar form in both sexes; neither the second nor the seventh pair of legs of males modified; first legs of male with 1 to 6 joints . . . . NEMASOMIDAE (p. 122)
   Mandible with 7 or 8 pectinate lamellae; gnathochilarium different in the two sexes; first legs of male with 6 joints and much thickened, the second and often the seventh legs also modified . . . . PARAIULIDAE (p. 129)

Family NEMASOMIDAE Bollman

Nemasominae Bollman, 1893, U. S. Nat. Mus. Bull. 46, p. 156.

Blaniulidae (in part) Sinclair, 1895, Myriopoda, *in* The Cambridge natural history, vol. 5, p. 44.

Nemasomidae Silvestri, 1896, Ann. Mus. Civ. Stor. Nat. Genova, ser. 2, vol. 16, p. 183.—Chamberlin, 1922, Proc. Biol. Soc. Washington, vol. 35, p. 9.

Protoiulidae Verhoeff, 1896, Verh. Naturh. Vereins Rheinlands, Westfalens, und Osnabrück, vol. 53, p. 210.

Blaniulinae Attems, 1909, Arkiv för Zoologi, vol. 5, No. 3, p. 35.

Blaniulidae Brölemann, 1921, Arch. Zool. Expér. Gén., vol. 60, Notes et Revue, No. 1, p. 1; 1923, Arch. Zool. Expér. Gén., vol. 61, p. 110.

Genus BLANIULUS Gervais

Blaniulus Gervais, 1836, L'Institut, vol. 4, p. 435; 1836; Extraits Soc. Philom. Paris, p. 72.—Attems, 1909, Arkiv för Zoologi, vol. 5, No. 3, p. 44—Brölemann, 1923, Arch. Zool. Expér. Gén., vol. 61, p. 283.

GENEROTYPE: *Julus guttulatus* Bosc.
RANGE: Western Europe; introduced into other regions.
SPECIES: Four; one is established in North America.

Blaniulus guttulatus (Bosc)

Julus guttulatus Bosc, 1791, Bull. Soc. Philom. Paris, p. 10.
Julus pulchellus Leach, 1815, Trans. Linn. Soc. London, vol. 11, p. 379
(type locality: England; location of type unknown).
Blaniulus guttulatus Gervais, 1836, L'Institut, vol. 4, p. 435.—Chamberlin,
1921, Proc. Biol. Soc. Washington, vol. 34, p. 83.—Jawlowski, 1939,
Frag. Faun. Mus. Zool. Polonici, vol. 4, p. 152.
TYPE: Not known to exist.
TYPE LOCALITY: France.
RANGE: Widespread over Europe, now established generally in cultivated
areas of the United States and Canada.

Genus CHONEIULUS Brölemann

Choneiulus Brölemann, 1921, Arch. Zool. Expér. Gén., vol. 60, Notes et
Revue, No. 1, p. 4.
GENEROTYPE: *Blaniulus palmatus* Němec, by original designation.
RANGE: Central western Europe; introduced into other areas.
SPECIES: Five, of which one occurs in North America.

Choneiulus palmatus (Němec)

Blaniulus palmatus Němec, 1895, Sitz.-ber. Böhmischen Ges. Wiss., art. 38,
p. 5, figs. 7–11.
Choneiulus palmatus Brölemann, 1923, Arch. Zool. Expér. Gén., vol. 61,
p. 211, figs. 132–136.
Nopoiulus palmatus Jawlowski, 1939, Frag. Faun. Mus. Zool. Polonici,
vol. 4, p. 153.
TYPE: Location unknown.
TYPE LOCALITY: Bohemia.
RANGE: Eastern and central, and, as introduced, northern Europe. In
North America, where also introduced, known definitely from Nova Scotia
(Jawlowski) and likely to be found in the eastern States as a synanthropic
species.

Genus NEMASOMA Koch

Nemasoma Koch, 1847, *in* Krit. Rev. Insect. Deutschlands, vol. 3, p. 47,
116.—Bollman, 1893, U. S. Nat. Mus. Bull. 46, p. 157.—Chamberlin,
1922, Proc. Biol. Soc. Washington, vol. 35, p. 9.
Isobates Menge, 1851, Neueste Schrift. Naturf. Ges. Danzig, vol. 4, Heft
4, p. 6; also most recent European authors.
Utoiulus Chamberlin, 1943, Proc. Biol. Soc. Washington, vol. 56, p. 145
(generotype: *Nemasoma uta* Chamberlin).

GENEROTYPE: *Nemasoma varicorne* Koch.
RANGE: Europe and North America.
SPECIES: Four or five species known from North America.

Nemasoma leechi Chamberlin

Nemasoma leechi Chamberlin, 1951, Chicago Acad. Sci. Nat. Hist. Misc. No. 87, p. 10.
TYPE: Prov. Mus., British Columbia.
TYPE LOCALITY: Trinity Valley, British Columbia.
RANGE: Known only from type locality.

Nemasoma nigrius Chamberlin

Nemasoma nigrius Chamberlin, 1943, Bull. Univ. Utah, biol. ser., vol. 8, No. 2, p. 9, fig. 22.
TYPE: Chicago Nat. Hist. Mus.
TYPE LOCALITY: Gatlinburg, Sevier County, Tennessee.
RANGE: The Great Smoky Mountains, Tennessee and North Carolina.

Nemasoma pium Chamberlin [8]

Nemasoma pium Chamberlin, 1918, Ann. Ent. Soc. Amer., vol. 11, p. 373.
TYPE: Mus. Comp. Zool.
TYPE LOCALITY: Creston, Natchitoches Parish, Louisiana.
RANGE: Known only from type locality.

Nemasoma sayanum Bollman

Julus punctatus Say, 1821, Journ. Acad. Nat. Sci. Philadelphia, vol. 2, p. 102 (preoccupied by *Julus punctatus* Leach, 1815).
Julus stigmatosus Brandt, 1841, Recueil, p. 88 (substitute name for *punctatus* Say, but also preoccupied by *Julus stigmatosus* Eichwald, 1830).
Nemasoma sayanum Bollman, 1893, U. S. Nat. Mus. Bull. 46, p. 145.
TYPE: Not known to exist.
TYPE LOCALITY: Probably vicinity of Philadelphia, Pennsylvania.
RANGE: Reported from Ohio, Indiana, Virginia, and other southeastern States, but the identity of Say's species has never been proven with certainty, and the form to which Bollman applied the name has likewise never been adequately described or figured.

Nemasoma uta Chamberlin

Nemasoma uta Chamberlin, 1912, Ann. Ent. Soc. Amer., vol. 5, p. 162; 1951, Chicago Acad. Sci. Nat. Hist. Misc. No. 87, p. 9, g. 21.
Utoiulus utus Chamberlin, 1943, Proc. Biol. Soc. Washington, vol. 56, p. 145.
TYPE: Collection of R. V. Chamberlin.
TYPE LOCALITY: Mill Creek Canyon, Salt Lake County, Utah

---

[8] The position of this poorly known species in *Nemasoma* is somewhat doubtful.

RANGE: Canyons of the Wasatch Mountains, in Salt Lake, Davis, and Utah Counties, Utah.

Genus NOPOIULUS Menge

Nopoiulus Menge, 1851, Neueste Schrift. Naturf. Ges. Danzig, vol. 4, Heft 4, p. 7.

GENEROTYPE: *Nopoiulus punctulatus* Menge (= *N. venustus* of Latzel).

RANGE: Europe; introduced and now established in eastern North America.

SPECIES: Six, of which one has been introduced in our area.

Nopoiulus minutus (Brandt)

Julus pusillus Say, 1821, Journ. Acad. Nat. Sci. Philadelphia, vol. 2, p. 105 (preoccupied by *J. pusillus* Leach 1815).

Julus minutus Brandt, 1841, Recueil, p. 89 (substitute name for *pusillus* Say).

Julus lineatus McNeill, 1887, Proc. U. S. Nat. Mus., vol. 10, p. 324 (type locality: Pensacola, Florida; location of type unknown).

Nopoiulus minutus Chamberlin, 1922, Proc. Biol. Soc. Washington, vol. 35, p. 9.

TYPE: Not known to exist.

TYPE LOCALITY: "Eastern shore of Virginia" (Say).

RANGE: Europe, introduced and widespread over eastern United States and Canada, occurring as far south as Delaware and Virginia and west to Tennessee, sporadically as far west as Utah.

Genus PROTEROIULUS Silvestri

Blaniulus (in part) Am Stein, 1857, Jahresb. Naturf. Ges. Graubündens, new ser., vol. 2, p. 139.

Proteroiulus Silvestri, 1897, Ann. Mus. Civ. Stor. Nat. Genova, ser. 2, vol. 18, p. 650.

GENEROTYPE: *Blaniulus fuscus* Am Stein, by original designation.

RANGE: Europe. Introduced into North America.

SPECIES: Two, of which one is known from one area.

Proteroiulus fuscus (Am Stein)

Blaniulus fuscus Am Stein, 1857, Jahresb. Naturf. Ges. Graubündens, new ser., vol. 2, p. 139.—Latzel, 1884, Myr. Öst.-Ung., Monarch., vol. 2, p. 248.

Proteroiulus fuscus Jawlowski, 1939, Frag. Faun. Zool. Mus. Polonici, vol. 4, p. 152.—Palmén, 1952, Ann. Zool. Soc. 'Vanamo', vol. 15, No. 1, p. 17, fig. 21.

TYPE: Unknown.

TYPE LOCALITY: Northern Europe.

RANGE: Known in North America from Newfoundland, Nova Scotia, and eastern United States.

Genus TIVIULUS Chamberlin

Tiviulus Chamberlin, 1941, Bull. Univ. Utah, biol. ser., vol. 6, No. 4, p. 17.
GENEROTYPE: *Tiviulus expressus* Chamberlin, by original designation.
RANGE: Washington.
SPECIES: One.

Tiviulus expressus Chamberlin

Tiviulus expressus Chamberlin, 1941, Bull. Univ. Utah, biol. ser., vol. 6, No. 4, p. 17, figs. 27, 28.
TYPE: Collection of R. V. Chamberlin.
TYPE LOCALITY: Arlington, Snohomish County, Washington.
RANGE: Known only from type locality.

Family PAEROMOPIDAE Cook

Paeromopidae Cook, 1895, Ann. New York Acad. Sci., vol. 9, p. 6.—
Chamberlin, 1949, Chicago Acad. Sci. Nat. Hist. Misc. No. 52, p. 1.
Californiulidae Verhoeff, 1938, Zool. Anz., vol. 122, Nos. 5–6, p. 114.

Genus AIGON Chamberlin

Aigon Chamberlin, 1949, Chicago Acad. Sci. Nat. Hist. Misc. No. 52, p. 1.
GENEROTYPE: *Aigon rodocki* Chamberlin, by original designation.
RANGE: Idaho, Montana.
SPECIES: Two.

Aigon parvior (Chamberlin)

Klansolus parvior Chamberlin, 1940, Pomona Coll. Journ. Ent. and Zool., vol. 32, No. 4, p. 83.
Aigon parvior Chamberlin, 1949, Chicago Acad. Sci. Nat. Hist. Misc. No. 52, p. 1.
TYPE: Collection of R. V. Chamberlin.
TYPE LOCALITY: Flathead Lake, Lake County, Montana.
RANGE: Known only from type locality.

Aigon rodocki Chamberlin

Aigon rodocki Chamberlin, 1949, Chicago Acad. Sci. Nat. Hist. Misc. No. 52, p. 2, figs. 1, 2.
TYPE: Collection of R. V. Chamberlin.
TYPE LOCALITY: Sweetwater, Nez Perce County, Idaho.
RANGE: Known only from type locality.

Genus ATOPOLUS Chamberlin

Atopolus Chamberlin, 1949, Chicago Acad. Sci. Nat. Hist. Misc. No. 52, p. 3.
GENEROTYPE: *Paeromopus chamberlini* Brölemann, by original designation.
RANGE: California.
SPECIES: One.

Atopolus chamberlini (Brölemann)

Paeromopus chamberlini Brölemann, 1922, Ann. Ent. Soc. Amer., vol. 15, p. 289, figs. 6–9, 53–57.
TYPE: Probably Paris Museum.
TYPE LOCALITY: Mount Shasta, Shasta County, California.
RANGE: Known only from type locality.

Genus CALIFORNIULUS Verhoeff

Californiulus Verhoeff, 1938, Zool. Anz., vol. 122, Nos. 5–6, p. 114.
GENEROTYPE: *Californiulus dorsovittatus* Verhoeff, by monotypy.
RANGE: California.
SPECIES: One.

Californiulus dorsovittatus Verhoeff

Californiulus dorsovittatus Verhoeff, 1938, Zool. Anz., vol. 122, Nos. 5–6, p. 118, figs. 1–7.
TYPE: Verhoeff collection.
TYPE LOCALITY: Mount Harkness, near Berkeley, Alameda County, California.
RANGE: Known only from type locality.

Genus KLANSOLUS Chamberlin

Klansolus Chamberlin, 1938, Proc. Biol. Soc. Washington, vol. 51, p. 205.
GENEROTYPE: *Klansolus euphanus* Chamberlin, by original designation.
RANGE: Northern California and Oregon.
SPECIES: Five.

Klansolus euphanus Chamberlin

Klansolus euphanus Chamberlin, 1938, Proc. Biol. Soc. Washington, vol. 51, p. 205.
TYPE: Collection of R. V. Chamberlin.
TYPE LOCALITY: Boyer (location unknown), Oregon.
RANGE: Known only from type locality.

Klansolus socius Chamberlin

Klansolus socius Chamberlin, 1941, Bull. Univ. Utah, biol. ser., vol. 6, No. 4, p. 16, figs. 19–23.

Type: Collection of R. V. Chamberlin.
Type Locality: 8 miles west of Wallowa, Wallowa County, Oregon.
Range: Known only from type locality.

Klansolus vicinus (Chamberlin)

Californiulus vicinus Chamberlin, 1943, Bull. Univ. Utah, biol. ser., vol. 8, No. 2, p. 12, figs. 40–42.
Klansolus vicinus Chamberlin, 1949, Chicago Acad. Sci. Nat. Hist. Misc. No. 52, p. 5.
Type: Collection of R. V. Chamberlin.
Type Locality: Dickson Flats, Shasta County, California.
Range: Known only from type locality.

Klansolus yosemitensis (Chamberlin)

Californiulus yosemitensis Chamberlin, 1941, Bull. Univ. Utah, biol. ser., vol. 6, No. 4, p. 17.
Klansolus yosemitensis Chamberlin, 1949, Chicago Acad. Sci. Nat. Hist. Misc. No. 52, p. 5.
Type: Collection of R. V. Chamberlin.
Type Locality: Yosemite National Park, California.
Range: Known only from type locality.

Klansolus zantus Chamberlin

Klansolus zantus Chamberlin, 1949, Chicago Acad. Sci. Nat. Hist. Misc. No. 52, p. 5.
Type: Collection of R. V. Chamberlin.
Type Locality: 12 miles east of Cave Junction, Josephine County, Oregon.
Range: Known only from type locality.

Genus PAEROMOPUS Karsch

Paeromopus Karsch, 1881, Zeitschr. Naturw., vol. 54 (ser. 3, vol. 6), p. 12.
Paeromopellus Verhoeff, 1938, Zool. Anz., vol. 122, Nos. 5–6, p. 124 (generotype, *P. sphinx* Verhoeff, [=*lysiopetalinus* Karsch]).
Generotype: *Paeromopus lysiopetalinus* Karsch, by monotypy.
Range: California.
Species: Four, plus one doubtful.

Paeromopus angusticeps (Wood)[9]

Spirobolus angusticeps Wood, 1864, Proc. Acad. Nat. Sci. Philadelphia, p. 16: 1865, Trans. Amer. Phil. Soc., vol. 13, p. 210, figs. 37, 37a.
Type: Location unknown.
Type Locality: California: San Francisco.
Range: Known only from type locality.

---

[9] Assignation to this genus somewhat tentative, as Wood's type was a female.

Paeromopus cavicolens Chamberlin

Paeromopus cavicolens Chamberlin, 1953, Proc. Biol. Soc. Washington, vol. 66, p. 68, figs. 3, 4.

TYPE: Collection of R. V. Chamberlin.

TYPE LOCALITY: Windeler Cavern, Tuolumne County, California.

RANGE: Known only from type locality.

Paeromopus eldoradus Chamberlin

Paeromopus eldoradus Chamberlin, 1941, Bull. Univ. Utah, biol. ser., vol. 6, No. 5, p. 7, figs. 10, 11.

TYPE: Collection of R. V. Chamberlin.

TYPE LOCALITY: Coloma, Eldorado County, California.

RANGE: Known only from type locality.

Paeromopus lysiopetalinus Karsch

Paeromopus lysiopetalinus Karsch, 1881, Zeitschr. Naturw., vol. 54 (ser. 3, vol. 6), p. 12.

Paeromopellus sphinx Verhoeff, 1938, Zool. Anz., vol. 122, Nos. 5–6, p. 125, figs. 8, 9 (new name for *lysiopetalinus* Karsch).

TYPE: Zool. Mus. Univ. Berlin.

TYPE LOCALITY: California.

RANGE: Definite localities not known.

Paeromopus pistus Chamberlin

Paeromopus pistus Chamberlin, 1941, Bull. Univ. Utah, biol. ser., vol. 6, No. 5, p. 7, figs. 8, 9.

TYPE: Collection of R. V. Chamberlin.

TYPE LOCALITY: Stanford, Palo Alto County, California.

RANGE: Known only from type locality.

Family PARAIULIDAE Bollman

Paraiulinae Bollman, 1893, U. S. Nat. Mus. Bull. 46, p. 156.

Paraiulidae Cook, 1895, Ann. New York Acad. Sci., vol. 9, p. 6.—Pocock, 1903, Diplopoda, *in* Biol. Centr.-Amer., p. 53.

Uroblaniulinae Attems, 1909, Ark. Zool., vol. 5, No. 3, p. 47.

Genus ALIULUS Causey

Aliulus Causey, 1950, Proc. Arkansas Acad. Sci., vol. 3, p. 45.

GENEROTYPE: *Aliulus carrollus* Causey, by original designation.

RANGE: Western Arkansas and adjacent Oklahoma.

SPECIES: Three.

Aliulus caddoensis Causey

Aliulus caddoensis Causey, 1950, Proc. Arkansas Acad. Sci., vol. 3, p. 46, figs. 5, 6.

TYPE: Acad. Nat. Sci., Philadelphia.
TYPE LOCALITY: Caddo County, Oklahoma.
RANGE: Known only from type locality.

Aliulus carrollus Causey

Aliulus carrollus Causey, 1950, Proc. Arkansas Acad. Sci., vol. 3, p. 45, figs. 1–4.
TYPE: Acad. Nat. Sci., Philadelphia.
TYPE LOCALITY: Blue Spring, Carroll County, Arkansas.
RANGE: Carroll and Washington Counties, Arkansas.

Aliulus rugosus (Bollman)

Parajulus rugosus Bollman, 1887, Ent. Amer., vol. 3, p. 81; 1893, U. S. Nat. Mus. Bull. 46, p. 105.
Aliulus rugosus Causey, 1952, Proc. Arkansas Acad. Sci., vol. 5, p. 22, fig. 5.
TYPE: U. S. Nat. Mus. (No. 129).
TYPE LOCALITY: Washington County, Pennsylvania.
RANGE: Pennsylvania, Ohio, Indiana, Illinois.

Genus ANIULUS Chamberlin

Aniulus Chamberlin, 1940, Bull. Univ. Utah, biol. ser., vol. 5, No. 7, p. 3.
GENEROTYPE: *Aniulus adelphus* Chamberlin, by original designation.
RANGE: United States, from New York to Georgia west as far as Utah, Colorado, and Arizona.
SPECIES: Twelve.

Aniulus adelphus Chamberlin

Aniulus adelphus Chamberlin, 1940, Bull. Univ. Utah, biol. ser. vol. 5, No. 7, p. 3, figs. 1–3.
TYPE: Collection of R. V. Chamberlin.
TYPE LOCALITY: Southwest of Boerne, Kendall County, Texas.
RANGE: Known only from type locality.

Aniulus austinensis Chamberlin

Aniulus austinensis Chamberlin, 1940, Bull. Univ. Utah, biol. ser., vol. 5, No. 7, p. 4, figs. 4, 5.
TYPE: Collection of R. V. Chamberlin.
TYPE LOCALITY: Austin, Travis County, Texas.
RANGE: Known only from the type locality.

Aniulus bollmani Causey

Julus impressus (not Say) Wood, 1865, Trans. Amer. Philos. Soc., vol. 13, p. 196.
Julus venustus (in part) Wood, 1864, Proc. Acad. Nat. Sci. Philadelphia, p. 10; 1865, Trans. Amer. Philos. Soc., vol. 13, p. 196.

Parajulus impressus (not Say) Bollman, 1887, Ann. New York Acad. Sci., vol. 4, p. 34; 1893, U. S. Nat. Mus. Bull. 46, pp. 52, 154.—Williams and Hefner, 1928, Bull. Ohio Biol. Surv., No. 18, p. 127, fig. 21.

Paraiulus impressus Hefner, 1929, Journ. Morph. Physiol., vol. 48, p. 153, 4 pls.

Aniulus impressus Causey, 1950, Proc. Arkansas Acad. Sci., vol. 3, p. 46, figs. 7, 8.

Aniulus bollmani Causey, 1952, Proc. Arkansas Acad. Sci., vol. 5, p. 19.

TYPE: Amer. Mus. Nat. Hist.

TYPE LOCALITY: Winslow, Stephenson County, Illinois.

RANGE: From western Pennsylvania and West Virginia westward to Wisconsin and North Dakota.

Aniulus brazonus Chamberlin

Aniulus brazonus Chamberlin, 1940, Bull. Univ. Utah, biol. ser., vol. 5, No. 7, p. 4, figs. 6, 7.

TYPE: Collection of R. V. Chamberlin.

TYPE LOCALITY: Brazos County, Texas.

RANGE: Known only from type locality.

Aniulus craterus Chamberlin

Aniulus craterus Chamberlin, 1940, Bull. Univ. Utah, biol. ser., vol. 5, No. 7, p. 5, figs. 9, 10.

TYPE: Collection of R. V. Chamberlin.

TYPE LOCALITY: Raven Ranch, Kerr County, Texas.

RANGE: Known only from type locality.

Aniulus dorophor Chamberlin

Aniulus dorophor Chamberlin, 1940, Bull. Univ. Utah, biol. ser., vol. 5, No. 7, p. 5, figs. 11–13.

TYPE: Collection of R. V. Chamberlin.

TYPE LOCALITY: South of Three Rivers, Live Oak County, Texas.

RANGE: Known only from type locality.

Aniulus fluviatilis Chamberlin

Aniulus fluviatilis Chamberlin, 1940, Bull. Univ. Utah, biol. ser., vol. 5, No. 7, p. 6, figs. 14, 15.

TYPE: Collection of R. V. Chamberlin.

TYPE LOCALITY: Brazos County, Texas.

RANGE: Known only from type locality, and from Polk County, Texas.

Aniulus hopius Chamberlin

Aniulus hopius Chamberlin, 1941, Bull. Univ. Utah, biol. ser., vol. 6, No. 4, p. 19, figs. 30, 31.

TYPE: Collection of R. V. Chamberlin.

TYPE LOCALITY: Greaterville, Pima County, Arizona.
RANGE: Known only from type locality.

Aniulus oreines Chamberlin

Aniulus oreines Chamberlin, 1940, Bull. Univ. Utah, biol. ser., vol. 5, No. 7, p. 6, figs. 19, 20.
TYPE: Collection of R. V. Chamberlin.
TYPE LOCALITY: 2 miles west of Glenwood, Garfield County, Colorado.
RANGE: Also known from Salt Lake County, Utah.

Aniulus orientalis Causey

Aniulus orientalis Causey, 1952, Proc. Arkansas Acad. Sci., vol. 5, p. 20, figs. 1–4.
TYPE: Amer. Mus. Nat. Hist.
TYPE LOCALITY: Probably Durham, North Carolina.
RANGE: Known only from type locality.

Aniulus orthodoxus Chamberlin

Aniulus orthodoxus Chamberlin, 1946, Proc. Biol. Soc. Washington, vol. 59, p. 32, figs. 3, 4.
TYPE: Collection of R. V. Chamberlin.
TYPE LOCALITY: Reelfoot Lake, Obion County, Tennessee.
RANGE: Known only from type locality.

Aniulus prosoicus Chamberlin

Aniulus prosoicus Chamberlin, 1940, Bull. Univ. Utah, biol. ser., vol. 5, No. 7, p. 7, figs. 16–18.
TYPE: Collection of R. V. Chamberlin.
TYPE LOCALITY: Edinburg, Hildalgo County, Texas.
RANGE: Known only from type locality.

Genus BOLLMANIULUS Verhoeff

Bollmaniulus Verhoeff, 1926, Zool. Anz., vol. 68, p. 65.
Caliulus Chamberlin, 1940, Bull. Univ. Utah, biol. ser., vol. 5, No. 7, p. 15.
GENEROTYPE: *Iulus furcifer* Harger, by original designation.
RANGE: California to Washington, Montana.
SPECIES: Ten.

Bollmaniulus catalinae (Chamberlin)

Caliulus catalinae Chamberlin, 1940, Bull. Univ. Utah, biol. ser., vol. 5, No. 7, p. 17, figs. 57, 58.
TYPE: Collection of R. V. Chamberlin.
TYPE LOCALITY: Catalina Island, California.
RANGE: Known only from type locality.

Bollmaniulus concolor (Chamberlin)

Caliulus concolor Chamberlin, 1940, Bull. Univ. Utah, biol. ser., vol. 5, No. 7, p. 18, figs. 56a, 59.

TYPE: Collection of R. V. Chamberlin.

TYPE LOCALITY: Redlands, San Bernardino County, California.

RANGE: Known only from type locality.

Bollmaniulus furcifer (Harger)

Iulus furcifer Harger, 1872, Amer. Journ. Sci. Arts, vol. 4, p. 119.

Bollmaniulus furcifer Verhoeff, 1926, Zool. Anz., vol. 68, p. 65.

Taijulus furcifer Chamberlin, 1938, Proc. Biol. Soc. Washington, vol. 51, p. 205.

Caliulus furcifer Chamberlin, 1940, Bull. Univ. Utah, biol. ser., vol. 5, No. 7, p. 15.

TYPE: Not known to exist.

TYPE LOCALITY: John Day Valley, Oregon.

RANGE: California to British Columbia.

Bollmaniulus pachysomus (Chamberlin)

Caliulus pachysomus Chamberlin, 1940, Bull. Univ. Utah, biol. ser., vol. 5, No. 7, p. 15, fig. 56.

TYPE: Collection of R. V. Chamberlin.

TYPE LOCALITY: Yosemite National Park, California.

RANGE: Known only from type locality.

Bollmaniulus pearcei (Chamberlin)

Caliulus pearcei Chamberlin, 1943, Bull. Univ. Utah, biol. ser., vol. 8, No. 2, p. 12, fig. 39.

TYPE: Collection of R. V. Chamberlin.

TYPE LOCALITY: South fork of Bishop Creek, Inyo County, California.

RANGE: Known only from type locality.

Bollmaniulus pugetensis (Chamberlin)

Caliulus pugetensis Chamberlin, 1940, Bull. Univ. Utah, biol. ser., vol. 5, No. 7, p. 16, figs. 61, 62.

TYPE: Collection of R. V. Chamberlin.

TYPE LOCALITY: Puget Sound, Washington.

RANGE: Known only from type locality.

Bollmaniulus rhodogeus (Chamberlin)

Caliulus rhodogeus Chamberlin, 1940, Bull. Univ. Utah, biol. ser., vol. 5, No. 7, p. 17, fig. 60.

TYPE: Collection of R. V. Chamberlin.

TYPE LOCALITY: Redlands, San Bernardino County, California.

RANGE: Known only from type locality.

Bollmaniulus sinampus (Chamberlin)

Paraiulus furcifer var. *sinampus* Chamberlin, 1910, Ann. Ent. Soc. Amer., vol. 3, p. 256, pl. 41, figs. 5–8, and pl. 42, figs. 1, 2.

TYPE: Probably lost.

TYPE LOCALITY: Portland, Oregon.

RANGE: Known only from type locality.

Bollmaniulus signifer (Chamberlin)

Caliulus signifer Chamberlin, 1941, Bull. Univ. Utah, biol. ser., vol. 6, No. 4, p. 19, fig. 32.

TYPE: Collection of R. V. Chamberlin.

TYPE LOCALITY: Portland, Oregon.

RANGE: Known only from type locality.

Bollmaniulus spenceri (Chamberlin)

Bollmaniulus spenceri Chamberlin, 1951, Chicago Acad. Sci. Nat. Hist., Misc. No. 87, p. 10, figs. 22, 23.

TYPE: Collection of R. V. Chamberlin.

TYPE LOCALITY: Kamloops, British Columbia.

RANGE: Known only from type locality.

Genus CODIULUS Chamberlin

Codiulus Chamberlin, 1940, Bull. Univ. Utah, biol. ser., vol. 5, No. 7, p. 19.

GENEROTYPE: *Codiulus oulogon* Chamberlin, by original designation.

RANGE: Southern California.

SPECIES: Two.

Codiulus etirus Chamberlin

Codiulus etirus Chamberlin, 1941, Bull. Univ. Utah, biol. ser., vol. 6. No. 4, p. 18, fig. 29.

TYPE: Collection of R. V. Chamberlin.

TYPE LOCALITY: Cardiff, San Diego County, California.

RANGE: Known only from type locality.

Codiulus oulogon Chamberlin

Codiulus oulogon Chamberlin, 1940, Bull. Univ. Utah, biol. ser., vol. 5, No. 7, p. 19, fig. 66.

TYPE: Collection of R. V. Chamberlin.

TYPE LOCALITY: Box Springs Grade, Riverside County, California.

RANGE: Known only from type locality.

Genus ETHOIULUS Chamberlin

Ethoiulus Chamberlin, 1918, Canadian Ent., vol. 50, p. 361.

Illiulus Causey, 1950, Proc. Arkansas Acad. Sci., vol. 3, p. 47 (generotype: *I. illinoensis* Causey).

GENEROTYPE: *Ethoiulus amphelictus* Chamberlin, by original designation.
RANGE: Southern United States, from Florida to Texas; Illinois and Arkansas.
SPECIES: Five.

Ethoiulus amphelictus Chamberlin

Ethoiulus amphelictus Chamberlin, 1918, Canadian Ent., vol. 50, p. 361.
TYPE: Mus. Comp. Zool.
TYPE LOCALITY: Covington, St. Tammany Parish, Louisiana.
RANGE: Known only from type locality.

Ethoiulus bufonius Chamberlin

Ethojulus bufonius Chamberlin, 1938, Proc. Biol. Soc. Washington, vol. 51, p. 206.
TYPE: Collection of R. V. Chamberlin.
TYPE LOCALITY: Gainesville, Alachua County, Florida.
RANGE: Known only from north-central Florida.

Ethoiulus illinoensis (Causey)

Illiulus illinoensis Causey, 1950, Proc. Arkansas Acad. Sci., vol. 3, p. 47, figs.
TYPE: Illinois Nat. Hist. Surv.
TYPE LOCALITY: LaRue, Union County, Illinois.
RANGE: Southern Illinois, west to northwestern Arkansas.

Ethoiulus ligifer (Chamberlin)

Parajulus ligifer Chamberlin, 1919, Proc. Biol. Soc. Washington, vol. 32, p. 119.
Hakiulus ligifer Causey, 1952, Texas Journ. Sci., vol. 4, p. 200.
Ethoiulus geniculatus Causey, 1952, Texas Journ. Sci., vol. 4, p. 201, figs. 8–10 (type locality: Fort Bend County, Texas; type: Amer. Mus. Nat. Hist.).
TYPE: Mus. Comp. Zool.
TYPE LOCALITY: Victoria, Victoria County, Texas.
RANGE: Victoria, Fort Bend, and Goliad Counties, Texas.

Ethoiulus robustior (Chamberlin)

Paraiulus robustior Chamberlin, 1918, Ann. Ent. Soc. America, vol. 11, p. 373.
Ethoiulus unilictus Causey, 1953, Amer. Midl. Nat., vol. 50, p. 152, figs. 1–4 (type locality: Ruston, Lincoln Parish, Louisiana; type: Amer. Mus. Nat. Hist.).
TYPE: Mus. Comp. Zool.
TYPE LOCALITY: Creston, Natchitoches Parish, Louisiana.
RANGE: Known from Natchitoches and Lincoln Parishes, Louisiana.

Genus HAKIULUS Chamberlin

Hakiulus Chamberlin, 1940, Bull. Univ. Utah, biol. ser., vol. 5, No. 7, p. 10.

GENEROTYPE: *Hakiulus amophor* Chamberlin, by original designation.

RANGE: Central and western United States, from Ohio west and south to Colorado and New Mexico. Most of the species occur in Texas.

SPECIES: Eleven.

Hakiulus amophor Chamberlin

Hakiulus amophor Chamberlin, 1940, Bull. Univ. Utah, biol. ser., vol. 5, No. 7, p. 11, figs. 36–39.

TYPE: Collection of R. V. Chamberlin.

TYPE LOCALITY: Turtle Creek, Kerr County, Texas.

RANGE: Recorded from Kerr and Live Oak Counties, Texas.

Hakiulus cyaneus (Chamberlin)

Ethojulus cyaneus Chamberlin, 1920, Proc. Biol. Soc. Washington, vol. 33, p. 41.

TYPE: Mus. Comp. Zool.

TYPE LOCALITY: Bay City, Matagorda County, Texas.

RANGE: Known only from type locality.

Hakiulus diversifrons (Wood)

Julus diversifrons Wood, 1867, Proc. Acad. Nat. Sci. Philadelphia, vol. 19, p. 43.

Parajulus castaneus Bollman, 1887, Ent. Amer., vol. 2, p. 226 (type locality: Fort Snelling, Minnesota; type: U. S. Nat. Mus., No. 95).

Iulus ellipticus Bollman, 1887, Amer. Nat., vol. 21, p. 82 (type locality: Fort Snelling, Minnesota; type: U. S. Nat. Mus.).

Parajulus diversifrons Williams and Hefner, 1928, Bull. Ohio Biol. Surv., No. 18, p. 128, fig. 20.

TYPE: Not known to exist.

TYPE LOCALITY: Southern Illinois.

RANGE: Ohio and Michigan, west to Illinois and Minnesota.

Hakiulus minori Causey

Hakiulus minori Causey, 1952, Texas Journ. Sci., vol. 4, p. 200, figs. 1–3.

TYPE: Amer. Mus. Nat. Hist.

TYPE LOCALITY: Lufkin, Angelina County, Texas.

RANGE: Recorded from Angelina and Polk Counties, in eastern Texas.

Hakiulus neomexicanus (Chamberlin)

Paraiulus neomexicanus Chamberlin, 1903, Proc. Acad. Nat. Sci. Philadelphia, vol. 55, p. 38.

Hakiulus neomexicanus Chamberlin, 1940, Bull. Univ. Utah, biol. ser., vol. 5, No. 7, p. 11.

TYPE: Present location unknown.
TYPE LOCALITY: Beulah, San Miguel County, New Mexico.
RANGE: Known only from type locality.

Hakiulus orthodox Chamberlin

Hakiulus orthodox Chamberlin, 1940, Bull. Univ. Utah, biol. ser., vol. 5, No. 7, p. 11, fig. 40.
TYPE: Collection of R. V. Chamberlin.
TYPE LOCALITY: College Station, Brazos County, Texas.
RANGE: Known only from type locality.

Hakiulus parallelus (Chamberlin)

Ethoiulus diversifrons Chamberlin, 1931, Ent. News, vol. 42, p. 98.
Hakiulus parallelus Chamberlin, 1940, Bull. Univ. Utah, biol. ser., vol. 5, No. 7, p. 12, figs. 41–43.
TYPE: Collection of R. V. Chamberlin.
TYPE LOCALITY: Cleveland County, Oklahoma.
RANGE: Recorded from Oklahoma, Texas, Arkansas, Colorado, and Iowa, suggesting a wide range over the Great Plains.

Hakiulus texanus (Chamberlin)

Paraiulus texanus Chamberlin, 1916, Psyche, vol. 23, p. 35.
TYPE: Mus. Comp. Zool.
TYPE LOCALITY: Victoria, Victoria County, Texas.
RANGE: Known only from type locality.

Hakiulus texensis Causey

Hakiulus texensis Causey, 1952, Texas Journ. Sci., vol. 4, No. 2, p. 201, figs. 6, 7.
TYPE: Amer. Mus. Nat. Hist.
TYPE LOCALITY: Kilgore, Gregg County, Texas.
RANGE: Known only from type locality.

Hakiulus victorianus (Chamberlin)

Paraiulus victorianus Chamberlin, 1916, Psyche, vol. 23, p. 33.
TYPE: Mus. Comp. Zool.
TYPE LOCALITY: Victoria, Victoria County, Texas.
RANGE: Known only from type locality.

Hakiulus zakiwanus (Chamberlin)

Paraiulus zakiwanus Chamberlin, 1910, Ann. Ent. Soc. Amer., vol. 3, No. 4, p. 253, pl. 39, figs. 6, 7; pl. 40, figs. 1–5.
TYPE: Present location unknown.
TYPE LOCATION: Sacramento Mountains, New Mexico.
RANGE: Central New Mexico.

Genus GOSIULUS Chamberlin

Gosiulus Chamberlin, 1940, Bull. Univ. Utah, biol. ser., vol. 5, No. 7, p. 10.

GENEROTYPE: *Gosiulus conformatus* Chamberlin, by original designation.

RANGE: Texas.

SPECIES: One.

Gosiulus conformatus Chamberlin

Gosiulus conformatus Chamberlin, 1940, Bull. Univ. Utah, biol. ser., vol. 5, No. 7, p. 10, figs. 32–35.

TYPE: Collection of R. V. Chamberlin.

TYPE LOCALITY: South of Three Rivers, Live Oak County, Texas.

RANGE: Reported from Live Oak, Brooks, and McCulloch Counties, in southern Texas.

Genus LITIULUS Chamberlin

Litiulus Chamberlin, 1940, Bull. Univ. Utah, biol. ser., vol. 5, No. 7, p. 19.

GENEROTYPE: *Paraiulus alaskanus Cook,* by original designation.

RANGE: Alaska, British Columbia, northern Washington.

SPECIES: One.

Litiulus alaskanus (Cook)

Paraiulus alaskanus Cook, 1904, *in* Harriman Alaska Exped., vol. 8, p. 70, pl. 5, figs. 4a–k.

TYPE: U. S. Nat. Mus. (No. 792).

TYPE LOCALITY: Metlakatla, Alaska.

RANGE: Southern coast of Alaska, south as far as Chinook, Washington.

Genus MULAIKIULUS Chamberlin

Mulaikiulus Chamberlin, 1941, Bull. Univ. Utah, biol. ser., vol. 6, No. 5, p. 8.

GENEROTYPE: *Mulaikiulus stanleius* Chamberlin, by original designation.

RANGE: California.

SPECIES: One.

Mulaikiulus stanleius Chamberlin

Mulaikiulus stanleius Chamberlin, 1941, Bull. Univ. Utah, biol. ser., vol. 6, No. 5, p. 8, figs. 12, 13.

TYPE: Collection of R. V. Chamberlin.

TYPE LOCALITY: 12 miles north of Hammond, Tulare County, California.

RANGE: Known only from type locality.

Genus OKLIULUS Causey

Okliulus Causey, 1950, Proc. Arkansas Acad. Sci., vol. 3, p. 46.

GENEROTYPE: *Okliulus carpenteri* Causey, by original designation.

RANGE: Oklahoma and Arkansas.
SPECIES: Two.

Okliulus beveli Causey

Okliulus beveli Causey, 1953, Amer. Midl. Nat., vol. 50, p. 152, figs. 5–7.
TYPE: Amer. Mus. Nat. Hist.
TYPE LOCALITY: Junction City, Union County, Arkansas.
RANGE: Known only from type locality.

Okliulus carpenteri Causey

Okliulus carpenteri Causey, 1950, Proc. Arkansas Acad. Sci., vol. 3, p. 46,
figs. 9–12.
TYPE: Acad. Nat. Sci. Philadelphia.
TYPE LOCALITY: Wilburton, Latimer County, Oklahoma.
RANGE: Oklahoma and Arkansas.

Genus ORIULUS Chamberlin

Oriulus Chamberlin, 1940, Bull. Univ. Utah, biol. ser., vol. 5, No. 7, p. 7.
GENEROTYPE: *Oriulus medianus* Chamberlin, by original designation.
RANGE: Northeastern and central United States, west as far as Montana,
Utah, and New Mexico.
SPECIES: Nine.

Oriulus annectans (Chamberlin)

Parajulus annectans Chamberlin, 1921, Canadian Ent., vol. 53, p. 233,
figs. 1.1, 1.2.
TYPE: Mus. Comp. Zool.
TYPE LOCALITY: Knox County, Tennessee.
RANGE: Known only from type locality.

Oriulus delus Chamberlin

Oriulus delus Chamberlin, 1940, Bull. Univ. Utah, biol. ser., vol. 5, No. 7,
p. 8, figs. 28, 29.
TYPE: Collection of R. V. Chamberlin.
TYPE LOCALITY: Plattsburg, Clinton County, New York.
RANGE: Southern New York, New Jersey, south as far as Albemarle
County, Virginia.

Oriulus eutypus Chamberlin

Oriulus eutypus Chamberlin, 1940, Bull. Univ. Utah, biol. ser., vol. 5,
No. 7, p. 8, figs. 23, 24.
TYPE: Collection of R. V. Chamberlin.
TYPE LOCALITY: Minneapolis, Minnesota.
RANGE: Known only from type locality.

Oriulus georgicolens Chamberlin

Oriulus georgicolens Chamberlin, 1940, Bull. Univ. Utah, biol. ser., vol. 5, No. 7, p. 9.

TYPE: Collection of R. V. Chamberlin.

TYPE LOCALITY: Barrington, McIntosh County, Georgia.

RANGE: Known only from type locality.

Oriulus grayi Causey

Oriulus grayi Causey, 1950, Proc. Arkansas Acad. Sci., vol. 3, p. 50, figs. 37–42.

TYPE: Acad. Nat. Sci. Philadelphia.

TYPE LOCALITY: DeValls Bluff, Prairie County, Arkansas.

RANGE: Known only from type locality.

Oriulus medianus Chamberlin

Oriulus medianus Chamberlin, 1940, Bull. Univ. Utah, biol. ser., vol. 5, No. 7, p. 7, figs. 21, 22.

TYPE: Collection of R. V. Chamberlin.

TYPE LOCALITY: Yellowstone National Park, Wyoming.

RANGE: Reported from numerous localities in Iowa, Nebraska, Montana, Utah, Colorado, Wyoming, and New Mexico.

Oriulus nigrans (Chamberlin)

Parajulus nigrans Chamberlin, 1918, Psyche, vol. 25, p. 27.

TYPE: Mus. Comp. Zool.

TYPE LOCALITY: Near Nashville, Davidson County, Tennessee.

RANGE: Known only from type locality.

Oriulus notus Chamberlin

Oriulus notus Chamberlin, 1940, Bull. Univ. Utah, biol. ser., vol. 5, No. 7, p. 8, figs. 25–27.

TYPE: Collection of R. V. Chamberlin.

TYPE LOCALITY: Gallatin River, near Taylor's Fork, Greenville County, South Carolina.

RANGE: Known only from type locality.

Oriulus venustus (Wood)

Julus venustus Wood, 1864, Proc. Acad. Nat. Sci. Philadelphia, p. 10.

Paraiulus venustus Bollman, 1889, Proc. U. S. Nat. Mus., vol. 11, p. 344—Williams and Hefner, 1928, Bull. Ohio Biol. Surv., No. 18, p. 128, fig. 22.

TYPE: Not known to exist.

TYPE LOCALITY: Illinois (restricted by Causey (in litt.) to West Frankfort, Franklin County).

RANGE: New York westward to Colorado and Utah. The southern limits of the range not known.

Genus PSEUDOJULUS Bollman

Pseudojulus Bollman, 1887, Ann. New York Acad. Sci., vol. 4, p. 37 (as subgenus of *Parajulus*).

Pseudoiulus Silvestri, 1896, Ann, Mus. Civ. Stor. Nat. Genova, ser. 2, vol. 16, pp. 138, 177.

GENEROTYPE: *Parajulus* (*Pseudojulus*) *obtectus* Bollman, by original designation.

RANGE: Western Florida.

SPECIES: One.

Pseudojulus obtectus [10] Bollman

Parajulus (*Pseudojulus*) *obtectus* Bollman, 1887, Ann. New York Acad. Sci., vol. 4, p. 37.

TYPE: If extant, probably at U. S. Nat. Mus.

TYPE LOCALITY: Restricted to Pensacola, Escambia County, Florida.

RANGE: Known only from type locality.

Genus PTYOIULUS Cook

Ptyoiulus Cook, 1895, Ann. New York Acad. Sci., vol. 9, p. 6.

GENEROTYPE: *Julus pennsylvanicus* Brandt [=*Julus impressus* Say], by original designation.

RANGE: Appalachian region from New York southward to Georgia, west to Illinois.

SPECIES: Four.

Ptyoiulus impressus (Say) [11]

Julus impressus Say, 1821, Journ. Acad. Nat. Sci. Philadelphia, vol. 2, p. 102.

Julus pennsylvanicus Brandt, 1841, Recueil, p. 85.

Julus pilosiscutis Wood, 1864, Proc. Acad. Nat. Sci. Philadelphia, p. 11; 1865, Trans. Amer. Philos. Soc., vol. 13, p. 198 (type locality: Susquehanna County, Pennsylvania; type: Acad. Nat. Sci. Philadelphia).

Julus montanus Cope, 1869, Proc. Amer. Philos. Soc., vol. 11, p. 181 (type locality: Montgomery County, Virginia; location of type unknown).

---

[10] This name was based upon immature specimens, probably of two different species, from Pensacola, Florida, and Bloomington, Indiana. Dr. Nell Causey (in litt.) has proposed restricting Bollman's name to a species occurring at Pensacola, the male of which presents distinctive generic characters and which justifies retention of Bollman's generic and specific name for its designation.

[11] The present allocation of Say's *J. impressus* has been arrived at after a careful reconsideration of details of Say's description in connection with his remarks on habitat and abundance. To these conditions no other form is thought to conform as well as the species that has long been commonly known under Brandt's name *pennsylvanicus*.

Ptyoiulus pennsylvanicus Cook, 1895, Ann. New York Acad. Sci., vol. 9,
　　p. 5.—Chamberlin, 1940, Bull. Univ. Utah, biol. ser., vol. 5, No. 7,
　　p. 15, figs. 71–73.
Paraiulus pennsylvanicus Brölemann, 1922, Ann. Ent. Soc. Amer., vol.
　　15, p. 291, figs. 22–27.
TYPE: Probably no longer in existence.
TYPE LOCALITY: Vicinity of Philadelphia, Pennsylvania.
RANGE: Northeastern United States, west to Indiana, and south to western North Carolina and Kentucky.

Ptyoiulus coveanus Chamberlin

Ptyoiulus coveanus Chamberlin, 1943, Bull. Univ. Utah, biol. serv., vol. 8,
　　No. 2, p. 10, figs. 24, 25.
Ptyoiulus ectenes Causey, 1952, Proc. Arkansas Acad. Sci., vol. 5, p. 23.
TYPE: Chicago Nat. Hist. Mus.
TYPE LOCALITY: Greenbriar Cove, Sevier County, Tennessee.
RANGE: Tennessee, Illinois.　Some of the earlier Tennessee records for
P. pennsylvanicus may apply to this species.

Ptyoiulus ectenes (Bollman)

Paraiulus ectenes Bollman, 1888, Proc. U. S. Nat. Mus., vol. 10, p. 617;
　　1893, U. S. Nat. Mus. Bull. 46, p. 34.
TYPE: U. S. Nat. Mus. (No. 659).
TYPE LOCALITY: Chapel Hill, Orange County, North Carolina.
RANGE: Known definitely only from type locality.　Identification of this
species with the preceding, without comparison of types, is regarded as
premature.

Ptyoiulus georgiensis Chamberlin

Ptyoiulus georgiensis Chamberlin, 1943, Bull. Univ. Utah, biol. ser.,
　　vol. 8, No. 2, p. 12, figs. 26, 27.
TYPE: Collection of R. V. Chamberlin.
TYPE LOCALITY: Northwest of Clayton, Rabun County, Georgia.
RANGE: Definitely known only from type locality.　Immature specimens
from Macon County, North Carolina, are probably this species.

Genus SAIULUS Chamberlin

Saiulus Chamberlin, 1940, Bull. Univ. Utah, biol. ser., vol. 5, No. 7,
p. 12.
GENEROTYPE: *Saiulus setifer* Chamberlin, by original designation.
RANGE: Washington.
SPECIES: One.

Saiulus setifer Chamberlin

Saiulus setifer Chamberlin, 1940, Bull. Univ. Utah, biol. ser., vol. 5,
　　No. 7, p. 12, figs. 44–47.

TYPE: Collection of R. V. Chamberlin.
TYPE LOCALITY: Region of Puget Sound, Washington.
RANGE: Known only from type locality.

Genus SHOSHONIULUS Chamberlin

Shoshoniulus Chamberlin, 1951, Great Basin Nat., vol. 11, p. 23.
GENEROTYPE: *Saiulus atlantus* Chamberlin, by original designation.
RANGE: North Georgia; Idaho.
SPECIES: Two.

Shoshoniulus atlantus (Chamberlin)

Saiulus atlantus Chamberlin, 1946, Ent. News, vol. 57, p. 149, figs. 1–5.
Shoshoniulus atlantus Chamberlin, 1951, Great Basin Nat., vol. 11, p. 23.
TYPE: Collection of R. V. Chamberlin.
TYPE LOCALITY: Atlanta, Fulton County, Georgia.
RANGE: Known only from type locality.

Shoshoniulus idahoanus (Chamberlin)

Uroblaniulus idahoanus Chamberlin, 1950, Chicago, Acad. Sci. Nat. Hist.
    Misc. No. 68, p. 5, fig. 2.
Shoshoniulus idahoanus Chamberlin, 1951, Great Basin Nat., vol. 11,
    p. 23.
TYPE: Collection of R. V. Chamberlin.
TYPE LOCALITY: Pierce, Clearwater County, Idaho.
RANGE: Known only from type locality.

Genus SIMIULUS Chamberlin

Simiulus Chamberlin, 1940, Bull. Univ. Utah, biol. ser., vol. 5, No. 7,
    p. 20.
GENEROTYPE: *Parajulus arius* Chamberlin, by original designation.
RANGE: Southern California.
SPECIES: One.

Simiulus arius (Chamberlin)

Parajulus arius Chamberlin, 1918, Pomona Coll. Journ. Ent. and Zool.,
    vol. 10, No. 1, p. 10.
TYPE: Mus. Comp. Zool.
TYPE LOCALITY: Stanford, Santa Clara County, California.
RANGE: Known only from type locality.

Genus SOPHIULUS Chamberlin

Sophiulus Chamberlin, 1940, Bull. Univ. Utah, biol. ser., vol. 5, No. 7,
    p. 18.
GENEROTYPE: *Paraiulus tivius* Chamberlin, by original designation.
RANGE: Central California.
SPECIES: Two.

Sophiulus lomondus Chamberlin

Sophiulus lomondus Chamberlin, 1941, Bull. Univ. Utah, biol. ser., vol. 6, No. 4, p. 20, figs. 33, 34.

TYPE: Collection of R. V. Chamberlin.

TYPE LOCALITY: Ben Lomond, Santa Cruz County, California.

RANGE: Known only from type locality.

Sophiulus tivius (Chamberlin)

Paraiulus tivius Chamberlin, 1912, Ann. Ent. Soc. America, vol. 5, p. 163, pl. 11, figs. 1–7.

Sophiulus tivius Chamberlin, 1940, Bull. Univ. Utah, biol. ser., vol. 5, No. 7, p. 18, fig. 64.

TYPE: Mus. Comp. Zool.

TYPE LOCALITY: Mill Valley, Marin County, California.

RANGE: Vicinity of San Francisco Bay (Stanford, Mill Valley, San Francisco).

Genus SPATHIULUS Chamberlin

Spathiulus Chamberlin, 1940, Bull. Univ. Utah, biol. ser., vol. 5, No. 7, p. 14.

GENEROTYPE: *Spathiulus leptus* Chamberlin, by original designation.

RANGE: Eastern central California.

SPECIES: Four.

Spathiulus elegantulus Causey

Spathiulus elegantulus Causey, 1950, Proc. Arkansas Acad. Sci., vol. 3, p. 47, figs. 18–21.

TYPE: Illinois Nat. Hist. Survey.

TYPE LOCALITY: Happy Isle, Yosemite National Park, Maricopa County, California.

RANGE: Known only from type locality.

Spathiulus leptus Chamberlin

Spathiulus leptus Chamberlin, 1940, Bull. Univ. Utah, biol. ser., vol. 5, No. 7, p. 14, figs. 53–55.

TYPE: Collection of R. V. Chamberlin.

TYPE LOCALITY: Yosemite National Park, Maricopa County, California.

RANGE: Known only from type locality.

Spathiulus tribolus Chamberlin

Spathiulus tribolus Chamberlin, 1941, Bull. Univ. Utah, biol. ser., vol. 6, No. 5, p. 8, figs. 14, 16.

TYPE: Collection of R. V. Chamberlin.

TYPE LOCALITY: Sequoia National Park, 12 miles north of Hammond, Tulare County, California.

RANGE: Known only from type locality.

Spathiulus tuolumnus Chamberlin

Spathiulus tuolumnus Chamberlin, 1950, Chicago Acad. Sci. Nat. Hist. Misc. No. 68, p. 4, fig. 1.

TYPE: Collection of R. V. Chamberlin.

TYPE LOCALITY: Pinecrest, Tuolumne County, California.

RANGE: Known only from type locality.

Genus TAIJULUS Chamberlin

Taijulus Chamberlin, 1938, Proc. Biol. Soc. Washington, vol. 51, p. 205. *Taiulus* authors (emendation of *Taijulus*).

GENEROTYPE: *Paraiulus tiganus* Chamberlin, by original designation.

RANGE: Utah, Wyoming, Idaho, and Washington.

SPECIES: Two.

Taijulus olympus (Causey)

Taiulus olympus Causey 1953, Amer. Midl. Nat., vol. 50, p. 154, figs. 8–10.

TYPE: Amer. Mus. Nat. Hist.

TYPE LOCALITY: Olympic Hot Springs, Washington.

RANGE: Known only from type locality.

Taijulus tiganus Chamberlin

Paraiulus tiganus Chamberlin, 1910, Ann. Ent. Soc. Amer., vol. 3, No. 4, p. 254, pl. 40, figs. 6–8, and pl. 41, figs. 1–4; Brölemann, 1922, Ann. Ent. Soc. Amer., vol. 15, p. 290.

Taijulus tiganus Chamberlin, 1938, Proc. Biol. Soc. Washington, vol. 51, p. 205.

TYPE: Collection of R. V. Chamberlin.

TYPE LOCALITY: Wahsatch Mountains, Salt Lake County, Utah.

RANGE: Northern Utah, Idaho, and Wyoming.

Genus TENIULUS Chamberlin

Teniulus Chamberlin, 1951, Great Basin Nat., vol. 11, Nos. 1–2, p. 21.

GENEROTYPE: *Teniulus parvior* Chamberlin, by original designation.

RANGE: Eastern Tennessee.

SPECIES: Two known.

Teniulus parvior Chamberlin

Teniulus parvior Chamberlin, 1951, Great Basin Nat., vol. 11, Nos. 1–2, p. 23, figs. 10–12.

TYPE: Collection of R. V. Chamberlin.

TYPE LOCALITY: Gatlinburg, Sevier County, Tennessee.

RANGE: Known only from type locality.

Teniulus setosior Chamberlin

Teniulus setosior Chamberlin, 1951, Great Basin Nat., vol. 11, Nos. 1–2, p. 21, figs. 6–9.

TYPE: Collection of R. V. Chamberlin.
TYPE LOCALITY: Gatlinburg, Sevier County, Tennessee.
RANGE: Known only from type locality.

Genus TUNIULUS Chamberlin

Tuniulus Chamberlin, 1941, Bull. Univ. Utah, biol. ser., vol. 6, No. 4, p. 18.
GENEROTYPE: *Codiulus milpetanus* Chamberlin, by original designation.
RANGE: California, Oregon, British Columbia.
SPECIES: Three.

Tuniulus hewitti (Chamberlin)

Paraiulus hewitti Chamberlin, 1919, Canadian Ent., vol. 51, p. 119, fig. 21.
Codiulus hewitti Chamberlin, 1940, Bull. Univ. Utah, biol. ser., vol. 5, No. 7, p. 20, pl. 7, fig. 67, and pl. 8 [sic], figs. 67–69.
TYPE: Mus. Comp. Zool.
TYPE LOCALITY: Agassiz, British Columbia.
RANGE: Reported also from Rainier National Park, Washington.

Tuniulus milpetanus (Chamberlin)

Codiulus milpetanus Chamberlin, 1940, Bull. Univ. Utah, biol. ser., vol. 5, No. 7, p. 20, fig. 70.
TYPE: Collection of R. V. Chamberlin.
TYPE LOCALITY: Milpetas,, Santa Clara County, California.
RANGE: Known only from type locality.

Tuniulus oregonensis (Wood)

Julus oregonensis Wood, 1864, Proc. Acad. Nat. Sci. Philadelphia, vol. 16, p. 11; 1865, Trans. Amer. Philos. Soc., vol. 13, p. 199, fig. 31.
Codiulus oregonensis Chamberlin, 1940, Bull. Univ. Utah, biol. ser., vol. 5, No. 7, p. 19.
TYPE: Unknown.
TYPE LOCALITY: "Oregon."
RANGE: No definite localities known.

Genus UROBLANIULUS Attems

Uroblaniulus Attems, 1902, Mitt. Naturh. Mus. Hamburg, vol. 18, p. 113.—
Chamberlin and Hoffman, 1950, Chicago Acad. Sci. Nat. Hist. Misc. No. 71, p. 6.
GENEROTYPE: *Uroblaniulus megalodus* Attems [=*Julus canadensis* Newport] by monotypy.
RANGE: Boreal North America, Ontario and Vermont south to Georgia, west to Illinois and Michigan.
SPECIES: Nine.

Uroblaniulus canadensis (Newport)

Iulus canadensis Newport, 1844, Ann. Mag. Nat. Hist., vol. 13, p. 268.—
Wood, 1865, Trans. Amer. Philos. Soc., vol. 13, p. 200.

Spirostreptus nutans Koch, 1847, *in* Krit. Rev. Insect. Deutschlands, vol.
3, p. 104 (type locality: North America; type unknown).

Spirostreptus clavipes Koch, 1847, *in* Krit. Rev. Insect. Deutschlands, vol.
3, p. 105 (type locality: Pennsylvania; type unknown).

Paraiulus canadensis Bollman, 1893, U. S. Nat. Mus. Bull. 46, p. 150.

Uroblaniulus mcgalodus Attems, 1902, Mitt. Naturh. Mus. Hamburg, vol.
18, p. 114, pl. 1, figs. 1–5 (type locality: Vermont; type: Hamburg
Museum).

Uroblaniulus canadensis Chamberlin and Hoffman, 1950, Chicago Acad.
Sci. Nat. Hist. Misc. No. 71, p. 6.

Saiulus jerseyi Causey, 1950, Proc. Arkansas Acad. Sci., vol. 3, p. 48, figs.
27–30 (type locality: Rockaway, New Jersey; type: Acad. Nat. Sci.
Philadelphia).

TYPE: British Mus. (Nat. Hist.).

TYPE LOCALITY: Albany River, Hudson's Bay, Ontario, Canada.

RANGE: Northeastern United States and eastern Canada, south in the
Appalachians at least as far as northern Virginia.

Uroblaniulus carolinensis Causey

Uroblaniulus carolinensis Causey, 1953, Amer. Midl. Nat., vol. 50, p. 154,
figs. 11–12.

TYPE: Amer. Mus. Nat. Hist.

TYPE LOCALITY: Raleigh, North Carolina.

RANGE: Known only from type locality.

Uroblaniulus dixinus Chamberlin

Uroblaniulus dixinus Chamberlin, 1951, Great Basin Nat., vol. 11, Nos.
1–2, p. 21, figs. 4, 5.

TYPE: Collection of R. V. Chamberlin.

TYPE LOCALITY: Gatlinburg, Tennessee.

RANGE: Known only from type locality.

Uroblaniulus dux (Chamberlin)

Paraiulus dux Chamberlin, 1914, Canadian Ent., vol. 46, p. 304.—Williams
and Hefner, 1928, Bull. Ohio Biol. Surv., No. 18, p. 126, fig. 18.

TYPE: Mus. Comp. Zool.

TYPE LOCALITY: Douglas Lake, Cheboygan County, Michigan.

RANGE: Cheboygan, Allen, and Logan Counties, Michigan.

Uroblaniulus exul Chamberlin

Uroblaniulus exul Chamberlin, 1951, Great Basin Nat., vol. 11, Nos. 1–2,
p. 19, figs. 1–3.

TYPE: Collection of R. V. Chamberlin.

TYPE LOCALITY: Gatlinburg, Tennessee.
RANGE: Known only from type locality.

Uroblaniulus fumans (Chamberlin)

Saiulus fumans Chamberlin, 1943, Bull. Univ. Utah, biol. ser., vol. 8, No. 3, p. 10, fig. 23.
Uroblaniulus fumans Chamberlin, 1951, Great Basin Nat., vol. 11, Nos. 1–2, p. 19.
TYPE: Chicago Nat. Hist. Mus.
TYPE LOCALITY: Gatlinburg, Sevier County, Tennessee.
RANGE: Great Smoky Mountains, Tennessee.

Uroblaniulus immaculatus (Wood)

Julus immaculatus Wood, 1864, Proc. Acad. Nat. Sci. Philadelphia, p. 12; 1865, Trans. Amer. Philos. Soc., vol. 13, p. 200.
Parajulus immaculatus Bollman, 1887, Ann. New York Acad. Sci., vol. 4, p. 44.—Brölemann, 1922, Ann. Ent. Soc. Amer., vol. 15, No. 4, p. 292, figs. 28–34.
Saiulus immaculatus Causey, 1950, Proc. Arkansas Acad. Sci., vol. 3, p. 49, figs. 31–36.
TYPE: Acad. Nat. Sci., Philadelphia.
TYPE LOCALITY: Catskill Mountains, New York.
RANGE: Known definitely from Vermont (Grafton County), New York (Catskill Mountains), Pennsylvania (Charteroak).

Uroblaniulus montanus (Hoffman)

Saiulus montanus Hoffman, 1949, Proc. Biol. Soc. Washington, vol. 62, p. 81, figs. 5, 6.
TYPE: U. S. Nat. Mus. (No. 1847).
TYPE LOCALITY: Mount Rogers, Grayson County, Virginia.
RANGE: High mountains in southwestern Virginia, in Grayson, Bland, Tazewell, Giles, and Alleghany Counties. This form is probably a southern subspecies of *U. immaculatus* (Wood).

Uroblaniulus sandersoni (Causey)

Saiulus sandersoni Causey, 1950, Proc. Arkansas Acad. Sci., vol. 3, p. 48, figs. 22–26.
TYPE: Illinois Nat. Hist. Survey.
TYPE LOCALITY: LaRue, Illinois.
RANGE: Southern Illinois (Thebes and LaRue).

Uroblaniulus stolidus Causey

Uroblaniulus stolidus Causey, 1952, Proc. Arkansas Acad. Sci., vol. 5, p. 22, figs. 6–9.
TYPE: Amer. Mus. Nat. Hist.
TYPE LOCALITY: Peninsular State Park, Door County, Wisconsin.
RANGE: Known only from type locality.

Genus ZINIULUS Chamberlin

Ziniulus Chamberlin, 1940, Bull. Univ. Utah, biol. ser., vol. 5, No. 7, p. 13.
GENEROTYPE: *Ziniulus aethes* Chamberlin, by original designation.
RANGE: Texas, New Mexico.
SPECIES: Three.

Ziniulus aethes Chamberlin

Ziniulus aethes Chamberlin, 1940, Bull. Univ. Utah, biol. ser., vol. 5,
    No. 7, p. 13, figs. 48–50.
TYPE: Collection of R. V. Chamberlin.
TYPE LOCALITY: Austin, Travis County, Texas.
RANGE: Known only from type locality.

Ziniulus medicolens Chamberlin

Ziniulus medicolens Chamberlin, 1940, Bull. Univ. Utah, biol. ser., vol. 5,
    No. 7, p. 13, figs. 51–51.
TYPE: Collection of R. V. Chamberlin.
TYPE LOCALITY: Raven Ranch, Kerr County, Texas.
RANGE: Known only from type locality.

Ziniulus navajo Chamberlin

Ziniulus navajo Chamberlin, 1943, Proc. Biol. Soc. Washington, vol. 56,
    p. 146, fig. 6.
TYPE: Collection of R. V. Chamberlin.
TYPE LOCALITY: 6 miles south of Mountainair, Torrance County, New
Mexico.
RANGE: Lincoln and Torrance Counties, New Mexico.

Paraiulidae of uncertain systematic position

Julus caesius Wood

Julus caesius Wood, 1867, Proc. Acad. Nat. Sci. Philadelphia, p. 43.
Parajulus caesius Bollman, 1893, U. S. Nat. Mus. Bull. 46, p. 119.
TYPE: Present location unknown.
TYPE LOCALITY: Texas.
Bollman was correct in referring this form to the Paraiulidae, but the
generic position and specific characters of *caesius* remain obscure.

Paraiulus garius Chamberlin

Paraiulus garius Chamberlin, 1912, Ann. Ent. Soc. Amer., vol. 5, p. 167.
TYPE: Present location unknown.
TYPE LOCALITY: Tolland, Gilpin County. Colorado.
Based upon a female. Collection of topotypes will be necessary to make
a generic placement certain.

Parajulus perditus Chamberlin

Parajulus perditus Chamberlin, 1920, Canadian Ent., vol. 52, p. 167.
TYPE: Mus. Comp. Zool.
TYPE LOCALITY: Waterton Lake, British Columbia.
Known only from females, and not at present to be placed with certainty.

Parajulus varius Bollman

Parajulus varius Bollman, 1887, Ann. New York Acad. Sci., vol. 4, p. 38.
TYPE: U. S. Nat. Mus.
TYPE LOCALITY: San Diego, California.
RANGE: Reported by Bollman from Ukiah and Rosario Mission, California, but probably more than one species were involved.
The type most probably is a *Bollmaniulus* or a *Codiulus*.

Parajulus zonatus Bollman

Parajulus zonatus Bollman, 1887, Proc. U. S. Nat. Mus., vol. 10, p. 618.
TYPE: U. S. Nat Mus.
TYPE LOCALITY: Chehalis, Lewis County, Washington.
This species is probably referrable to *Bollmaniulus*.

Family ZOSTERACTIIDAE Loomis

Zosteractiidae Loomis, 1943, Bull. Mus. Comp. Zool., vol. 92, No. 7, p. 393.

Genus ZOSTERACTIS Loomis

Zosteractis Loomis, 1943, Bull. Mus. Comp. Zool., vol. 92, No. 7, p. 394.
GENEROTYPE: *Zosteractis interminata* Loomis, by original designation.
RANGE: Missouri.
SPECIES: One.

Zosteractis interminata Loomis

Zosteractis interminata Loomis, 1943, Bull. Mus. Comp. Zool., vol. 92, No. 7, p. 395, figs. 11a–i.
TYPE: Mus. Comp. Zool.
TYPE LOCALITY: South Rankin Cave, 4 miles east of Eureka, St. Louis County, Missouri.
RANGE: Caves in St. Louis and St. Genevieve Counties, Missouri.

Julida of uncertain systematic position

Julus cinerefrons Wood

Julus cinerefrons Wood, 1864, Proc. Acad. Nat. Sci. Philadelphia, p. 13.
TYPE: Present location unknown.
TYPE LOCATION: Oregon.
Wood based this species on a single badly mutilated female, now apparently lost. It seems impossible to identify the form again, even to family, with any degree of certainty.

Julus milesi Wood

Julus milesi Wood, 1864, Proc. Acad. Nat. Sci. Philadelphia, p. 13.

TYPE: Present location unknown.

TYPE LOCALITY: Michigan.

A form not identifiable with certainty. It was probably based on immature specimens.

Order SPIROBOLIDA

Spirobolinae Bollman, 1893, U. S. Nat. Mus. Bull. 46, p. 156.

Spirobolidae (in part) Verhoeff, 1893, Zool. Anz., vol. 16, p. 481.—
Pocock, 1894, Chilopoda, Symphyla and Diplopoda . . . , *in* Weber,
Zool. Erg. Reise Niederl. Ost-Ind., vol. 3, p. 388.

Anocheta Cook, 1895, Ann. New York Acad. Sci., vol. 9, p. 7.

Spiroboloidea Attems, 1926, *in* Kükenthal-Krumbach, Handbuch der
Zoologie, vol. 4, p. 192.

KEY TO THE NORTH AMERICAN FAMILIES OF SPIROBOLIDA

1. Prozonites of some of the segments usually with a pair of dorsal pits (scobinae);
   sternite of anterior gonopods produced distally; telopodite of posterior gonopods
   distally biramous (tibiotarsus with a separate solenomerite), usually very slender.
   .... RHINOCRICIDAE (p. 151)

   Scobinae never present; sternite of anterior gonopods not conspicuously produced
   distad; telopodite of posterior gonopods not very slender and usually without a free
   and conspicuous solenomerite 2

2. Second tergite extending well below level of the collum, latter with ends generally
   rounded; coxite and telopodite of posterior gonopods attached to each other in
   the same axis . . . . SPIROBOLIDAE (p. 159)

   Second tergite not extending below level of ends of collum, latter typically more
   acute; posterior gonopods with coxite and telopodite attached to form a right
   angle . . . . ATOPETHOLIDAE (p. 152)

Family RHINOCRICIDAE Brölemann

Rhinocricidae Brölemann, 1914, Ann. Soc. Ent. France, vol. 83, p. 476.—
Schubart, 1951, Anais Acad. Brasileira Ciénc., vol. 23, p. 221.

Genus EURHINOCRICUS Brölemann

Eurhinocricus Brölemann, 1903, Ann. Soc. Ent. France, vol. 72, p. 131.—
Pocock, 1907, Diplopoda, *in* Biol. Centr.-Amer., pp. 68, 73.—Hoffman, 1953, Proc. Biol. Soc. Washington, vol. 66, p. 179.

GENEROTYPE: *Eurhinocricus biolleyi* Brölemann, by original designation.

RANGE: Middle America, from southern California south to Panama;
Jamaica.

SPECIES: Twenty, of which one occurs, in our area.

Eurhinocricus tidus (Chamberlin)

Rhinocricus tidus Chamberlin, 1947, Proc. Acad. Nat. Sci. Philadelphia, vol. 99, p. 37, figs. 25, 26.

Eurhinocricus tidus Hoffman, 1953, Proc. Biol. Soc. Washington, vol. 66, p. 183.

TYPE: Acad. Nat. Sci. Philadelphia.

TYPE LOCALITY: Fort Tejon, Kern County, California.

RANGE: Known only from type locality.

Genus RHINOCRICUS Karsch

Rhinocricus Karsch, 1881, Zeitschr. Naturw., vol. 54 (ser. 3, vol. 6), p. 68 (as subgenus of *Spirobolus*).

Rhinocricus Pocock, 1894, Journ. Linn. Soc. London, vol. 24 (Zool.), p. 485.

GENEROTYPE: *Spirobolus* (*Rhinocricus*) *parcus* Karsch, by subsequent designation of Pocock, 1894.

RANGE: Neotropical and Austral regions.

SPECIES: Two are known from our limits; more than a hundred have been described from the tropics.

Rhinocricus vagans Chamberlin

Rhinocricus vagans Chamberlin, 1947, Proc. Acad. Nat. Sci. Philadelphia, vol. 99, p. 37, figs. 23, 24.

TYPE: Acad. Nat. Sci. Philadelphia (No. 9959).

TYPE LOCALITY: Fort Tejon, Kern County, California.

RANGE: Known only from type locality.

Rhinocricus vancouveri Chamberlin

Rhinocricus vancouveri Chamberlin, 1951, Chicago Acad. Sci. Nat. Hist. Misc. No. 87, p. 11, figs. 24–26.

TYPE: Prov. Mus. British Columbia.

TYPE LOCALITY: Clayoquot Sound, Vancouver Island, British Columbia.

RANGE: Known only from type locality.

Family ATOPETHOLIDAE Chamberlin

Atopetholidae Chamberlin, 1918, Proc. Biol. Soc. Washington, vol. 31, p. 167; 1949, Journ. Washington Acad. Sci., vol. 39, p. 168.

Onychelidae Verhoeff, 1938, Zool. Anz., vol. 122, p. 273.

Genus ANELUS Cook

Anelus Cook, 1911, Proc. U. S. Nat. Mus., vol. 40, p. 160.

GENEROTYPE: *Anelus reduncus* Cook, by original designation.

RANGE: Texas.

SPECIES: One in our area, another in Mexico.

Anelus reduncus Cook

Anelus reduncus Cook, 1911, Proc. U. S. Nat. Mus., vol. 40, p. 162.
TYPE: U. S. Nat. Mus. (No. 798).
TYPE LOCALITY: Brownsville, Cameron County, Texas.
RANGE: Known only from type locality.

Genus ARINOLUS Chamberlin

Arinolus Chamberlin, 1940, Pomona Coll. Journ. Ent. and Zool., vol. 32,
p. 81.
GENEROTYPE: *Arinolus torynophor* Chamberlin, by original designation.
RANGE: Arizona, southern California, and Mexico.
SPECIES: Ten, nine in our area.

Arinolus apachellus Chamberlin

Arinolus apachellus Chamberlin, 1941, Bull. Univ. Utah, biol. ser., vol. 6,
No. 4, p. 10, figs. 12–14.
TYPE: Collection of R. V. Chamberlin.
TYPE LOCALITY: Covered Wells, Pima County, Arizona.
RANGE: Known only from type locality.

Arinolus chiricahuanus Chamberlin

Arinolus chiricahuanus Chamberlin, 1947, Proc. Acad. Nat. Sci. Phila-
delphia, vol. 99, p. 50, figs. 56–58.
TYPE: Acad. Nat. Sci. Philadelphia.
TYPE LOCALITY: White Tail Canyon, Chiricahua Mountains, Arizona.
RANGE: Known only from type locality.

Arinolus dentatus (Cook)

Onychelus dentatus Cook, 1911, Proc. U. S. Nat. Mus., vol. 40, p. 158.
Onychelus suturatus Cook, 1911, Proc. U. S. Nat. Mus., vol. 40, p. 159
(type locality: Fort Huachuca, Arizona; type: U. S. Nat. Mus.,
No. 805).
Arinolus dentatus Loomis, 1950, Journ. Washington Acad. Sci., vol. 40,
p. 164.
TYPE: U. S. Nat. Mus. (No. 804).
TYPE LOCALITY: Fort Huachuca, Cochise County, Arizona.
RANGE: Known only from type locality.

Arinolus hopinus Chamberlin

Arinolus hopinus Chamberlin, 1941, Bull. Univ. Utah, biol. ser., vol. 6,
No. 4, p. 12, fig. 16.
TYPE: Collection of R. V. Chamberlin.
TYPE LOCALITY: 15 miles east of Tucson, Pima County, Arizona.
RANGE: Known only from type locality.

Arinolus hospes (Cook)

Onychelus hospes Cook, 1911, Proc. U. S. Nat. Mus., vol. 40, p. 157.
Arinolus hospes Loomis, 1950, Journ. Washington Acad. Sci., vol. 40, p. 164.
TYPE: U. S. Nat Mus. (No. 803).
TYPE LOCALITY: Tucson, Pima County, Arizona.
RANGE: Known only from the type locality.

Arinolus latus Loomis

Arinolus latus Loomis, 1953, Journ. Washington Acad. Sci., vol. 43, p. 418, figs. 10–12.
TYPE: U.S. Nat. Mus. (No. 2090).
TYPE LOCALITY: Antelope Valley, between Lancaster and Palmdale, Los Angeles County, California.
RANGE: Known only from type locality.

Arinolus nogalanus Chamberlin

Arinolus nogalanus Chamberlin, 1941, Bull. Univ. Utah, biol. ser., vol. 6, No. 4, p. 11, fig. 15.
TYPE: Collection of R. V. Chamberlin.
TYPE LOCALITY: Nogales, Santa Cruz County, Arizona.
RANGE: Known only from type locality.

Arinolus pimus Chamberlin

Arinolus pimus Chamberlin, 1941, Bull. Univ. Utah, biol. ser., vol. 6, No. 4, p. 12.
TYPE: Collection of R. V. Chamberlin.
TYPE LOCALITY: Litchfield Park, Maricopa County, Arizona.
RANGE: Known only from type locality.

Arinolus torynophor Chamberlin

Arinolus torynophor Chamberlin, 1940, Pomona Coll. Journ. Ent. and Zool., vol. 32, p. 81, figs. A, B.
TYPE: Collection of R. V. Chamberlin.
TYPE LOCALITY: Fish Creek, Maricopa County, Arizona.
RANGE: Known only from type locality.

Genus ATOPETHOLUS Chamberlin

Atopetholus Chamberlin, 1918, Proc. Biol. Soc. Washington, vol. 31, p. 167.
GENEROTYPE: *Atopetholus californicus* Chamberlin, by original designation.
RANGE: California.
SPECIES: Seven.

Atopetholus angelus Chamberlin

Atopetholus aneglus Chamberlin, 1920, Proc. Biol. Soc. Washington, vol. 33, p. 101.

TYPE: U. S. Nat. Mus.

TYPE LOCALITY: Edendale, Los Angeles County, California.

RANGE: Known only from type locality.

Atopetholus barbaranus Chamberlin

Atopetholus barbaranus Chamberlin, 1949, Journ. Washington Acad. Sci., vol. 39, p. 168.

TYPE: Collection of R. V. Chamberlin.

TYPE LOCALITY: Santa Barbara County, California.

RANGE: Known only from type locality.

Atopetholus californicus Chamberlin

Atopetholus californicus Chamberlin, 1918, Proc. Biol. Soc. Washington, vol. 31, p. 168.

TYPE: Mus. Comp. Zool.

TYPE LOCALITY: Claremont, Los Angeles County, California.

RANGE: Known only from type locality.

Atopetholus carmelitus Chamberlin

Atopetholus carmelitus Chamberlin, 1940, Pomona Coll. Journ. Ent. and Zool., vol. 32, p. 81, figs. C–E.

TYPE: Collection of R. V. Chamberlin.

TYPE LOCALITY: Hastings Reservation, Monterey County, California.

RANGE: Known only from type locality.

Atopetholus fraternus Chamberlin

Atopetholus fraternus Chamberlin, 1918, Proc. Biol. Soc. Washington, vol. 31, p. 168.

TYPE: Mus. Comp. Zool.

TYPE LOCALITY: Friant, Fresno County, California.

RANGE: Known only from type locality.

Atopetholus paroicus Chamberlin

Atopetholus paroicus Chamberlin, 1941, Bull. Univ. Utah. biol. ser., vol. 6, No. 4, p. 7, fig. 5.

TYPE: Collection of R. V. Chamberlin.

TYPE LOCALITY: Mountain Spring, San Diego County, California.

RANGE: Known only from type locality.

Atopetholus pearcei Chamberlin

Atopetholus pearcei Chamberlin, 1950, Chicago Acad. Sci. Nat. Hist. Misc. No. 68, p. 6, fig. 3.

TYPE: Collection of R. V. Chamberlin.

Type Locality: Oildale, Kern County, California.
Range: Known only from type locality.

Genus EURELUS Cook

Eurelus Cook, 1911, Proc. U. S. Nat. Mus., vol. 40, p. 151.
Generotype: *Eurelus soleatus* Cook, by original designation.
Range: Western Texas; New Mexico.
Species: Four.

Eurelus kerrensis Chamberlin and Mulaik

Eurelus kerrensis Chamberlin and Mulaik, 1941, Journ. New York Ent.
  Soc., vol. 49, p. 61.
Type: Collection of R. V. Chamberlin.
Type Locality: Kerr County, Texas.
Range: Known only from type locality.

Eurelus mulaiki Chamberlin

Eurelus mulaiki Chamberlin, 1943, Proc. Biol. Soc. Washington, vol. 56,
  p. 147, figs. 7–11.
Type: Collection of R. V. Chamberlin.
Type Locality: North of Glencoe, Lincoln County, New Mexico.
Range: Known from Lincoln and Torrance Counties, New Mexico.

Eurelus proximus Chamberlin and Mulaik

Eurelus proximus Chamberlin and Mulaik, 1941, Journ. New York Ent.
  Soc., vol. 49, p. 62.
Type: Collection of R. V. Chamberlin.
Type Locality: Edinburg, Hidalgo County, Texas.
Range: Known only from type locality.

Eurelus soleatus Cook

Eurelus soleatus Cook, 1911, Proc. U. S. Nat. Mus., vol. 40, p. 153.
Type: U. S. Nat. Mus. (No. 801).
Type Locality: Falfurrias, Brooks County, Texas.
Range: Known only from type locality.

Genus HESPEROLUS Chamberlin

Hesperolus Chamberlin, 1918, Proc. Biol. Soc. Washington, vol. 31, p. 169.
Generotype: *Hesperolus wheeleri* Chamberlin, by original designation.
Range: California.
Species: One.

Hesperolus wheeleri Chamberlin

Hesperolus wheeleri Chamberlin, 1918, Proc. Biol. Soc. Washington,
  vol. 31, p. 169.
Type: Mus. Comp. Zool.

TYPE LOCALITY: Cold Spring Canyon, Santa Inez Mountains, California.
RANGE: Known only from type locality.

Genus ONYCHELUS Cook

Onychelus Cook, 1904, in Harriman Alaska Exped., vol. 8, p. 67.
Gosichelus Chamberlin, 1949, Journ. Washington Acad. Sci., vol. 39,
   p. 168 (generotype, *Onychelus jaegeri* Chamberlin).
GENEROTYPE: *Onychelus obustus* Cook, by original designation.
RANGE: California and Arizona.
SPECIES: Three.

Onychelus jaegeri Chamberlin

Onychelus jaegeri Chamberlin, 1947, Proc. Acad. Nat. Sci. Philadelphia,
   vol. 99, p. 50, figs. 53, 54.
Gosichelus jaegeri Chamberlin, 1949, Journ. Washington Acad. Sci., vol.
   39, p. 168.
TYPE: Acad. Nat. Sci. Philadelphia (No. 9972).
TYPE LOCALITY: Indio Mudhills, about ten miles northeast of Palm Springs,
Riverside County, California.
RANGE: Known only from type locality.

Onychelus medolus Chamberlin

Onychelus medolus Chamberlin, 1941, Bull. Univ. Utah, biol. ser., vol.
   6, No. 4, p. 13, figs. 17, 18.
TYPE: Collection of R. V. Chamberlin.
TYPE LOCALITY: Olberg, Pinal County, Arizona.
RANGE: Known only from type locality.

Onychelus obustus Cook

Onychelus obustus Cook, 1904, *in* Harriman Alaska Exped., vol. 4, p. 68.
TYPE: U. S. Nat. Mus. (No. 797).
TYPE LOCALITY: Colorado Desert, Imperial County, California.
RANGE: Known only from type locality.

Genus ORTHICHELUS Chamberlin and Hoffman

Orthichelus Chamberlin and Hoffman, 1950, Chicago Acad. Sci. Nat. Hist.
   Misc. No. 71, p. 7.
GENEROTYPE: *Onychelus phanus* Chamberlin, by original designation.
RANGE: California.
SPECIES: One.

Orthichelus michelbacheri (Verhoeff)

Onychelus michelbacheri Verhoeff, 1938, Zool. Anz., vol. 122, Nos. 11–12,
   p. 276, figs. 1–3.

387630—58——11

Onychelus phanus Chamberlin, 1941, Bull. Univ. Utah, biol. ser., vol. 6,
    No. 5, p. 6, figs. 6, 7.   (type locality: 6 miles west of Freeman, Kern
    County, California; type: collection of R. V. Chamberlin).
TYPE: Verhoeff collection.
TYPE LOCALITY: Walker's Pass, west of Freeman, Kern County, California.
RANGE: Known only from Kern County, California.

Genus PIEDOLUS Chamberlin

Piedolus Chamberlin, 1930, Pan-Pacific Ent., vol. 6, p. 117.
GENEROTYPE: *Piedolus utus* Chamberlin, by original designation.
RANGE: Southern Utah.
SPECIES: One.

Piedolus utus Chamberlin

Piedolus utus Chamberlin, 1930, Pan-Pacific Ent., vol. 6, p. 118, fig.
TYPE: Collection of R. V. Chamberlin.
TYPE LOCALITY: St. George, Washington County, Utah.
RANGE: Known only from type locality.

Genus TIDOLUS Chamberlin

Tidolus Chamberlin, 1949, Journ. Washington Acad. Sci., vol. 39, No. 5,
    p. 169.
GENEROTYPE: *Atopetholus parvus* Chamberlin, by original designation.
RANGE: Southern California.
SPECIES: One.

Tidolus parvus (Chamberlin)

Atopetholus parvus Chamberlin, 1918, Proc. Biol. Soc. Washington, vol.
    31, p. 168.
Tidolus parvus Chamberlin, 1949, Journ. Washington Acad. Sci., vol. 39,
    p. 169.
TYPE: Mus. Comp. Zool.
TYPE LOCALITY: Claremont, Los Angeles County, California.
RANGE: Known only from type locality.

Genus TOLTECOLUS Chamberlin

Toltecolus Chamberlin, 1943, Bull. Univ. Utah, biol. ser., vol. 8, No. 3,
    p. 27.
GENEROTYPE: *Toltecolus garcianus* Chamberlin, by original designation.
RANGE: Texas, Chihuahua, Nuevo León.
SPECIES: Three, one of which occurs in our area.

Toltecolus parvunguis Hoffman

Toltecolus parvunguis Hoffman, 1949, Chicago Acad. Sci. Nat. Hist. Misc.
    No. 46, p. 1, figs. A, B.
TYPE: U. S. Nat. Mus. (No. 1853).

TYPE LOCALITY: Frio State Park, Frio County, Texas.
RANGE: Known only from type locality.

Genus WATICHELUS Chamberlin

Watichelus Chamberlin, 1949, Journ. Washington Acad. Sci., vol. 39, p. 169.
GENEROTYPE: *Onychelus smithi* Chamberlin, by original designation.
RANGE: Southern California, and adjacent Baja California.
SPECIES: Four in our area, two extralimital.

Watichelus edentatus Loomis

Watichelus edentatus Loomis, 1949, Journ. Washington Acad. Sci., vol. 39, p. 241, figs. 3, 4.
TYPE: U. S. Nat. Mus.
TYPE LOCALITY: Between El Centro and San Diego, California.
RANGE: Known only from type locality.

Watichelus parallelus Loomis

Watichelus parallelus Loomis, 1949, Journ. Washington Acad. Sci., vol. 39, p. 244, figs. 9, 10.
TYPE: U. S. Nat. Mus.
TYPE LOCALITY: Chula Vista, San Diego County, California.
RANGE: Known only from type locality.

Watichelus robustus Loomis

Watichelus robustus Loomis, 1949, Journ. Washington Acad. Sci., vol. 39, p. 241, figs. 1, 2.
TYPE: U. S. Nat. Mus.
TYPE LOCALITY: Chula Vista, San Diego County, California.
RANGE: Known only from type locality.

Watichelus smithi (Chamberlin)

Onychelus smithi Chamberlin, 1947, Proc. Acad. Nat. Sci. Philadelphia, vol. 99, p. 49, figs. 52, 53.
Watichelus smithi Chamberlin, 1949, Journ. Washington Acad. Sci., vol. 39, p. 169.
TYPES Acad. Nat. Sci., Philadelphia.
TYPE LOCALITY: Murray Canyon, Riverside County, California.
RANGE: Known only from type locality.

Family SPIROBOLIDAE Bollman

Spirobolinae (in part) Bollman, 1893, U. S. Nat. Mus. Bull. 46, p. 156.
Spirobolidae (in part) Verhoeff, 1893, Zool. Anz., vol. 16, p. 481.—Pocock, 1894, Chilopoda, Symphyla and Diplopoda, . . . , *in* Weber, Zool. Erg. Reise Niederl. Ost-Ind., vol. 3, p. 388.—Cook, 1895, Ann. New York Acad. Sci., vol. 9, p. 7.
Spirobolidae Brölemann, 1914, Ann. Soc. Ent. France, vol. 83, p. 1.

Genus AUXOBOLUS Chamberlin

Auxobolus Chamberlin, 1949, Journ. Washington Acad. Sci., vol. 39, p. 163.

GENEROTYPE: *Auxobolus ergus* Chamberlin, by original designation.
RANGE: Southern California.
SPECIES: Eight.

Auxobolus castaneus (Chamberlin)

Tylobolus castaneus Chamberlin, 1918, Proc. Biol. Soc. Washington, vol. 31, p. 166.
Auxobolus castaneus Chamberlin, 1949, Journ. Washington Acad. Sci., vol. 39, p. 163.

TYPE: Mus. Comp. Zool.
TYPE LOCALITY: Brookdale, Santa Cruz County, California.
RANGE: Known only from the type locality.

Auxobolus claremontus (Chamberlin)

Tylobolus claremontus Chamberlin, 1918, Proc. Biol. Soc. Washington, vol. 31, p. 165.
Auxobolus claremontus Chamberlin, 1949, Journ. Washington Acad. Sci., vol. 39, p. 163, figs. 1, 2.

TYPE: Mus. Comp. Zool.
TYPE LOCALITY: Claremont, Los Angeles County, California.
RANGE: Known only from type locality.

Auxobolus discipulus Chamberlin

Auxobolus discipulus Chamberlin, 1949, Journ. Washington Acad. Sci., vol. 39, p. 165, figs. 3, 4.

TYPE: Collection of R. V. Chamberlin.
TYPE LOCALITY: Ione, Amador County, California.
RANGE: Also known from vicinity of Stanford University, in central California.

Auxobolus ergus Chamberlin

Auxobolus ergus Chamberlin, 1949, Journ. Washington Acad. Sci., vol. 39, p. 163, figs. 5–7.

TYPE: Collection of R. V. Chamberlin.
TYPE LOCALITY: Tollhouse, Fresno County, California.
RANGE: Central-eastern California, from Kern County north to Madera County.

Auxobolus friantus Chamberlin

Auxobolus friantus Chamberlin, 1949, Journ. Washington Acad. Sci., vol. 39, p. 165, figs. 8, 9.

TYPE: Collection of R. V. Chamberlin.

TYPE LOCALITY: Friant, Fresno County, California.
RANGE: Known only from type locality.

Auxobolus monachus Chamberlin

Auxobolus monachus Chamberlin, 1949, Journ. Washington Acad. Sci., vol. 39, p. 165, figs. 10, 11.
TYPE: Collection of R. V. Chamberlin.
TYPE LOCALITY: Hastings Reservation, Monterey County, California.
RANGE: Known only from Monterey County, California.

Auxobolus simulatus Chamberlin

Auxobolus simulatus Chamberlin, 1949, Journ. Washington Acad. Sci., vol. 39, p. 165, figs. 12, 13.
TYPE: Collection of R. V. Chamberlin.
TYPE LOCALITY: Riverside, Riverside County, California.
RANGE: Known only from type locality.

Auxobolus stebbinsi (Chamberlin)

Tylobolus stebbinsi Chamberlin, 1944, Proc. Biol. Soc. Washington, vol. 57, p. 113, figs. 4, 5.
Auxobolus stebbinsi Chamberlin, 1949, Journ. Washington Acad. Sci., vol. 39, p. 165.
TYPE: Collection of R. V. Chamberlin.
TYPE LOCALITY: Meadow Canyon, Santa Monica Mountains, Los Angeles County, California.
RANGE: Known only from Los Angeles County, California.

Genus CALIFORNIBOLUS Verhoeff

Californibolus Verhoeff, 1944, Bull. Southern California Acad. Sci., vol. 43, p. 53.—Chamberlin, 1949, Journ. Washington Acad. Sci., vol. 39, p. 165.
GENEROTYPE: *Californibolus michelbacheri* Verhoeff, by original designation.
RANGE: Oregon, California, southwestern Utah.
SPECIES: Seven.

Californibolus fredricksoni Causey

Californibolus fredricksoni Causey, 1955, Journ. Kansas Ent. Soc., vol. 28, p. 78, figs. 1c, 4, 5.
TYPE: Snow Ent. Mus., Univ. Kansas.
TYPE LOCALITY: Douglas County, Kansas.
RANGE: Eastern Kansas, probably also Nebraska and Iowa.

Californibolus michelbacheri Verhoeff

Californibolus michelbacheri Verhoeff, 1944, Bull. Southern California Acad. Sci., vol. 43, p. 56, pl. 12, figs. 1–3.

TYPE: Verhoeff collection.
TYPE LOCALITY: Vicinity of Fort Seward, Humboldt County, California.
RANGE: Known only from type locality.

Californibolus oregonus Chamberlin

Californibolus oregonus Chamberlin, 1949, Journ. Washington Acad. Sci., vol. 39, p. 166, figs. 14, 15.
TYPE: Collection of R. V. Chamberlin.
TYPE LOCALITY: Springfield, Lane County, California.
RANGE: Known only from type locality.

Californibolus pontis Chamberlin

Californibolus pontis Chamberlin, 1949, Journ. Washington Acad. Sci., vol. 39, p. 166, figs. 18, 19.
TYPE: Collection of R. V. Chamberlin.
TYPE LOCALITY: Bridgeville, Humboldt County, California.
RANGE: Known only from type locality.

Californibolus rectus Chamberlin

Californibolus rectus Chamberlin, 1949, Journ. Washington Acad. Sci., vol. 39, p. 166, figs. 16, 17.
TYPE: Collection of R. V. Chamberlin.
TYPE LOCALITY: Solano County, California.
RANGE: Known only from type locality.

Californibolus uncigerus (Wood)

Spirobolus uncigerus Wood, 1864, Proc. Acad. Nat. Sci. Philadelphia, p. 15; 1865, Trans. Amer. Philos. Soc., vol. 13, p. 209, fig. 36.
Californibolus uncigerus Chamberlin, 1949, Journ. Washington Acad. Sci., vol. 39, p. 166.
TYPE: Not known to exist.
TYPE LOCALITY: California, without further locality.
RANGE: Recorded from Shasta County, California, by Causey (1955).

Californibolus utahensis (Chamberlin)

Tylobolus utahensis Chamberlin, 1925, Pan-Pacific Ent., vol. 2, No. 2, p. 60.
TYPE: Collection of R. V. Chamberlin.
TYPE LOCALITY: Zion National Park, Washington County, Utah.
RANGE: Known only from type locality.

Genus CHICOBOLUS Chamberlin

Chicobolus Chamberlin, 1947, Proc. Acad. Nat. Sci. Philadelphia, vol. 99, p. 46.—Causey, 1955, Journ. Kansas Ent. Soc., vol. 28, p. 75.
GENEROTYPE: *Chicobolus pilsbryi* Chamberlin, by original designation.
RANGE: Florida.
SPECIES: Three.

Chicobolus jucundus Causey

Chicobolus jucundus Causey, 1955, Journ. Kansas Ent. Soc., vol. 28, p. 77.

TYPE: Amer. Mus. Nat. Hist.

TYPE LOCALITY: Pensacola, Escambia County, Florida.

RANGE: Known only from type locality.

Chicobolus pilsbryi Chamberlin

Chicobolus pilsbryi Chamberlin, 1947, Proc. Acad. Nat. Sci. Philadelphia, vol. 99, p. 46, figs. 46, 47.

TYPE: Acad. Nat. Sci. Philadelphia (No. 9968).

TYPE LOCALITY: Boca Chica Key, Dade County, Florida.

RANGE: Known only from type locality.

Chicobolus spinigerus (Wood)

Spirobolus spinigerus Wood, 1864, Proc. Acad. Nat. Sci. Philadelphia, p. 15.

Spirobolus paludis Chamberlin, 1918, Ann. Ent. Soc. Amer., vol. 11, p. 374 (type locality: Okefenokee Swamp, Georgia; type: Mus. Comp. Zool.).

Chicobolus spinigerus Causey, 1955, Journ. Kansas Ent. Soc., vol. 28, p. 76, fig. 1b.

TYPE: Acad. Nat. Sci. Philadelphia.

TYPE LOCALITY: "Florida and South Carolina" (Wood), restricted by Causey to Everglades National Park, Florida.

RANGE: Peninsular Florida, south to Charleston, South Carolina, northwest as far as Leon County, Florida.

Genus HILTONIUS Chamberlin

Hiltonius Chamberlin, 1918, Proc. Biol. Soc. Washington, vol. 31, p. 166; 1949, Journ. Washington Acad. Sci., vol. 39, p. 166.

GENEROTYPE: *Hiltonius pulchrus* Chamberlin, by original designation.

RANGE: Southern California and Arizona, south on the Mexican Plateau as far as the State of Guerrero.

SPECIES: Fifteen, of which eight are found within our limits.

Hiltonius congregans Chamberlin

Hiltonius congregans Chamberlin, 1941, Bull. Univ. Utah, biol. ser., vol. 6, No. 4, p. 9, fig. 10.

TYPE: Collection of R. V. Chamberlin.

TYPE LOCALITY: Mountain Spring, San Diego County, California.

RANGE: Known only from type locality.

Hiltonius conservatus Chamberlin

Hiltonius conservatus Chamberlin, 1947, Proc. Acad. Nat. Sci. Philadelphia, vol. 99, p. 53, figs. 61–63.

TYPE: Acad. Nat. Sci. Philadelphia.

TYPE LOCALITY: Fort Tejon, Kern County, California.

RANGE: Known only from the type locality.

Hiltonius hebes (Bollman)

Spirobolus hebes Bollman, 1887, Ann. New York Acad. Sci., vol. 4, p. 31.

Hiltonius balboanus Chamberlin, 1941, Bull. Univ. Utah, biol. ser., vol. 6, No. 4, p. 10, fig. 11 (type locality: San Diego, California; types in Chamberlin Collection).

Hiltonius hebes Loomis and Hoffman, 1948, Proc. Biol. Soc. Washington, vol. 61, p. 51.

TYPE: U. S. Nat. Mus.

TYPE LOCALITY: San Diego, California.

RANGE: Known only from type locality.

Hiltonius mimus Chamberlin

Hiltonius mimus Chamberlin, 1941, Bull. Univ. Utah, biol. ser., vol. 6, No. 4, p. 9, figs. 8, 9.

TYPE: Collection of R. V. Chamberlin.

TYPE LOCALITY: Mountain Spring, San Diego County, California.

RANGE: Known only from type locality.

Hiltonius palmaris Loomis

Hiltonius palmaris Loomis, 1953, Journ. Washington Acad. Sci., vol. 43, p. 418, figs. 8, 9.

TYPE: U. S. Nat. Mus. (No. 2089).

TYPE LOCALITY: Palm Canyon, Palm Springs, Riverside County, California.

RANGE: Known only from type locality.

Hiltonius pius Chamberlin

Hiltonius pius Chamberlin, 1941, Bull. Univ. Utah, biol. ser., vol. 6, No. 4, p. 7, fig. 6.

TYPE: Collection of R. V. Chamberlin.

TYPE LOCALITY: Mountain Spring, San Diego County, California.

RANGE: Known only from type locality.

Hiltonius pulchrus Chamberlin

Hiltonius pulchrus Chamberlin, 1918, Proc. Biol. Soc. Washington, vol. 31, p. 167.

TYPE: Mus. Comp. Zool.

TYPE LOCALITY: Claremont, Los Angeles County, California.
RANGE: Known only from type locality.

Hiltonius thebanus Chamberlin

Hiltonius thebanus Chamberlin, 1941, Bull. Univ. Utah, biol. ser., vol. 6, No. 4, p. 8, fig. 7.
TYPE: Collection of R. V. Chamberlin.
TYPE LOCALITY: Theba, Maricopa County, Arizona.
RANGE: Known only from type locality.

Genus NARCEUS Rafinesque

Narceus Rafinesque, 1820, Annals of nature, p. 9.—Hoffman and Crabill, 1953, Florida, Ent., vol. 36, p. 80.
Rhexenor Rafinesque, 1820, Annals of nature, p. 9 (generotype: *R. annularis* Rafinesque, by monotypy).
Spirobolus (not Brandt) Wood, 1865, Trans. Amer. Philos. Soc., new ser., vol. 13, p. 207.—Bollman, 1893, U. S. Nat. Mus. Bull. 46, p. 118.—Brölemann, 1914, Ann. Soc. Ent. France, vol. 83, p. 31.—Chamberlin, 1947, Proc. Acad. Nat. Sci. Philadelphia, vol. 99, p. 44.
Arctobolus Cook, 1904, *in* Harriman Alaska Exped., vol. 8, p. 64 (generotype: *A. onandaga* Cook).
GENEROTYPE: *Narceus tinctorius* Rafinesque, by monotypy.
RANGE: North America east of the Great Plains. The entirely provisional statement of ranges in this genus must be emphasized. Many of the names admitted to this list will doubtless fall as synonyms when adequate studies have been made.
SPECIES: Fourteen.

Narceus americanus (Beauvois)

Julus americanus Beauvois, 1805, Insectes recueillis en Afrique et Amérique, . . . , Aptères, pl. 4, figs. 3a–c (the name "americae borealis" appears on page 155 of the text).
Spirobolus marginatus (not Say) Wood, 1865, Trans. Amer. Philos. Soc., new ser., vol. 13, p. 207 (this citation follows Bollman, whose identification of Say's *marginatus* with the Floridian species does not seem to be beyond challenge and which is here only provisionally accepted).
Spirobolus agilis Cope, 1869, Proc. Amer. Philos. Soc., vol. 11, p. 181 (type locality: Montgomery County, Virginia; types probably not extant).
Spirobolus americae-borealis Bollman, 1893, U. S. Nat. Mus. Bull. 46, p. 145.
Spirobolus americanus Hoffman, 1951, Florida Ent., vol. 34, p. 15.
TYPE: Location unknown.
TYPE LOCALITY: North America, without further indication.

RANGE: Atlantic Coast States, at least from Maryland to Georgia and Alabama, exact limits unknown.

Narceus annularis (Rafinesque)

Rhexenor annularis Rafinesque, 1820, Annals of nature, p. 9.

Arctobolus onandaga Cook, 1904, *in* Harriman Alaska Exped., vol. 8, p. 64 (type locality: Kirkville, Onandaga County, New York; type: U. S. Nat. Mus., No. 1881).

Narceus annularis Hoffman and Crabill, 1953, Florida Ent., vol. 36, p. 81.

TYPE: Probably none extant.

TYPE LOCALITY: "Highland Hills of New York," here restricted to vicinity of Catskill, Greene County, New York.

RANGE: Exact limits unknown, but specimens have been seen from several localities in central New York State.

Narceus atratus (Girard)

Julus atratus Girard, 1853, *in* Marcy, Exploration of the Red River of Louisiana . . . in 1852, Appendix F, p. 244.

TYPE: Originally belonging to the Smithsonian Institution, present location unknown.

TYPE LOCALITY: Prairie Mer Rouge, Louisiana.

RANGE: Known only from type locality.

Narceus dolleyi (Loomis)

Arctobolus dolleyi Loomis, 1943, Bull. Mus. Zool., vol. 92, No. 7, p. 398, figs. 13a–f.

TYPE: Mus. Comp. Zool.

TYPE LOCALITY: Feemster's Lake near Tupelo, Lee County, Mississippi.

RANGE: Central Mississippi to northern Alabama, western North Carolina, Tennessee, and southwest Virginia.

Narceus gordanus (Chamberlin)

Spirobolus gordanus Chamberlin, 1943, Bull. Univ. Utah, biol. ser., vol. 8, No. 2, p. 5, figs. 6–11.

TYPE: Chicago Nat. Hist. Mus.

TYPE LOCALITY: Punta Gorda, Charlotte County, Florida.

RANGE: Known only from type locality.

Narceus keysi (Loomis)

Arctobolus keysi Loomis, 1944, Psyche, vol. 50, p. 169, fig. 2.

TYPE: Mus. Comp. Zool.

TYPE LOCALITY: Lantana, Palm Beach County, Florida.

RANGE: Known only from type locality.

Narceus melanior (Chamberlin)

Spirobolus melanior Chamberlin, 1943, Bull. Univ. Utah, biol. ser., vol. 8, No. 2, p. 9.

TYPE: Chicago Nat. Hist. Mus.

TYPE LOCALITY: Stephen E. Austin State Park, 5 miles east of Scaley, Austin County, Texas.

RANGE: Known only from type locality.

Narceus oklahomae (Chamberlin)

Spirobolus oklahomae Chamberlin, 1931, Ent. News, vol. 42, p. 98, pl. 2, fig. 1.

TYPE: Collection of R. V. Chamberlin.

TYPE LOCALITY: Murray County, Oklahoma.

RANGE: Murray, Comanche, and Pushmahata Counties, Oklahoma.

Narceus orophilus (Chamberlin)

Spirobolus orophilus Chamberlin, 1943, Bull. Univ. Utah, biol. ser., vol. 8, No. 2, p. 8, figs. 17–21.

TYPE: Chicago Nat. Hist. Mus.

TYPE LOCALITY: Gatlinburg, Sevier County, Tennessee.

RANGE: Eastern Tennessee and southeastern Kentucky.

Narceus pensacolae (Bollman)

Spirobolus pensacolae Bollman, 1887, Ent. Amer., vol. 1, p. 228.

TYPE: U. S. Nat. Mus. (No. 110).

TYPE LOCALITY: Pensacola, Escambia County, Florida.

RANGE: Known only from type locality.

Narceus ramstadti (Chamberlin)

Spirobolus ramstadti Chamberlin, 1943, Bull. Univ. Utah, biol. ser., vol. 8, No. 2, p. 7, figs. 12–16.

TYPE: Chicago Nat. Hist. Mus.

TYPE LOCALITY: Punta Gorda, Charlotte County, Florida.

RANGE: Known only from type locality.

Narceus scotti (Chamberlin)

Spirobolus scotti Chamberlin, 1943, Proc. Biol. Soc. Washington, vol. 56, p. 148, figs. 12–14.

TYPE: Collection of R. V. Chamberlin.

TYPE LOCALITY: Houston, Harris County, Texas.

RANGE: Known only from type locality.

Narceus tinctorius Rafinesque

Narceus tinctorius Rafinesque, 1820, Annals of nature, p. 9.

TYPE: Probably none in existance.

TYPE LOCALITY: Here restricted to the "Knobs" in Estill County, Kentucky.

RANGE: Known definitely only from the type locality, but doubtless ranging over much of the Cumberland Plateau and adjacent regions.

Narceus woodi (Humbert and Saussure)

Spirostreptus woodi Humbert and Saussure, 1870, Rev. Mag. Zool., ser. 2, vol. 22, p. 177.

TYPE: Geneva Museum.

TYPE LOCALITY: St. Louis, Missouri.

RANGE: No definite localities known.   Placement of this name in *Narceus* is tentative.

Genus TYLOBOLUS Cook

Tylobolus Cook, 1904 *in* Harriman Alaska Exped., vol. 8, p. 65.

GENEROTYPE: *Tylobolus deses* Cook, by original designation.

RANGE: California.

SPECIES: One.

Tylobolus deses Cook

Tylobolus deses Cook, 1904, *in* Harriman Alaska Exped., vol. 8, p. 65, pl. 4, figs. 3a–3b.

TYPE: U. S. Nat. Mus. (No. 796).

TYPE LOCALITY: California; exact locality not known but probably either the vicinity of Stanford or of Claremont.

RANGE: No definite localities known.

Spirobolida of uncertain systematic position

Spirostreptus californicus Humbert and Saussure

Spirostreptus californicus Humbert and Saussure, 1870, Rev. Mag. Zool., ser. 2, vol. 22, p. 177.

TYPE: ?Geneva Museum.

TYPE LOCALITY: California.

Spirostreptus ignobilis Humbert and Saussure

Spirostreptus ignobilis Humbert and Saussure, 1870, Rev. Mag. Zool., ser. 2, vol. 22, p. 177.

TYPE: ?Geneva Museum.

TYPE LOCALITY: "North America."

Tylobolus viduus Chamberlin

Tylobolus viduus Chamberlin, 1940. Pomona Coll. Journ. Ent. and Zool., vol. 32, p. 81.

TYPE: Collection of R. V. Chamberlin.

TYPE LOCALITY: Known only from the female type specimen, probably not a true *Tylobolus* in its restricted sense.

Order SPIROSTREPTIDA

Spirostreptidea Brandt, 1833, Bull. Soc. Nat. Moscou, vol. 6, p. 200.

Spirostreptidae Pocock, 1894, Chilopoda, Symphyla and Diplopoda . . . ,
    in Weber, Zool. Erg. Reise Niederl. Ost-Ind., vol. 3, p. 378.
Spirostreptoidea Cook, 1895, Ann. New York Acad. Sci., vol. 9, p. 5.—
    Attems, 1914, Zoologica, vol. 25, Heft 65–66, p. 52.—Verhoeff, 1931,
    in Bronn, Klass. und Ordn. des Tier-Reichs, Band. 5, Abt. 2, Lief. 11,
    pp. 1675, 1704.
Spirostreptomorpha Attems, 1926, in Kükenthal-Krumbach, Handbuch der
    Zoologie, vol. 4, p. 197.

KEY TO NORTH AMERICAN FAMILIES OF SPIROSTREPTIDA

1. Lingual laminae of gnathochilarium separated by the mentum; telopodite of anterior
   gonopod fused with the basiopodite, without apparent seminal groove.

   CHOCTELLIDAE (p. 169)

   Lingual laminae of gnathochilarium not separated by the mentum; telopodite of
   anterior gonopod long, slender, partly embraced by the folded coxite but always
   freely moveable and with a distinct seminal groove . . . SPIROSTREPTIDAE (p. 169)

Family CHOCTELLIDAE Chamberlin and Hoffman

Choctellidae Chamberlin and Hoffman, 1950, Chicago Acad. Sci., Nat.
    Hist. Misc. No. 71, p. 7.

Genus CHOCTELLA Chamberlin

Choctella Chamberlin, 1918, Psyche, vol. 25, p. 25.
GENEROTYPE: Choctella cumminsi Chamberlin, by original designation.
RANGE: Alabama and Tennessee.
SPECIES: One.

Choctella cumminsi Chamberlin

Choctella cumminsi Chamberlin, 1918, Psyche, vol. 25, p. 25.—Loomis,
    1943, Bull. Mus. Comp. Zool., vol. 92, No. 7, p. 391, fig. 9.
TYPE: Mus. Comp. Zool.
TYPE LOCALITY: Glendale Hills, Davidson County, Tennessee.
RANGE: Cumberland Plateau and adjacent region, from the vicinity of
Nashville, Tennessee, south to the vicinity of Guntersville, Marshall County,
Alabama.

Family SPIROSTREPTIDAE Attems

Spirostreptidae Attems, 1914, Zoologica, Vol. 25, Heft. 65–66, p. 52 (The
    first usage of the name Spirostreptidae in its current restricted sense,
    i. e., exclusive of the Harpagophoridae and Odontopygidae).

Genus ORTHOPORUS Silvestri

Orthoporus Silvestri, 1897, Boll. Mus. Zool. Anat. Comp. Univ. Torino, vol.
    12, No. 283, p. 7.
GENEROTYPE: Orthoporus diaporoides Silvestri, by monotypy.

RANGE: Tropical America, ?Africa.

SPECIES: About 50, of which 10 occur in our area. In addition to the forms recorded below, Bollman listed *Spirostreptus montezumae* Saussure (now referable to *Orthoporus*) as occurring in Texas at El Paso. As the evidence makes it reasonably certain that the El Paso species is not the same as Saussure's, *O. montezumae* is not cataloged herein.

Orthoporus arizonicus Loomis

Orthoporus arizonicus Loomis, 1953, Journ. Washington Acad. Sci., vol. 43, No. 12, p. 418, figs. 4, 5.

TYPE: U. S. Nat. Mus (No. 2088).

TYPE LOCALITY: Patagonia, Santa Cruz County, Arizona.

RANGE: Known only from type locality.

Orthoporus boreus Chamberlin

Orthoporus boreus Chamberlin, 1947, Proc. Acad. Nat. Sci. Philadelphia, vol. 99, p. 55, fig. 69.

TYPE: Acad. Nat. Sci. Philadelphia (No. 9979).

TYPE LOCALITY: Snake River Desert at Taber, Bingham County, Idaho.

RANGE: Known only from type locality.

Orthoporus crotonus Chamberlin

Orthoporus crotonus Chamberlin, 1952, Great Basin Nat., vol. 12, Nos. 1–4, p. 24.

TYPE: Chicago Nat. Hist. Mus.

TYPE LOCALITY: Croton Springs, north of Chisos Mountains, Brewster County, Texas.

RANGE: Known only from type locality.

Orthoporus entomacis Chamberlin and Mulaik

Othoporus entomacis Chamberlin and Mulaik, 1941, Journ. New York Ent. Soc., vol. 49, p. 63.

TYPE: Collection of R. V. Chamberlin.

TYPE LOCALITY: Duncan, Greenlee County, Arizona.

RANGE: Known only from type locality.

Orthoporus flavior Chamberlin and Mulaik

Orthoporus flavior Chamberlin and Mulaik, 1941, Journ. New York Ent. Soc., vol. 49, p. 63.

TYPE: Collection of R. V. Chamberlin.

TYPES LOCALITY: 4 miles east of Dryden, Terrel County, Texas.

RANGE: Known only from type locality.

Orthoporus ornatus (Girard)

Julus ornatus Girard, 1853, *in* Marcy, Exploration of the Red River of Louisiana . . . in 1852, Appendix F, p. 274.

Spirobolus ornatus Wood, 1865, Trans. Amer. Philos. Soc., vol. 13, p. 208.

Orthoporus ornatus Causey, 1954, Tulane Stud. Zool., vol. 2, No. 4, p. 67, fig. 10.

TYPE: Not known to exist.

TYPE LOCALITY: Headwaters of the Prairiedog Town River, in the northern Panhandle of Texas. Considered by Causey (op. cit.) to be "either within or near the present Palo Duro Canyon State Park, Randall County, Texas."

RANGE: Known only from Randall County, Texas.

Orthoporus pontis Chamberlin

Orthoporus pontis Chamberlin, 1947, Proc. Acad. Nat. Sci Philadelphia, vol. 99, p. 53, fig. 66.

TYPE: Acad. Nat. Sci. Philadelphia (No. 9977).

TYPE LOCALITY: "High Bridge", on the Pecos River, Texas.

RANGE: Known only from type locality.

Orthoporus producens Chamberlin

Orthoporus producens Chamberlin, 1947, Proc. Biol. Soc. Washington, vol. 60, p. 11, fig. 8.

TYPE: Collection of R. V. Chamberlin.

TYPE LOCALITY: Benson, Cochise County, Arizona.

RANGE: Known only from type locality.

Orthoporus sanctus Chamberlin

Orthoporus sanctus Chamberlin, 1947, Proc. Acad. Nat. Sci. Philadelphia, vol. 99, p. 55, fig. 68.

TYPE: Acad. Nat. Sci Philadelphia (No. 9978).

TYPE LOCALITY: St. Augustine, St. Johns County, Florida.

RANGE: Known only from the type locality. In view of the considerable separation of this location from the rest of the range occupied by *Orthoporus* in the United States, confirmation is very desirable.

Orthoporus vallicolens Chamberlin

Orthoporus vallicolens Chamberlin, 1943, Proc. Biol. Soc. Washington, vol. 56, p. 149, fig. 15.

TYPE: Collection of R. V. Chamberlin.

TYPE LOCALITY: Fort Hancock, Hudspeth County, Texas.

RANGE: Known only from type locality.

Orthoporus wichitanus Chamberlin

Orthoporus wichitanus Chamberlin, 1931, Ent. News, vol. 42, p. 99, pl. 2, fig. 2.

TYPE: Collection of R. V. Chamberlin.

TYPE LOCALITY: Elk Mountain, Wichita Reserve, Comanche County, Oklahoma.

RANGE: Known only from type locality.

Genus SCAPHIOSTREPTUS Brölemann

Scaphiostreptus Brölemann, 1902, Rev. Mus. Paulista, vol. 5, p. 152 (as subgenus of *Spirostreptus*).

Scaphiostreptus Attems, 1914, Zoologica, vol. 25, Heft 65–66, p. 75; 1950, Ann. Naturh. Mus. Wien, vol. 57, p. 225.

GENEROTYPE: *Spirostreptus fuscipes* Porat, by present designation.

RANGE: Tropical America, from southern Brasil north to Texas.

SPECIES: About 40, only one of which is known with certainty to occur in the United States. One or more other species, among the several based upon females and here placed under *Orthoporus,* may belong to *Scaphiostreptus.*

Scaphiostreptus texicolens (Chamberlin)

Orthoporus texicolens Chamberlin, 1938, Proc. Biol. Soc. Washington, vol. 51, p. 207.

TYPE: Collection of R. V. Chamberlin.

TYPE LOCALITY: Edinburg, Hidalgo County, Texas.

RANGE: Southern Texas.

Spirostreptidae of uncertain systematic position

Spirobolus miles Chamberlin

Spirobolus miles Chamberlin, 1918, Pomona Coll. Journ. Ent. and Zool., vol. 10, p. 11.

TYPE: Mus. Comp. Zool.

TYPE LOCALITY: Fort Boutelle, Arizona.

RANGE: Known only from type locality. This species is clearly a spirostreptoid, but its correct generic position cannot be determined in the absence of males.

Julus multiannulatus McNeill

Inlus (sic) *multiannulatus* McNeill, 1887, Proc. U. S. Nat. Mus., vol. 10, p. 331.

TYPE: Location unknown.

TYPE LOCALITY: Fort Madison, Lee County, Iowa.

RANGE: Known only from the type locality. This is rather considerably out of the known range of spirostreptids in this country, and since none have subsequently been found near Iowa, there is some doubt about the provenance of the type specimen.

Order CAMBALIDA

Cambalinae Bollman, 1893, U. S. Nat. Mus., Bull. 46, p. 156.

Cambaloidea Cook, 1895, Ann. New York Acad. Sci., vol. 9, p. 6.—Silvestri, 1897, Ann. Mus. Civ. Stor. Nat. Genova, ser. 2, vol. 18, p. 650.

Cambalida Chamberlin, 1943, Bull. Univ. Utah, biol. ser. vol. 8, No. 3, p. 4.

KEY TO NORTH AMERICAN FAMILIES OF CAMBALIDA

1. Mentum divided, the promentum clearly set off . . . . . CAMBALIDAE (p. 173)
   Mentum entire, no separate promentum . . . . LEIODERIDAE (p. 179)

Family CAMBALIDAE Bollman

Cambalinae Bollman, 1893, U. S. Nat. Mus. Bull. 46, p. 157.
Cambalidae Cook, 1895, Ann. New York Acad. Sci., vol 9, p. 6.—Loomis,
1938, Proc. U. S. Nat. Mus., vol. 86, p. 31.

Genus ALAKENE Chamberlin

Alakene Chamberlin, 1941, Bull. Univ. Utah, biol. ser., vol. 6, No. 5, p. 3.
GENEROTYPE: *Akalene simplex* Chamberlin, by original designation.
RANGE: California.
SPECIES: One.

Alakene simplex Chamberlin

Alakene simplex Chamberlin, 1941, Bull. Univ. Utah, biol. serv., vol. 6,
No. 5, p. 3, fig. 2.
TYPE: Collection of R. V. Chamberlin.
TYPE LOCALITY: 5 miles northeast of Lemoncove, Tulare County,
California.
RANGE: Known only from type locality.

Genus BUWATIA Chamberlin

Buwatia Chamberlin, 1912, Ann. Ent. Soc. America, vol. 5, p. 159.
GENEROTYPE: *Buwatia monterea* Chamberlin, by original designation.
RANGE: Southern California.
SPECIES: One.

Buwatia monterea Chamberlin

Buwatia monterea Chamberlin, 1912, Ann. Ent. Soc. America, vol. 5, p.
159, pl. 10, fig. 7.
TYPE: Mus. Comp. Zool.
TYPE LOCALITY: Pacific Grove, Monterey County, California.
RANGE: Known only from type locality.

Genus CAMBALA Gray

Cambala Gray, 1832, Insecta, *in* Griffith, The animal kingdom . . . by
the Baron Cuvier, vol. 15, pl. 135.—Loomis, 1938, Proc. U. S. Nat.
Mus., vol. 86, p. 37.
GENEROTYPE: *Julus annulatus* Say, by monotypy.
RANGE: Eastern United States.
SPECIES: Ten.

Cambala annulata (Say)

Julus annulatus Say, 1821, Journ. Acad. Nat. Sci. Philadelphia, vol. 2, p. 103.

Cambala annulata Gray, 1832, Insecta, *in* Griffith, The animal kingdom . . . by the Baron Cuvier, vol. 15, pl. 135.—Loomis, 1938, Proc. U. S. Nat. Mus., vol. 86, p. 37, fig. 11.

TYPE: Present location unknown, possibly in British Mus. (Nat. Hist.).

TYPE LOCALITY: Southeastern United States.

RANGE: Virginia and Kentucky, south to Florida and Louisiana. Exact limits of range unknown, owing to past confusion with *C. cristula.*

Cambala arkansana Chamberlin

Cambala arkansana Chamberlin, 1942, Bull. Univ. Utah, biol. ser., vol. 6, No. 8, p. 3, figs. 2, 3.

TYPE: Collection of R. V. Chamberlin.

TYPE LOCALITY: 1 mile north of Pocahontas, Randolph County, Arkansas.

RANGE: Known only from type locality.

Cambala cara Causey

Cambala cara Causey, 1953, Amer. Midl. Nat., vol. 50, p. 156, figs. 13, 14.

TYPE: Amer. Mus. Nat. Hist.

TYPE LOCALITY: Cave Springs, Benton County, Arkansas.

RANGE: Arkansas and northern Louisiana.

Cambala caeca Loomis

Cambala caeca Loomis, 1953, Journ. Washington Acad. Sci., vol. 43, No. 12, p. 417, figs. 1–3.

TYPE: U. S. Nat. Mus. (No. 2087).

TYPE LOCALITY: Sonora, Sutton County, Texas.

RANGE: Caves in Sutton County, Texas.

Cambala cristula Loomis

Cambala cristula Loomis, 1938, Proc. U. S. Nat. Mus., vol. 86, p. 39, fig. 12.

TYPE: U. S. Nat. Mus. (No. 1305).

TYPE LOCALITY: Etowah, Monroe County, Tennessee.

RANGE: Southwestern Virginia, eastern Tennessee, North and South Carolina, western Panhandle of Florida.

Cambala minor Bollman

Cambala annulata minor Bollman, 1888, Proc. U. S. Nat. Mus., vol. 11, p. 404.

Cambala annulata Williams and Hefner, 1928, Bull. Ohio Biol. Surv., No. 18, p. 123, fig. 17b.

Cambala minor Loomis, 1938, Proc. U. S. Nat. Mus., vol. 86, p. 40.

TYPE: U. S. Nat. Mus.

TYPE LOCALITY: Here restricted to Bloomington, Monroe County, Indiana.
RANGE: Ohio and Indiana, southwest to Arkansas.

Cambala ochra Chamberlin

Cambala ochra Chamberlin, 1942, Bull. Univ. Utah, biol. ser., vol. 6, No. 8, p. 3, fig. 1.
TYPE: Collection of R. V. Chamberlin.
TYPE LOCALITY: Darlington, Ste. Helena Parish, Louisiana.
RANGE: Known only from type locality.

Cambala saltillona Chamberlin

Cambala saltillona Chamberlin, 1943, Bull. Univ. Utah, biol. ser., vol. 8, No. 2, p. 3, figs. 1, 2.
TYPE: Chicago Nat. Hist. Mus.
TYPE LOCALITY: Saltillo, Stephens County, Texas.
RANGE: Known only from type locality.

Cambala texana Loomis

Cambala texana Loomis, 1938, Proc. U. S. Nat. Mus., vol. 86, p. 40, fig. 13.
TYPE: U. S. Nat. Mus. (No. 1306).
TYPE LOCALITY: Nacogdoches County, Texas.
RANGE: Known only from type locality.

Cambala washingtonensis Causey [12]

Cambala washingtonensis Causey, 1954, Ann. Ent. Soc. Amer., vol. 47, p. 85, fig. 9.
TYPE: Amer. Mus. Nat. Hist.
TYPE LOCALITY: Wilma, Garfield County, Washington.
RANGE: Known only from type locality.

Genus ECLOMUS Chamberlin

Eclytus (not Holmgren 1855) Chamberlin, 1952, Ent. News, vol. 63, p. 10.
Eclomus Chamberlin, 1952, Ent. News, vol. 63, p. 71.
GENEROTYPE: *Eclomus speobius* Chamberlin, by original designation.
RANGE: Texas.
SPECIES: One.

Eclomus speobius (Chamberlin)

Eclytus speobius Chamberlin, 1952, Ent. News, vol. 63, p. 11.
Eclomus speobius Chamberlin, 1952, Ent. News, vol. 63, p. 71.
TYPE: Collection of R. V. Chamberlin.
TYPE LOCALITY: Wyatt Cave, Sonora, Sutton County, Texas.
RANGE: Known only from type locality.

---

[12] Known only from a female and not impossibly will be found to be generically distinct from the eastern species of *Cambula*.

Genus MIMOLENE Chamberlin

Mimolene Chamberlin, 1941, Bull. Univ. Utah, biol. ser., vol. 6, No. 5, p. 3.
GENEROTYPE: *Mimolene oregona* Chamberlin, by original designation.
RANGE: Oregon.
SPECIES: One.

Mimolene oregona Chamberlin

Mimolene oregona Chamberlin, 1941, Bull. Univ. Utah, biol. ser., vol. 6, No. 5, p. 3.
TYPE: Collection of R. V. Chamberlin.
TYPE LOCALITY: Washington County, Oregon.
RANGE: Known only from type locality.

Genus NANNOLENE Bollman

Nannolene Bollman, 1887, Ann. New York Acad. Sci., vol. 4, p. 37.—
Chamberlin, 1922, Proc. U. S. Nat. Mus., vol. 61, art. 10, p. 2.—
Loomis, 1938, Proc. U. S. Nat. Mus., vol. 86, p. 42.
GENEROTYPE: *Julus burkei* Bollman, by original designation.
RANGE: Pacific Coast States.
SPECIES: Nine.

Nannolene burkei (Bollman)

Julus burkei Bollman, 1887, Amer. Nat., vol. 21, p. 82.
Nannolene burkei Bollman, 1887, Ann. New York Acad. Sci., vol. 4, p. 40.—
Chamberlin, 1922, Proc. U. S. Nat. Mus., vol. 61, art. 10, p. 2, pl. 1, figs. 4–10.
TYPE: U. S. Nat. Mus. (No. 80).
TYPE LOCALITY: Ukiah, Mendocino County, California.
RANGE: Known only from type locality.

Nannolene catalina Chamberlin

Nannolene catalina Chamberlin, 1941, Bull. Univ. Utah, biol. ser., vol. 6, No. 5. p. 5.
TYPE: Collection of R. V. Chamberlin.
TYPE LOCALITY: Santa Catalina Island, Los Angeles County, California.
RANGE: Known only from type locality.

Nannolene cincta Chamberlin

Nannolene cinta Chamberlin, 1941, Bull. Univ. Utah, biol. ser., vol. 6, No. 5, p. 4, fig. 1.
TYPE: Collection of R. V. Chamberlin.
TYPE LOCALITY: Arlington, Snohomish County, Washington.
RANGE: Known only from type locality.

Nannolene corticolens Chamberlin

Nannolene corticolens Chamberlin, 1951, Great Basin Nat., vol. 11, Nos. 1–2, p. 31, fig. 3.

TYPE: Collection of R. V. Chamberlin.

TYPE LOCALITY: Marsch Creek Springs, at base of Mount Diablo, near Concord, Contra Costa County, California.

RANGE: Known only from type locality.

Nannolene dorothea Chamberlin

Nannolene dorothea Chamberlin, 1941, Bull. Univ. Utah, biol. ser., vol. 6, No. 5, p. 4, fig. 3.

TYPE: Collection of R. V. Chamberlin.

TYPE LOCALITY: Kernville, Kern County, California.

RANGE: Known only from type locality.

Nannolene keiferi Chamberlin

Nannolene keiferi Chamberlin, 1943, Ent. News, vol. 54, p. 88.

TYPE: Collection of R. V. Chamberlin.

TYPE LOCALITY: Sacramento, Sacramento County, California.

RANGE: Known only from type locality.

Nannolene minor Loomis

Nannolene minor Loomis, 1938, Proc. U. S. Nat. Mus., vol. 86, p. 44, fig. 14.

TYPE: U. S. Nat. Mus. (No. 1307).

TYPE LOCALITY: Bakersfield, Kern County, California.

RANGE: Known only from type locality.

Nannolene personifer Chamberlin

Nannolene personifer Chamberlin, 1941, Bull. Univ. Utah, biol. ser., vol. 6, No. 5, p. 5, figs. 4, 5.

TYPE: Collection of R. V. Chamberlin.

TYPE LOCALITY: 9 miles north of Placerville, Eldorado County, California.

RANGE: Known only from type locality.

Nannolene violacea Loomis

Nannolene violacea Loomis, 1938, Proc. U. S. Nat. Mus., vol. 86, p. 46, fig. 15; pl. 2, fig. 3.

TYPE: U. S. Nat. Mus. (No. 1308).

TYPE LOCALITY: Atascadero, San Luis Obispo County, California.

RANGE: Known only from type locality.

Genus ODACHURUS Loomis

Odachurus Loomis, 1938, Proc. U. S. Nat. Mus., vol. 86, p. 54.

GENEROTYPE: *Odachurus petasatus* Loomis, by original designation.

RANGE: Southern California.

SPECIES: One.

Odachurus petasatus Loomis

Odachurus petasatus Loomis, 1938, Proc. U. S. Nat. Mus., vol. 86, p. 55, fig. 17.

TYPE: U. S. Nat. Mus. (No. 1311).

TYPE LOCALITY: Torrey Pines, La Jolla, San Diego County, California.

RANGE: Known only from type locality.

Genus PAITEYA Chamberlin

Paiteya Chamberlin, 1910, Ann. Ent. Soc. Amer., vol. 3, p. 258.

GENEROTYPE: *Paiteya errans* Chamberlin, by original designation.

RANGE: Southern California.

SPECIES: One.

Paiteya errans Chamberlin

Paiteya errans Chamberlin, 1910, Ann. Ent. Soc. Amer., vol. 3, p. 258, pl. 43, figs. 4–7.

TYPE: Location unknown.

TYPE LOCALITY: "Southern California."

RANGE: No definite localities known.

Genus PHARODERE Loomis

Pharodere Loomis, 1938, Proc. U. S. Nat. Mus., vol. 86, p. 51.

GENEROTYPE: *Pharodere radiata* Loomis, by original designation.

RANGE: Southern California.

SPECIES: One.

Pharodere radiata Loomis

Pharodere radiata Loomis, 1938, Proc. U. S. Nat. Mus., vol. 86, p. 53, fig. 16; pl. 2, fig. 1.

TYPE: U. S. Nat. Mus. (No. 1310).

TYPE LOCALITY: Torrey Pines, La Jolla, San Diego County, California.

RANGE: Known only from type locality.

Genus PLATYDERE Loomis

Platydere Loomis, 1938, Proc. U. S. Nat. Mus., vol. 86, p. 48.

GENEROTYPE: *Platydere caeca* Loomis, by original designation.

RANGE: California.

SPECIES: One.

Platydere caeca Loomis

Platydere caeca Loomis, 1938, Proc. U. S. Nat. Mus., vol. 86, p. 50.

TYPE: U. S. Nat. Mus. (No. 1309).

TYPE LOCALITY: Tajiguas, Santa Barbara County, California.

RANGE: Known only from type locality.

Genus TRIDERE Cook and Loomis

Tridere Cook and Loomis, 1938, Proc. U. S. Nat. Mus., vol. 86, p. 33.
GENEROTYPE: *Tridere chelopa* Cook and Loomis, by original designation.
RANGE: Southern California.
SPECIES: One.

Tridere chelopa Cook and Loomis

Tridere chelopa Cook and Loomis, 1938, Proc. U. S. Nat. Mus., vol. 86,
    p. 36, fig. 10; pl. 2, figs. 6, 7.
TYPE: U. S. Nat. Mus. (No. 1304.)
TYPE LOCALITY: 2 miles above Mountain Springs, between San Diego and
El Centro, San Diego County, California.
RANGE: Known only from type locality.

Family LEIODERIDAE Schubart

Leioderidae Schubart, 1946, Rev. Brasileira, Biol., vol. 6, No. 3, p. 404.
Cambalopsidae Cook (in part), 1895, Ann. New York Acad. Sci., vol 9,
    p. 6—Loomis, 1938, Proc. U. S. Nat. Mus., vol. 86, p. 32.— Chamber-
    lin, 1943, Bull. Univ. Utah, biol, ser., vol. 8, No. 2, p. 4.
Trachyiulidae Silvestri (in part), 1896, Ann. Mus. Civ. Stor. Nat. Genova,
    ser. 2, vol. 16, p. 168, fig. 15.

Genus DOILENE Chamberlin

Doilene Chamberlin, 1941, Bull. Univ. Utah, biol. serv., vol. 6, No. 4, p. 6.
GENEROTYPE: *Doilene carmela* Chamberlin, by original designation.
RANGE: California.
SPECIES: One.

Doilene carmela Chamberlin

Doilene carmela Chamberlin, 1941, Bull. Univ. Utah, biol. ser., vol. 6, No.
    4, p. 6.
TYPE: Collection of R. V. Chamberlin.
TYPE LOCALITY: Hastings Reservation, Monterey County, California.
RANGE: Known only from type locality.

Genus ENDERE Loomis

Endere Loomis, 1938, Proc. U. S. Nat. Mus., vol. 86, p. 57.
GENEROTYPE: *Endere disora* Loomis, by original designation.
RANGE: California.
SPECIES: One.

Endere disora Loomis

Endere disora Loomis, 1938, Proc. U. S. Nat. Mus., vol. 86, p. 59, fig. 18.
TYPE: U. S. Nat. Mus. (No. 1312).

TYPE LOCALITY: Sunnyside Mine, Seneca, Plumas County, California.
RANGE: Known only from type locality.

Genus LEIODERE Loomis

Leiodere Loomis, 1938, Proc. U. S. Nat. Mus., vol. 86, p. 60.
GENEROTYPE: *Leiodere torreyana* Loomis, by original designation.
RANGE: Southern California.
SPECIES: Four.

Leiodere angelorum Chamberlin

Leiodere angelorum Chamberlin, 1943, Bull. Univ. Utah, biol ser., vol. 8.
   No. 2, p. 5, fig. 5.
TYPE: Collection of R. V. Chamberlin.
TYPE LOCALITY: Los Angeles, California.
RANGE: Known only from type locality.

Leiodere dasyura Loomis

Leiodere dasyura Loomis, 1938, Proc. U. S. Nat. Mus., vol. 86, p. 64.
TYPE: U. S. Nat. Mus (No. 1315).
TYPE LOCALITY: Tajiguas, Santa Barbara County, California.
RANGE: Known only from type locality.

Leiodere nana Loomis

Leiodere nana Loomis, 1938, Proc. U. S. Nat. Mus., vol. 86, p. 62, fig. 20.
TYPE: U. S. Nat. Mus. (No. 1314).
TYPE LOCALITY: Between Vallejo and Cordelia, Solano County, California.
RANGE: Known only from type locality.

Leiodere torreyana Loomis

Leiodere torreyana Loomis, 1938, Proc. U. S. Nat. Mus., vol. 86, p. 61,
   fig. 18; pl. 2, figs. 4, 5.
TYPE: U. S. Nat. Mus. (No. 1313).
TYPE LOCALITY: Torrey Pines, La Jolla, San Diego County, California.
RANGE: Southern California and northern Baja California.

Genus TIGOLENE Chamberlin

Tigolene Chamberlin, 1941, Bull. Univ. Utah, biol. ser., vol. 6, No. 4,
   p. 5.
GENEROTYPE: *Tigolene clementinus* Chamberlin, by original designation.
RANGE: San Clemente Island, California.
SPECIES: One.

Tigolene clementinus Chamberlin

Tigolene clementinus Chamberlin, 1941, Bull. Univ. Utah, biol. ser., vol. 6,
   No. 4, p. 5, fig. 2.
TYPE: Collection of R. V. Chamberlin.

TYPE LOCALITY: San Clemente Island, Los Angeles County, California.
RANGE: Known only from type locality.

Genus TITSONA Chamberlin

Titsona Chamberlin, 1912, Ann. Ent. Soc. Amer., vol. 5, p. 160.
GENEROTYPE: *Titsona sima* Chamberlin, by original designation.
RANGE: California.
SPECIES: One.

Titsona sima Chamberlin

Titsona sima Chamberlin, 1912, Ann. Ent. Soc. Amer., vol. 5, p. 161, pl. 10, figs. 4–6.—Loomis, 1943, Bull. Mus. Comp. Zool., vol. 92, No. 7, p. 393, figs. 10a, b.
TYPE: Mus. Comp. Zool.
TYPE LOCALITY: Oroville, Butte County, California.
RANGE: Yolo and Butte Counties, California.

Superorder COLOBOGNATHA

Colobognatha Brandt, 1834, Oken's Isis, p. 704.—Latzel, 1884, Myr. Öst.-Ung. Monarch, vol. 2, p. 56.—Bollman, 1893, U. S. Nat. Mus. Bull. 46, p. 154—Cook and Loomis, 1928, Proc. U. S. Nat. Mus., vol. 72, art. 18, p. 4.
Siphonizantia Brandt, 1837, Bull. Sci. Acad. Sci. Saint-Pétersbourg, vol. 1 (1836, No. 23), p. 178.
Sugentia Wood, 1869, Trans. Amer. Philos. Soc., vol. 13, p. 248.

KEY TO ORDERS OF COLOBOGNATHA

1. Gnathochilarium having the usual parts represented in millipeds; tergites with a distinctly impressed median sulcus . . . . PLATYDESMIDA (p. 181)
2. Gnathochilarium represented by a single triangular plate, or the divisions at most indistinctly indicated; tergites without an impressed median sulcus.
POLYZONIIDA (p. 185)

Order PLATYDESMIDA

Platydesmiens Saussure, 1860, Mém. Soc. Phys. Hist. Nat. Genève, vol. 15, p. 83.
Platydesmia (in part) + Dolistenia Latzel, 1884, Myr. Öst.-Ung. Monarch., vol. 2, p. 356.
Platydesmini Pocock, 1887, Ann. Mag. Nat. Hist., ser. 5, vol. 20, p. 225.
Platydesminae + Andrognathinae Bollman, 1893, U. S. Nat. Mus. Bull. 46, p. 154.

Family ANDROGNATHIDAE Cope

Andrognathidae Cope, 1869, Proc. Amer. Philos. Soc., vol. 11, p. 182.—Cook and Loomis, 1928, Proc. U. S. Nat. Mus., vol. 72, art. 18, p. 18.

Genus ANDROGNATHUS Cope

Andrognathus Cope, 1869, Proc. Amer. Philos. Soc., vol. 11, p. 182.
GENEROTYPE: *Andrognathus corticarius* Cope, by monotypy.
RANGE: Eastern United States.
SPECIES: One.

Andrognathus corticarius Cope

Andrognathus corticarius Cope, 1869, Proc. Amer. Philos. Soc., vol. 11,
    p. 182—Cook and Loomis, 1928, Proc. U. S. Nat. Mus., vol. 72, art.
    18, p. 19.
TYPE: Unknown.
TYPE LOCALITY: Montgomery County, Virginia.
RANGE: Campbell, Roanoke, and Montgomery Counties, Virginia, west to
Crittenden, Kentucky, and south to Georgia and Tennessee. Also reported
from northern Florida.

Genus BRACHYCYBE Wood

Brachycybe Wood, 1864, Proc. Acad. Nat. Sci. Philadelphia, p. 187.—
    Cook and Loomis, 1928, Proc. U. S. Nat. Mus., vol. 72, art. 18, p. 22.
GENEROTYPE: *Brachycybe lecontei* Wood, by monotypy.
RANGE: Southeastern United States, and California.
SPECIES: Six.

Brachycybe lecontei Wood

Brachycybe lecontei Wood, 1864, Proc. Acad. Nat. Sci. Philadelphia, p.
    187.—Loomis, 1936, Proc. U. S. Nat. Mus., vol. 83, p. 366, fig. 322.
TYPE: U. S. Nat. Mus.
TYPE LOCALITY: Mountains of northern Georgia.
RANGE: Eastern Kentucky, West Virginia, and southwest Virginia, south
to western South Carolina and central Alabama. Also reported from
Arkansas.

Brachycybe petasata Loomis

Brachycybe petasata Loomis, 1936, Proc. U. S. Nat. Mus., vol. 83, p. 365,
    fig. 32.
TYPE: U. S. Nat. Mus. (No. 1160).
TYPE LOCALITY: Cherokee National Forest, Tennessee.
RANGE: The Great Smoky Mountains in North Carolina and Tennessee.

Brachycybe potterinus Chamberlin

Brachycybe potterinus Chamberlin, 1941, Bull. Univ. Utah, biol. ser.,
    vol. 6, No. 4, p. 4.
TYPE: Collection of R. V. Chamberlin.
TYPE LOCALITY: Potter Creek, Mendocino County, California.
RANGE: Known only from type locality.

Brachycybe producta Loomis

Brachycybe producta Loomis, 1936, Proc. U. S. Nat. Mus., vol. 83, p. 367, figs. 32 h, i.

TYPE: U. S. Nat. Mus. (No. 1161).

TYPE LOCALITY: Baja California.

RANGE: Reported from Marin County, California, by Causey (1954).

Brachycybe rosea Murray

Brachycybe rosea Murray, 1877, Economic entomology . . . Aptera, pt. 1, p. 21.—Loomis, 1936, Proc. U. S. Nat. Mus., vol. 83, p. 367, figs. 32f, g.

Platydesmus californicus Karsch, 1881, Mitth. Münchner Ent. Ver., vol. 4, p. 144 (type locality: "California"; type: Berlin Museum).

TYPE: Not known.

TYPE LOCALITY: California, without more specific locality.

RANGE: Central and southern California.

Brachycybe tuolumne Chamberlin

Brachycybe tuolumne Chamberlin, 1953, Proc. Biol. Soc. Washington, vol. 66, p. 70.

TYPE: Collection of R. V. Chamberlin.

TYPE LOCALITY: Windeler Cavern, Tuolumne County, California.

RANGE: Known only from type locality.

Genus EUCYBE Chamberlin

Eucybe Chamberlin, 1941, Bull. Univ. Utah, biol. ser., vol. 6, No. 4, p. 3.

GENEROTYPE: *Eucybe clarus* Chamberlin, by original designation.

RANGE: Central California.

SPECIES: Two.

Eucybe clarus Chamberlin

Eucybe clarus Chamberlin, 1941, Bull. Univ. Utah, biol. ser., vol. 6, No. 4, p. 3.

TYPE: Collection of R. V. Chamberlin.

TYPE LOCALITY: Hastings Reservation, Monterey County, California.

RANGE: Known only from type locality.

Eucybe longior Chamberlin

Eucybe longior Chamberlin, 1950, Chicago Acad. Sci. Nat. Hist. Misc., No. 68, p. 4.

TYPE: Collection of R. V. Chamberlin.

TYPE LOCALITY: 12 miles east of Hammond, Tulare County, California.

RANGE: Known only from type locality.

Genus GOSODESMUS Chamberlin

Gosodesmus Chamberlin, 1922, Pomona College Journ. Ent. and Zool., vol. 14, No. 1, p. 9.

GENEROTYPE: *Gosodesmus claremontanus* Chamberlin, by original designation.

RANGE: Southern California.

SPECIES: One.

Gosodesmus claremontanus Chamberlin

Gosodesmus claremontanus Chamberlin, 1922, Pomona Coll. Journ. Ent. and Zool., vol. 14, No. 1, p. 9.—Loomis, 1936, Proc. U. S. Nat. Mus., vol. 83, p. 364, fig. 32c.

TYPE: Mus. Comp. Zool.

TYPE LOCALITY: Claremont, Los Angeles County, California.

RANGE: Type locality, also the Santa Cruz Mts. and south of Pescadero, California.

Genus ISCHNOCYBE Cook and Loomis

Ischnocybe Cook and Loomis, 1928, Proc. U. S. Nat. Mus., vol. 72, art. 18, p. 21.

GENEROTYPE: *Ischnocybe plicata* Cook and Loomis, by original designation.

RANGE: California.

SPECIES: One.

Ischnocybe plicata Cook and Loomis

Ischnocybe plicata Cook and Loomis, 1928, Proc. U. S. Nat. Mus., vol. 72, art. 18, p. 22, fig. 6, pl. 1.

TYPE: U. S. Nat. Mus. (No. 980).

TYPE LOCALITY: 14 miles up North Fork of the Feather River from Belden, Plumas County, California.

RANGE: Known only from type locality and from Idaho County, Idaho.

Genus MITOCYBE Cook and Loomis

Mitocybe Cook and Loomis, 1928, Proc. U. S. Nat. Mus., vol. 72, art. 18, p. 19.

GENEROTYPE: *Mitocybe auriportae* Cook and Loomis, by original designation.

RANGE: California.

SPECIES: One.

Mitocybe auriportae Cook and Loomis

Mitocybe auriportae Cook and Loomis, 1928, Proc. U. S. Nat. Mus., vol. 72, art. 18, p. 19, fig. 5.

TYPE: U. S. Nat. Mus. (No. 979).

TYPE LOCALITY: Mount Tamalpais, Marin County, California.
RANGE: Known only from type locality.

Genus STENOCYBE Chamberlin

Stenocybe Chamberlin, 1950, Chicago Acad. Sci. Nat. Hist. Misc. No. 68, p. 3.
GENEROTYPE: *Stenocybe waipea* Chamberlin, by original designation.
RANGE: California.
SPECIES: One.

Stenocybe waipea Chamberlin

Stenocybe waipea Chamberlin, 1950, Chicago Acad. Sci. Nat. Hist. Misc. No. 68, p. 3.
TYPE: Collection of R. V. Chamberlain.
TYPE LOCALITY: Squaw Creek, Placer County, California.
RANGE: Known only from type locality.

Order POLYZONIIDA

Ommatophora Brandt, 1841, Recueil, p. 49.
Polyzonidae Gervais, 1844, Ann. Sci. Nat., ser. 3, vol. 2, p. 78.
Polyzoniidae Bollman, 1893, U. S. Nat. Mus. Bull. 46, p. 186.
Polyzonoidea Cook and Loomis, 1928, Proc. U. S. Nat. Mus., vol. 72, art. 18, p. 4.

KEY TO NORTH AMERICAN FAMILIES OF POLYZONIIDA

1. Eyes absent; head narrowed forward or prolonged into a beak; prozonites decidedly smaller than the metazonites producing constrictions between the latter; dorsum pilose and tuberculate . . . . SIPHONOPHORIDAE (p. 189)
   One or several ocelli on each side; head not strongly narrowed forward or produced into a beak; the prozonites not forming a constriction between the metazonites; dorsum without hairs or tubercules . . . . . POLYZONIIDAE (p. 185)

Family POLYZONIIDAE Gervais

Polyzonidae (in part) Gervais, 1844, Ann. Sci. Nat., ser. 3, vol. 2, p. 78.
Polyzoniidae (in part) Wood, 1865, Trans. Amer. Philos. Soc., vol. 13, p. 248.
Polyzoniinae Bollman, 1893, U. S. Nat. Mus. Bull. 46, p. 186.

Genus BDELLOZONIUM Cook and Loomis

Bdellozonium Cook and Loomis, 1928, Proc. U. S. Nat. Mus., vol. 72, art. 18, p. 15.
GENEROTYPE: *Bdellozonium cerviculatum* Cook and Loomis, by original designation.
RANGE: Central California north to Oregon.
SPECIES: Three.

Bdellozonium cerviculatum Cook and Loomis

Bdellozonium cerviculatum Cook and Loomis, 1928, Proc. U. S. Nat. Mus., vol. 72, art. 18, p. 16, fig. 3.

TYPE: U. S. Nat. Mus. (No. 978).

TYPE LOCALITY: Belden, Plumas County, California.

RANGE: Known also from Emigrant Gap, California.

Bdellozonium rothi Chamberlin

Bdellozonium rothi Chamberlin, 1950, Chicago, Acad. Sci. Nat. Hist. Misc. No. 68, p. 2.

TYPE: Collection of R. V. Chamberlin.

TYPE LOCALITY: 14 miles west of Grant's Pass, Oregon.

RANGE: Known only from type locality.

Bdellozonium sequoium Chamberlin

Bdellozonium sequoium Chamberlin, 1941, Bull. Univ. Utah, biol. ser., vol. 6, No. 5, p. 5.

TYPE: Collection of R. V. Chamberlin.

TYPE LOCALITY: 12 miles northeast of Hammond, Tulare County, California.

RANGE: Known only from type locality.

Genus BUOTUS Chamberlin

Buotus Chamberlin, 1940, Canadian Ent., vol. 72, p. 59.

GENEROTYPE: *Buotus carolinus* Chamberlin, by original designation.

RANGE: Central North Carolina.

SPECIES: One.

Buotus carolinus Chamberlin

Buotus carolinus Chamberlin, 1940, Canadian Ent., vol. 72, p. 59.

TYPE: Collection of R. V. Chamberlin.

TYPE LOCALITY: Duke Forest, Durham County, North Carolina.

RANGE: Known only from type locality.

Genus BUZONIUM Cook and Loomis

Buzonium Cook and Loomis, 1928, Proc. U. S. Nat. Mus., vol. 72, art. 18, p. 13.

GENEROTYPE: *Buzonium crassipes* Cook and Loomis, by original designation.

RANGE: California.

SPECIES: One.

Buzonium crassipes Cook and Loomis

Buzonium crassipes Cook and Loomis, 1928, Proc. U. S. Nat. Mus., vol. 72, art. 18, p. 14, fig. 2.

TYPE: U. S. Nat. Mus. (No. 977).
TYPE LOCALITY: Scneca, Plumas County, California.
RANGE: Known only from type locality.

Genus EUZONIUM Chamberlin

Euzonium Chamberlin, 1950, Chicago Acad. Sci. Nat. Hist. Misc. No. 68, p. 1.
GENEROTYPE: *Euzonium crucis* Chamberlin, by original designation.
RANGE: California.
SPECIES: One.

Euzonium crucis Chamberlin

Euzonium crucis Chamberlin, 1950, Chicago Acad. Sci. Nat. Hist. Misc. No. 68, p. 1.
TYPE: Collection of R. V. Chamberlin.
TYPE LOCALITY: Felbon, Santa Cruz County, California.
RANGE: Known only from type locality.

Genus HYPOZONIUM Cook

Hypozonium Cook, 1904, *in* Harriman Alaska Exped., vol. 8, p. 62.
GENEROTYPE: *Hypozonium anurum* Cook, by original designation.
RANGE: Washington.
SPECIES: One.

Hypozonium anurum Cook

Hypozonium anurum Cook, 1904, *in* Harriman Alaska Exped., vol. 8, p. 63, pl. 5, figs. 1a–d.—Cook and Loomis, 1928, Proc. U. S. Nat. Mus., vol. 72, art. 18, p. 17.
TYPE: U. S. Nat. Mus. (No. 791).
TYPE LOCALITY: Seattle, Washington.
RANGE: Known only from Seattle and Bremerton, Washington.

Genus PIZONIUM Chamberlin

Pizonium Chamberlin, 1950, Chicago Acad. Sci. Nat. Hist. Misc. No. 68, p. 2.
GENEROTYPE: *Pizonium crescentis* Chamberlin, by original designation.
RANGE: California.
SPECIES: One.

Pizonium crescentis Chamberlin

Pizonium crescentis Chamberlin, 1950, Chicago Acad. Sci. Nat. Hist. Misc. No. 68, p. 2.
TYPE: Collection of R. V. Chamberlin.
TYPE LOCALITY: 15 miles east of Crescent, Los Angeles County, California.
RANGE: Known from type locality only.

Genus POLYZONIUM Brandt

Polyzonium Brandt, 1834, Oken's Isis, p. 704; 1837, Bull. Sci. Acad. Sci. Saint Pétersbourg, vol. 1 (1836, No. 23), p. 178.

Octoglena Wood, 1864, Proc. Acad. Nat. Sci. Philadelphia, p. 186 (generotype: *O. bivirgata* Wood, by monotypy).

Petaserpes Cope, 1870, Trans. Amer. Ent. Soc., vol. 3, p. 65 (generotype: *P. rosalbus* Cope, by monotypy).

Hexaglena McNeill, 1887, Proc. U. S. Nat. Mus., vol. 10, p. 328 (generotype: *H. cryptocephala* McNeill.

GENEROTYPE: *Polyzonium germanicum* Brandt, by monotypy.

RANGE: Northern Europe; eastern United States.

SPECIES: About seven; three occur in our area.

Polyzonium bikermani Causey

Polyzonium bikermani Causey, 1951, Proc. Biol. Soc. Washington, vol. 64, p. 138, fig. 1.

TYPE: Acad. Nat. Sci. Philadelphia.

TYPE LOCALITY: Devil's Den State Park, Washington County, Arkansas.

RANGE: Known only from type locality.

Polyzonium bivirgatum (Wood)

Octoglena bivirgata Wood, 1864, Proc. Acad. Nat. Sci. Philadelphia, p. 186.

Petaserpes rosalbus Cope, 1870, Trans. Amer. Ent. Soc., vol. 3, p. 65 (type locality: ". . . western slope of the Cumberlands, in the northern part of East Tennessee." Location of type unknown).

Polyzonium bivirgatum Cook and Loomis, 1928, Proc. U. S. Nat. Mus., vol. 72, art. 18, p. 18.

TYPE: Location unknown, probably not in existence.

TYPE LOCALITY: Georgia.

RANGE: Eastern United States from Connecticut west as far as Ohio, south to Georgia in the mountains. Exact limits of range still poorly known.

Polyzonium cryptocephalum (McNeill) [13]

Hexaglena cryptocephala McNeill, 1887, Proc. U. S. Nat. Mus., vol. 10, p. 328.

Polyzonium mutabile Causey, 1951, Proc. Biol. Soc. Washington, vol. 64, p. 139, fig. 2.

TYPE: U. S. Nat. Mus.

TYPE LOCALITY: Bloomington, Monroe County, Indiana.

RANGE: Indiana, Illinois, Michigan, southern Ontario.

---

[13] Synonymy based on unpublished studies, including examination of the holotype of *cryptocephala.*

Genus SIPHONOTUS Brandt

Siphonotus Brandt, 1837, Bull. Sci. Acad. Sci. Saint-Pétersbourg, vol. 1, p. 179.

GENEROTYPE: *Siphonotus brasiliensis* Brandt, by monotypy.

RANGE: South America, West Indies.

SPECIES: About six.

Siphonotus purpureus Pocock

Siphonotus purpureus Pocock, 1894, Journ. Linn. Soc. London, vol. 24, p. 479, pl. 37, fig. 5.—Loomis, 1934, Smithsonian Misc. Coll., vol. 89, p. 9.

Siphonotus miamiensis Causey, 1953, Florida Ent., vol. 36, p. 71, figs. 1, 2 (type locality: Miami, Florida; type: Illinois Nat. Hist. Surv.).

TYPE: British Museum (Nat. Hist.).

TYPE LOCALITY: Brasil.

RANGE: Most of the Lesser Antilles; Hispaniola; northern coast of South America; southern Florida. Probably dispersed by commerce.

Family SIPHONOPHORIDAE Newport

Siphonophoridae Newport, 1845, Trans. Linn. Soc. London, vol. 19, p. 278.—Verhoeff, 1941, Zool. Anz., vol. 134, p. 212.—Attems, 1951, Mém. Mus. Nat. Hist. Nat., Paris, ser. A, Zoologie, vol. 3, fasc. 3, p. 221.

Genus ILLACME Cook and Loomis

Illacme Cook and Loomis, 1928, Proc. U. S. Nat. Mus., vol. 72, art. 18, p. 10.

GENEROTYPE: *Illacme plenipes* Cook and Loomis, by original designation.

RANGE: California.

SPECIES: One.

Illacme plenipes Cook and Loomis

Illacme plenipes Cook and Loomis, 1928, Proc. U. S. Nat. Mus., vol. 72, art. 18, p. 12.

TYPE: U. S. Nat. Mus. (No. 976).

TYPE LOCALITY: between Salinas and San Juan Bautista, in San Benito County, California.

RANGE: Known only from type locality.

Genus SIPHONACME Cook and Loomis

Siphonacme Cook and Loomis, 1928, Proc. U. S. Nat. Mus., vol. 72, art 18, p. 7.

GENEROTYPE: *Siphonacme lyttoni* Cook and Loomis, by original designation.

RANGE: Southern Arizona; northwestern Mexico.

SPECIES: Two, one of which occurs in the United States.

Siphonacme lyttoni Cook and Loomis

Siphonacme lyttoni Cook and Loomis, 1928, Proc. U. S. Nat. Mus., vol. 72, art. 18, p. 8, fig. 1 a–c.

TYPE: U. S. Nat. Mus. (No. 975).

TYPE LOCALITY: Crest of Pinal mountains, between Miami and Superior, in Gila County, Arizona.

RANGE: Known also from single localities in Yavapa and Cochise Counties, Arizona.

Genus SIPHONOPHORA Brandt

Siphonophora Brandt, 1837, Bull. Sci. Acad. Saint-Pétersbourg, vol. 1, p. 179.

GENEROTYPE: *Siphonophora portoricensis* Brandt, by subsequent designation of Silvestri, 1896.

RANGE: Tropical America and possibly also the Oriental region, but the extent of the genus in its strict sense has yet to be determined by study of the type species.

SPECIES: About 18 species are listed by Attems, in a sort of semi-restricted sense. Two species have been described in *Siphonophora* in the United States, but these may not be congeneric with *S. portoricensis.*

Siphonophora limitare Loomis

Siphonophora limitare Loomis, 1936, Proc. U. S. Nat. Mus., vol. 83, No. 2989, p. 362, 363, fig. 32 a, b.

TYPE: U. S. Nat. Mus. (No. 1159).

TYPE LOCALITY: Brownsville, Cameron County, Texas.

RANGE: Known only from the type locality.

Siphonophora texascolens Chamberlin and Mulaik

Siphonophora texascolens Chamberlin and Mulaik, 1941, Journ. New York Ent. Soc., vol. 49, p. 64.

TYPE: Collection of R. V. Chamberlin.

TYPE LOCALITY: Raven Ranch, Kerr County, Texas.

RANGE: Reported from Kerr, Kendall, and Bandera counties, in central Texas.

Addendum

The following species should appear on page 80, immediately preceding *Eurymerodesmus louisianae.*

Eurymerodesmus hispidipes (Wood)

Polydesmus hispidipes Wood, 1864, Proc. Acad. Nat. Sci. Philadelphia, p. 7; 1865, Trans. Amer. Philos. Soc., new ser., vol. 13, p. 220, fig. 48.

Eurymerodesmus hispidipes Brölemann, 1900, Mém. Soc. Zool. France, vol. 13, p. 101, pl. 6, fig. 32.—Causey, 1950, Ohio Journ. Sci., vol. 50, No. 6, p. 267, figs. 1–4.

TYPE: If extant, present location unknown.

TYPE LOCALITY: "Illinois."

RANGE: Dixon Springs, Lee County, Illinois, is the only definitely known locality for this rare species. The Louisiana record for *hispidipes* by Brölemann (op. cit.) doubtless applies to a different member of the genus.

Bibliography

AM STEIN, J. G.
1857. Aufzählung unde Beschreibung der Myriapoden und Crustaceen Graubündens. Jahresb. Naturf. Ges. Graubündens, new ser., vol. 2 (1855–1856), pp. 112–148.

ATTEMS, CARL.
1899. System der Polydesmiden. I Theil. Denkschr. Akad. Wiss., Wien (Math.-naturwiss. Classe), vol. 67, pp. 221–482, pls. 1–11, figs. 1–276.

1900. System der Polydesmiden. II Theil. Denkschr. Akad. Wiss., Wien (Math.-naturwiss. Classe), vol. 68, pp. 251–435, pls. 12–17, figs. 277–400.

1902. Neue durch den Schiffsverkehr in Hamburg eingeschleppte Myriapoden. Mitt. Naturh. Mus. Hamburg, vol. 18, pp. 109–116, pl. 1.

1903. Beiträge zur Myriopodenkunde. Zool. Jahrb., Abt. Syst., vol. 18, pp. 63–154, pls. 5, 6, figs. 1–37, pl. 7, figs 1–20, pls. 8–11, figs. 1–88.

1908. Note sur lse myriapodes, in Gadeau de Kerville, Voyage zoologique en Khroumirie (Tunisie) . . . 1906, . . ., pp. 112–113, pl. 24, figs. 10–12.

1909. Die Myriopoden der Vega-Expedition. Arkiv för Zoologi, vol. 5, No. 3, pp. 1–84, text figs. 1–27, pls. 1–5, figs. 1–86.

1914. Afrikanische Spirostreptiden nebst Überblick über die Spirostreptiden orbis terrarum. Zoologica, Stuttgart, vol. 25, Heft 65–66, pp. 1–233, figs. 1–36, pls. 1–15.

1914. Die indo-australischen Myriopoden. Arch. Naturg., Abt. A, vol. 80, No. 4, pp. 1–398, pls. 1–7, figs. 1–125.

1926. Myriopoda, in Kükenthal und Krumbach, Handbuch der Zoologie, vol. 4, pp. 1–402, figs. 1–477.

1931. Die Familie Leptodesmidae und andere Polydesmiden. Zoologica, Stuttgart, vol. 30, Lief. 3–4, pp. 1–149, figs. 1–245.

1937. Fam. Strongylosomidae, in Das Tierreich, Lief, 68 (Polydesmoidea I), pp. 1–300, figs. 1–343.

1938. Fam. Leptodesmidae, Platyrhachidae, Oxydesmidae, Gomphodesmidae, in Das Tierreich, Lief. 69 (Polydesmoida II), pp. 1–487, figs. 1–509.

1940. Fam. Polydesmidae, Vanhoeffeniidae, Cryptodesmidae, Oniscodesmidae, Sphaerotrichopidae, Peridontodesmidae, Rhachidesmidae, Macellolophidae, Pandirodesmidae, in Das Tierreich, Lief. 70 (Polydesmoidea III), pp. 1–577, figs. 1–719.

1950. Über Spirostreptiden (Diplpodoa). Ann. Naturh. Mus. Wien, vol. 57 (1949–50), pp. 179–257, figs. 1–96.

1951. Revision systématique des Colobognatha (Myriapodes Diplopodes) et description d'espèces nouvelles. Mém. Mus. Nat. Hist. Nat., ser. A, Zoologie, vol. 3, fasc. 3, pp. 193–231, figs. 1–72.

BARBER, HERBERT S.
1915. Migrating armies of myriopods. Proc. Ent. Soc. Washington, vol. 17, pp. 121–123.

1915. Fragmentary notes on the life-history of the myriopod Spirobolus marginatus. Proc. Ent. Soc. Washington, vol. 17, pp. 123–126.

BERG, CARLOS
1899. Substitución de nombres genéricos. III. Comun. Mus. Nac. Buenos Aires, vol. 1, No. 3, pp. 77–80.

BERLESE, ANTONIO
1884.   Studi critici sulla sistematica dei Chilognati conservati nella Raccolti del
        Museo zoologico della R. Università di Padova. Parte I, Julidae. Atti
        Rend. Inst. Veneto, ser. 6, vol. 2, pp. 247–280, pls. 1, 2.
1882–1895. Acari, Myriopoda et Scorpiones hucusque in Italia reperta, Fasc. 1–77.
        Padua.
BLOWER, GORDON
1953.   On three species of Cylindroiulus Verhoeff (Diplopoda, Iulidae) in Britain.
        Ann. Mag. Nat. Hist., ser. 12, vol. 6, pp. 305–316, figs. 1–4.
BOLLMAN, CHARLES HARVEY
1887.   Preliminary descriptions of ten new North American myriapods. Amer. Nat.,
        vol. 21, pp. 81–82.
1887.   Descriptions of new genera and species of North American Myriapoda
        (Julidae). Ent. Amer., vol. 2, pp. 225–229.
1887.   Notes on North American Julidae, with descriptions of new species. Ann.
        New York Acad. Sci., vol. 4, Nos. 1 and 2, pp. 25–44.
1887.   New genus and species of Polydesmidae. Ent. Amer., vol. 3, No. 1, pp. 45, 46.
1887.   New North American myriapods. Ent. Amer., vol. 3, No. 5, pp. 81–83.
1888.   A preliminary list of the Myriapoda of Arkansas, with descriptions of new
        species. Ent. Amer., vol. 4, pp. 1–8.
1888.   Notes upon a collection of Myriapoda from East Tennessee, with a descrip-
        tion of a new genus and six new species. Ann. New York Acad. Sci.,
        vol. 4, Nos. 3 and 4, pp. 106–112.
1888.   Descriptions of fourteen new species of North American myriapods. Proc.
        U. S. Nat. Mus., vol. 10, pp. 617–627.
1889.   Description of a new species of insect, Fontaria pulchella, from Strawberry
        Plains, Jefferson County, Tennessee. Proc. U. S. Nat. Mus., vol. 11, p. 316.
1889.   Notes on a collection of Myriapoda from Mossy Creek, Tenn., with a descrip-
        tion of a new species. Proc. U. S. Nat. Mus., vol. 11, pp. 339–342.
1889.   Notes upon some myriapods belonging to the U. S. National Museum. Proc.
        U. S. Nat. Mus., vol. 11, pp. 343–350.
1889.   Catalogue of the myriapods of Indiana. Proc. U. S. Nat. Mus., vol. 11,
        pp. 403–410.
1893.   The Myriapoda of North America. U. S. Nat. Mus. Bull. 46, pp. 1–210
        (edited by L. M. Underwood, containing the preceding papers and 14
        posthumously published articles, with introduction and literature review
        by Underwood).
BORRE, ALFRED PREUDHOMME DE
1884.   Tentamen catalogi lysiopetalidarum, julidarum, archijulidarum, polyzoni-
        darum, atque siphonophoridarum hucusque descriptarum. Ann. Soc. Ent.
        Belgique, vol. 28, pp. 46–82.
BOSC, LOUIS AUGUSTIN GUILLAUME
1791.   Description d'une nouvelle espèce d'iule. Bull. Soc. Philom. Paris, vol. 1,
        p. 10.
BRADE-BIRKS, HILDA K., AND S. GRAHAM
1919.   Notes on Myriapoda. XVII. (1): Pour réhabiliter quelques anciens noms
        spécifiques. [With notes by H. W. Brolemann.] Bull. Soc. Zool. France,
        vol. 44, pp. 63–68.
BRANDT, JOHANN FRIEDRICH
1833.   De nove insectorum multipedum seu myriapodum familia Pentazoniorum
        (glomeridorum) nomine designanda. Bull. Mém. Acad. Sci. St.-Péters-
        bourg, ser. 6 (Sci. Math. Phys.), vol. 2.

BRANDT, JOHANN FRIEDRICH—Continued

1833. Tentaminum quorundam monographicorum Insecta Myriapoda Chilognatha Latreillii spectantium. Bull. Soc. Nat. Moscou, vol. 6, pp. 194–209, pl. 5, figs. 22–47.

1834. (Note on Colobognatha). Oken's Isis (vol. 27), p. 704.

1834. (Note on the genus *Polyzonium Brandt*). Oken's Isis (vol. 27), p. 704.

1837. Note sur un ordre nouveau de la classe des Myriapodes et sur l'établissement des sections de cette classe d'animaux en général. Bull. Sci. Acad. Sci. Saint-Pétersbourg, vol. 1 (1836, No. 23), pp. 178, 179.

1841. Recueil de mémoires relatif à l'ordre des Insectes Myriapodes. Bull. Sci. Acad. Sci. Saint-Pétersbourg, vols. 5–9, 189 pp. [Individual titles are listed in Latzel, 1884, Myr. Öst.-Ung. Monarch., vol. 2, pp. 375–76.]

BRÖLEMANN, HENRY W.

1896. Liste de myriapodes des États-Unis, et principalement de la Caroline du Nord, faisant partie des collections de M. Eugène Simon. Ann. Soc. Ent. France, vol. 65, pp. 43–70, pls. 5–7.

1897. Julides d'Algérie. Ann. Sci. Nat., ser. 8, vol. 4 (1896), pp. 253–276, pls. 3, 4.

1898. Voyage de M. E. Simon au Venezuela. Myriapodes. Ann. Soc. Ent. France, vol. 67, pp. 241–313, pls. 20–27.

1900. Myriapodes d'Amérique. Mém. Soc. Zool. France, vol. 13, pp. 89–131, pls. 6–8., figs. 1–122.

1902. Le genre *Paraiulus* (Myriapodes-diplopodes). Ann. Soc. Ent. France, vol. 71, Nos. 1, 2, pp. 440–447, pls. 1, 2, figs. 1–18.

1902. Myriapodes du Musée de Sao Paulo. Rev. Mus. Paulista, vol. 5, pp. 35–237, pls. 1–9, figs. 1–271.

1903. Myriapodes recueillis à l'isla de Cocos par M. le Professeur P. Biolley. Ann. Soc. Ent. France, vol. 72, pp. 128–143, figs. 10, pls. 1.

1910. Biospeologica. XVII. Symphyles, psélaphognathes, polydesmoides et lysiopétaloides (myriapodes) (1 ʳᵉ série). Arch. Zool. Expér. Gén., Paris, ser. 5, vol. 5, pp. 339–378, pls. 4–7, figs. 1–50.

1913. Un nouveau systeme de spirobolides. Bull. Soc. Ent. France, No. 19, pp. 476–478.

1914. Étude sur les spirobolides. Ann. Soc. Ent. France, vol. 83, No. 1, pp. 1–38, figs. 1–9.

1916. Essai de classification des polydesmiens (myriapodes). Ann. Soc. Ent. France, vol. 84, No. 4 (1915), pp. 523–608, figs. 1–18.

1921. Clef dichotomique des divisions et des espèces de la famille des Blaniulidae (myriapodes). Arch. Zool. Expér. Gen., Paris, vol. 60, Notes et Revue, No. 1, pp. 1–10.

1922. Notes on female paraiulids, with description of a new species. Ann. Ent. Soc. Amer., vol. 15, No. 4, pp. 281–309, pls. 19–24, figs. 1–57.

1923. Biospeologica 48. Blaniulidae (myriapodes). Arch. Zool. Expér. Gen., Paris, vol. 61, fasc. 2, pp. 99–453, figs. 1–411, pls. 1–16.

1935. Myriapodes diplopodes (chilognathes I), *in* Faune de France, No. 29, pp. 1–369, figs. 1–750.

CARL, JOHANN

1902. Exotische Polydesmiden. Rev. Suisse Zool., vol. 10, pp. 563–679, pls. 10–12, figs. 1–109.

1903. Revision amerikanischer Polydesmiden. Rev. Suisse Zool., vol. 11, pp. 543–562, pls. 16–17, figs. 1–23.

CAUSEY, NELL BEVEL

1942. Six new diplopods of the family Xystodesmidae. Ent. News, vol. 53, pp. 165–170, figs. 1–9.

CAUSEY, NELL BEVEL—Continued

1943.   Studies on the life-history and the ecology of the hot-house millipede, *Orthomorpha gracilis* (C. L. Koch). Amer. Midl. Nat., vol. 29, No. 3, pp. 670–682, 3 figs.

1950.   A collection of xystodesmid millipeds from Kentucky and Tennessee. Ent. News, vol. 61, pp. 5–7, figs. 1–3.

1950.   Two new polydesmoid diplopods. Ent. News, vol. 61, pp. 37–39, figs. 1–5.

1950.   Five new Arkansas millipeds of the genera *Eurymerodesmus* and *Paresmus* (Xystodesmidae). Ohio Journ. Sci., vol. 50, No. 6, pp. 267–272, figs. 1–11.

1950.   A new genus and species of diplopod (Family Xystodesmidae). Chicago Acad. Sci. Nat. Hist. Misc., No. 73, pp. 1–3, figs. 1.

1950.   New genera and species of millipeds—Paraiulidae (Juloidea). Proc. Arkansas Acad. Sci., vol. 3, pp. 45–58, pls. 1–5, figs. 1–42.

1950.   Variations in the gonopods of a xystodesmid diplopod. Amer. Midl. Nat., vol. 44, No. 1, pp. 198–202, figs. 1–6.

1950.   On four new polydesmoid millipeds. Ent. News, vol. 61, No. 7, pp. 193–198, figs. 1–7.

1951.   On Eurymerodesmidae, a new family of Diplopoda (Strongylosomidea), and a new Arkansas species of *Eurymerodesmus*. Proc. Arkansas Acad. Sci., vol. 4, pp. 69–71, figs. 1–3.

1951.   The milliped assembly *Zinaria butlerii* isogen. (Xystodesmidae). Proc. Arkansas Acad. Sci., vol. 4, pp. 73–88, pls. 1, 2, figs. 1–12.

1951.   New genera and species of chordeumoid millipeds in the United States, and notes on some established species. Proc. Biol. Soc. Washington, vol. 64, pp. 117–124, figs. 1–18.

1951.   On two new colobognath millipeds and records of some established species from east of the Rocky Mountains. Proc. Biol. Soc. Washington, vol. 64, pp. 137–140, figs. 1–3.

1951.   New cleidogonid millipeds (Chordeumoidea). Journ. Washington Acad. Sci., vol. 41, No. 2, pp. 78–83, figs. 1–23.

1952.   On two new species and new distribution records of paraiulid millipeds from the eastern United States. Proc. Arkansas Acad. Sci., vol. 5, pp. 19–23, figs. 1–9.

1952.   Some records and descriptions of polydesmoid millipeds from the United States. Chicago Acad. Sci. Nat. Hist. Misc., No. 106, pp. 1–11, figs. 1–8.

1952.   New species and records of pariulid millipeds from Texas. Texas Journ. Sci., vol. 4, No. 2, pp. 200–203, figs. 1–10.

1952.   On three new eurymerodesmoid millipeds and notes on *Paresmus impurus* (Wood). Ent. News, vol. 63, No. 7, pp. 169–176, figs. 1–9.

1952.   Four chordeumoid millipeds from the United States. Proc. Biol. Soc. Washington, vol. 65, pp. 111–118, figs. 1–18.

1952.   New records of millipeds from southern Ontario. Canadian Field Nat., vol. 66, p. 145.

1953.   On a Florida milliped, *Siphonotus miamiensis*, n. sp. Florida Ent., vol. 36, No. 2, pp. 71–72, figs. 1, 2.

1953.   On five new North American millipeds and records of some established species. Amer. Midl. Nat., vol. 50, pp. 152–158, figs. 1–14.

1954.   The millipeds collected in the Pacific Northwest by Dr. M. H. Hatch. Ann. Ent. Soc. America, vol. 47, pp. 81–86, figs. 1–12.

1954.   New records and species of millipeds from the western United States and Canada. Pan-Pacific Ent., vol. 30, No. 3, pp. 221–227, figs. 1–5.

1954.   Three new species and new records of southern millipeds. Tulane Stud. Zool., vol. 2, No. 4, pp. 63–68, figs. 1–10.

CAUSEY, NELL BEVEL—Continued

1955. Spirobolidae (Spirobolida: Diplopoda) east of the Rocky Mountains. Journ. Kansas Ent. Soc., vol. 28, pp. 69–80, figs. 1–5.

1955. New records and descriptions of polydesmoid millipeds (Order Polydesmida) from the eastern United States. Proc. Biol. Soc. Washington, vol. 68, pp. 21–30, figs. 1–7.

1955. New records and descriptions of Californian Diplopoda. Proc. Biol. Soc. Washington, vol. 68, pp. 87–94, figs. 1–5.

CHAMBERLIN, RALPH VARY

1903. Myriapods from Beulah, New Mexico. Proc. Acad. Nat. Sci. Philadelphia, vol. 55, pp. 35–40.

1910. Diplopoda from the western states. Ann. Ent. Soc. Amer., vol. 3, No. 4, pp. 233–262, pls. 30–43.

1911. Notes on myriapods from Alaska and Washington. Canadian Ent., vol. 43, pp. 260–264, fig. 16.

1912. New North American chilopods and diplopods. Ann. Ent. Soc. America, vol. 5, No. 2, pp. 141–172, pls. 10–13.

1913. A new leptodesmid from Montana. Canadian Ent., vol. 45, pp. 424–426, fig. 17.

1914. A new diplopod from the Galapagos Is., with notes on the chilopods. Psyche, vol. 21, pp. 85–89.

1914. Notes on myriapods from Douglas Lake, Michigan. Canadian Ent., vol. 46, pp. 301–306.

1914. A new *Julus* from California. Canadian Ent., vol. 46, pp. 314–315, figs. 26, 27.

1916. Two new Texan Parajuli. Psyche, vol. 23, pp. 33–36.

1918. Four new western diplopods. Pomona Coll. Journ. Ent. and Zool., vol. 10, No. 1, pp. 9–11.

1918. Myriapods from Nashville, Tennessee. Psyche, vol. 25, pp. 23–30.

1918. The Chilopoda and Diplopoda of the West Indies. Bull. Mus. Comp. Zool., vol. 62, No. 5, pp. 149–262.

1918. Two new diplopods from Louisiana. Canadian Ent., vol. 50, pp. 361–363.

1918. New polydesmoid diplopods from Tennessee and Mississippi. Psyche, vol. 25, No. 6, pp. 122–127.

1918. Myriopods from Okefenokee swamp, Ga., and from Natchitoches Parish, Louisiana. Ann. Ent. Soc. Amer., vol. 11, No. 4, pp. 369–380.

1918. New spiroboloid diplopods. Proc. Biol. Soc. Washington, vol. 31, pp. 165–170.

1919. A new *Parajulus* from British Columbia. Canadian Ent., vol. 51, pp. 119–120, fig. 21.

1919. A new Texas *Parajulus*. Proc. Biol. Soc. Washington, vol. 32, pp. 119–120.

1920. (Note on the writings of H. C. Wood). Ent. News, vol. 31, pp. 117–118.

1920. Some records of Canadian myriopods. Canadian Ent., vol. 52, No. 4, pp. 94–95.

1920. Canadian myriapods collected in 1882–83 by J. B. Tyrrell, with additional records. Canadian Ent., vol. 52, No. 6, pp. 166–168, figs. 16, 17.

1920. A new diplopod from Texas and a new chilopod from Alaska. Proc. Biol. Soc. Washington, vol. 33, pp. 41–44.

1920. Corrections to Mr. Gunthorp's summary of Wood's Myriopoda papers. Canadian Ent., vol. 52, No. 7, pp. 202–203.

1920. A new leptodesmoid diplopod from Louisiana. Proc. Biol. Soc. Washington, vol. 33, pp. 97–100.

1920. A new diplopod of the genus *Atopetholus*. Proc. Biol. Soc. Washington, vol. 33, pp. 101–102.

1921. The Julidae and Isobatidae in North America. Proc. Biol. Soc. Washington, vol. 34, pp. 81–84.

CHAMBERLIN, RALPH VARY—Continued

1921. On some chilopods and diplopods from Knox Co., Tennessee. Canadian Ent., vol. 53, No. 10, pp. 230–233, fig. 1, pl. 9, figs. 1–4.

1922. A new platydesmoid diplopod from California. Pomona Coll. Journ. Ent. and Zool., vol. 14, No. 1, pp. 9–10, 1 fig.

1922. Further notes on the nomenclature of North American Julidae and Nemasomidae. Proc. Biol. Soc. Washington, vol. 35, pp. 7–10.

1922. A new milliped of the genus *Polyxenus* from the Florida Keys. Ent. News, vol. 33, No. 6, p. 165.

1922. Notes on West Indian millipeds. Proc. U. S. Nat. Mus., vol. 61, art. 10, pp. 1–19, pls. 1–6.

1923. An Algerian julid in America. Proc. Biol. Soc. Washington, vol. 36, pp. 191–192.

1925. Notes on some centipeds and millipeds from Utah. Pan-Pacific Ent., vol. 2, No. 2, pp. 55–63.

1928. Some chilopods and diplopods from Missouri. Ent. News, vol. 39, No. 5, pp. 153–155.

1928. Notes on chilopods and diplopods from southeastern Utah. Ent. News, vol. 39, No. 10, pp. 307–311.

1930. On some centipeds and millipeds from Utah and Arizona. Pan-Pacific Ent., vol. 6, No. 3, pp. 111–121, 11 figs.

1931. A new milliped of the genus *Fontaria* from Mississippi. (Chilognatha: Xystodesmidae). Ent. News, vol. 42, No. 3, pp. 78–79.

1931. On a collection of chilopods and diplopods from Oklahoma. Ent. News, vol. 42, No. 4, pp. 97–104, pl. 2, figs. 1–8.

1938. Diplopoda from Yucatan, *in* Pearse, Fauna of the caves of Yucatan. Carnegie Inst. Washington Publ., No. 491, pp. 165–182, figs. 1–55.

1938. New diplopods. Proc. Biol. Soc. Washington, vol. 51, pp. 205–208.

1939. On some diplopods of the family Fontariidae. Bull. Univ. Utah, biol. ser., vol. 5, No. 3, pp. 1–19, pls. 1–4, figs. 1–37.

1940. On some chilopods and diplopods from North Carolina. Canadian Ent., vol. 72, pp. 56–59.

1940. New genera and species of North American Paraiulidae. Bull. Univ. Utah, biol. ser., vol. 5, No. 7, pp. 1–39, pls. 1–8, figs. 1–73.

1940. Four new western millipeds. Pomona Coll. Journ. Ent. and Zool., vol. 32, No. 4, pp. 81–83, figs. a–f.

1940. Four new polydesmoid millipeds from North Carolina (Myriapoda). Ent. News, vol. 51, No. 10, pp. 282–284, figs. 1–4.

1941. New polydesmoid diplopods intercepted at quarantine. Proc. Ent. Soc. Washington, vol. 43, No. 2, pp. 32–35, 4 text figs.

1941. New American millipeds. Bull. Univ. Utah, biol. ser., vol. 6, No. 4, pp. 1–39, pls. 1–5, figs. 1–49.

1941. New western millipeds. Bull. Univ. Utah, biol. ser., vol. 6, No. 5, pp. 1–23, pls. 1–3, figs. 1–30.

1942. On a collection of myriopods from Iowa. Canadian Ent., vol. 74, No. 1, pp. 15–17, 4 figs.

1942. New southern millipeds. Bull. Univ. Utah, biol. ser., vol. 6, No. 8, pp. 1–19. pls. 1–4, figs. 1–40

1943. On nine North American polydesmoid millipeds. Proc. Biol. Soc. Washington, vol. 56, pp. 35–40, pls. 1, 2, figs. 1–11.

1943. A new *Polydesmus* from Missouri and Oklahoma (Diplopoda). Ent. News, vol. 54, pp. 15–16, figs. 1, 2.

1943. A new cambalid diplopod. Ent. News, vol. 54, pp. 88–89.

CHAMBERLIN, RALPH VARY—Continued

1943. On some genera and species of American millipeds. Bull. Univ. Utah, biol. ser., vol. 8, No. 2, pp. 1–20, figs. 1–42.

1943. Some records and descriptions of American diplopods. Proc. Biol. Soc. Washington, vol. 56, pp. 143–152, pls. 7–8, figs. 1–15.

1943. On Mexican millipeds. Bull. Univ. Utah, biol. ser., vol. 8, No. 3, pp. 1–103, pls. 1–16, figs. 1–172.

1944. Some records of myriopods collected by W. M. Pearce in California. Pan-Pacific Ent., vol. 20, pp. 79–80.

1944. Two millipeds from southern California. Proc. Biol. Soc. Washington, vol. 57, pp. 113–116, pl. 4, figs. 1–5.

1946. Two new species of the milliped genera *Chonaphe and Aniulus*. Proc. Biol. Soc. Washington, vol. 59, pp. 31–34, figs. 1–4.

1946. *Texophon*, a new genus in the diplopod family Lysiopetalidae. Ent. News, vol. 57, pp. 97–99, figs. 1–2.

1946. On some millipeds of Georgia. Ent. News, vol. 57, pp. 149–152, figs. 1–9.

1946. On four millipeds from Georgia and Mississippi. Proc. Biol. Soc. Washington, vol. 59, pp. 139–142, figs. 1–5.

1947. Seven new American millipeds. Proc. Biol. Soc. Washington, vol. 60, pp. 9–16, figs. 1–8.

1947. Some records and descriptions of diplopods chiefly in the collection of the Academy. Proc. Acad. Nat. Sci. Philadelphia, vol. 99, pp. 21–58, figs. 1–73.

1948. A third species in the chelodesmid genus *Semionellus*. Ent. News, vol. 59, p. 259, figs. 1–2.

1949. Some millipeds of the families Polydesmidae and Xystodesmidae. Journ. Washington Acad. Sci., vol. 39, No. 3, pp. 94–102, figs. 1–27.

1949. A new genus and four new species in the diplopod family Xystodesmidae. Proc. Biol. Soc. Washington, vol. 62, pp. 3–6, figs. 1–6.

1949. A new family in the diplopod order Chordeumida. Proc. Biol. Soc. Washington, vol. 62, pp. 7, 8, figs. 1, 2.

1949. On some western millipeds of the order Spirobolida. Journ. Washington Acad. Sci., vol. 39, No. 5, pp. 163–169, figs. 1–19.

1949. American millipeds of the family Paeromopidae. Chicago Acad. Sci. Nat. Hist. Misc., No. 52, pp. 1–6, figs. 1, 2.

1949. Some western millipeds of the family Chelodesmidae. Proc. Biol. Soc. Washington, vol. 63 [sic=62], pp. 125–132, figs. 1–11.

1950. Three new genera and eight new species of western millipeds. Chicago Acad. Sci. Nat. Hist. Misc., No. 68, pp. 1–6, figs. 1–3.

1950. Neotropical chilopods and diplopods in the collections of the Department of Tropical Research, New York Zoological Society. Zoologica, New York, vol. 35, No. 2, pp. 133–144, figs. 1–23.

1951. Eleven new western millipeds. Chicago Acad. Sci. Nat. Hist. Misc., No. 87, pp. 1–12, figs. 1–26.

1951. On eight new southern millipeds. Great Basin Nat., vol. 11, Nos. 1–2, pp. 19–27, figs. 1–16.

1951. Records of American millipeds and centipeds collected by Dr. D. Eldon Beck in 1950. Great Basin Nat., vol. 11, Nos. 1–2. pp. 27–35, figs. 1–3.

1952. Three cave-dwelling millipeds. Ent. News, vol. 63, pp. 10–12.

1952. *Eclomus*, nom. nov. Ent. News, vol. 63, p. 71.

1952. Two Oregon millipeds of the order Chordeumida. Chicago Acad. Sci. Nat. Hist. Misc., No. 113, pp. 1–4, figs. 1–6.

1952. American polydesmoid millipeds in the collection of the Chicago Museum of Natural History. Ann. Ent. Soc. Amer., vol. 45, pp. 553–584, figs. 1–47.

CHAMBERLIN, RALPH VARY—Continued

1952.   Further records and descriptions of American millipeds. Great Basin Nat.,
        vol. 12, Nos. 1–4, pp. 13–34, figs. 1–21.
1953.   Six new American millipeds, with notes on several cave-dwelling species.
        Proc. Biol. Soc. Washington, vol. 66, pp. 67–72, figs. 1–4.
1953.   Two new millipeds taken in California caves. Ent. News, vol. 64, pp. 93–95.
1953.   Some American millipeds of the order Spirobolida. Amer. Midl. Nat., vol. 50,
        pp. 138–151, figs. 1–31.

CHAMBERLIN, RALPH V., AND HOFFMAN, RICHARD L.

1950.   On some genera and families of North American diplopods. Chicago Acad.
        Sci. Nat. Hist. Misc., No. 71, pp. 1–7, figs. 1, 2.

CHAMBERLIN, RALPH V., AND MULAIK, STANLEY

1941.   On a collection of millipeds from Texas and New Mexico. Journ. New York
        Ent. Soc., vol. 49, No. 1, pp. 57–64.

COOK, ORATOR FULLER

1895.   Chordeumidae or Craspedosomatidae? Amer. Nat., vol. 29, pp. 862–864.
1895.   The genera of Lysiopetalidae. Amer. Nat., vol. 29, pp. 1017–1019.
1895.   Introductory note on the families of Diplopoda, in Cook and Collins, The
        Craspedosomatidae of North America. Ann. New York Acad. Sci., vol. 9,
        pp. 1–9.
1896.   On recent diplopod names. Brandtia, No. 2, pp. 5–8.
1896.   Cryptodesmus and its allies. Brandtia, No. 5, p. 25.
1896.   A spinning diplopod. Brandtia, No. 9, pp. 41–42.
1896.   An American glomeroid. Brandtia, No. 10, pp. 43–45.
1896.   Note on the classification of Diplopoda. Amer. Nat., vol. 30, pp. 681–684.
1898.   Myriapoda, in The fur seals and fur-seal islands of the North Pacific Ocean,
        edited by D. S. Jordan, vol. 4, pp. 350–351.
1898.   American oniscoid Diplopoda of the order Merocheta. Proc. U. S. Nat. Mus.,
        vol. 21, pp. 451–468, pls. 29–32.
1899.   The diplopod family Striariidae. Proc. U. S. Nat. Mus., vol. 21, pp. 667–676,
        pls. 53–54.
1904.   Myriapoda of northwestern North America, in Harriman Alaska Expedition,
        vol. 8 (Insects, pt. 1), pp. 47–82, pls. 3, 4, 5.
1911.   Notes on the distribution of millipeds in southern Texas, with descriptions of
        new genera and species from Texas, Arizona, Mexico, and Costa Rica.
        Proc. U. S. Nat. Mus., vol. 40, pp. 147–167.
1911.   The hothouse milliped as a new genus. Proc. U. S. Nat. Mus., vol. 40, pp.
        625–631.

COOK, ORATOR F., AND COLLINS, GEORGE N.

1895.   The Craspedosomatidae of North America. Ann. New York Acad. Sci., vol. 9,
        pp. 1–100, pls. 1–12, figs. 1–219. (Pp. 1–9 by O. F. Cook.)

COOK, ORATOR F., AND COOK, A. C.

1894.   A monograph of Scytonotus. Ann. New York Acad Sci., vol. 8, pp. 233–248,
        pls. 6–9, figs. 1–71.

COOK, ORATOR F., AND LOOMIS, HAROLD F.

1928.   Millipeds of the order Colobognatha, with descriptions of six new genera and
        type species, from Arizona and California. Proc. U. S. Nat. Mus., vol. 72,
        art. 18, pp. 1–26, figs. 1–6, pls. 1, 2.

COPE, EDWARD DRINKER

1869.   Synopsis of the extinct Mammalia of the cave formations in the United States,
        with observations on some Myriapoda found in and near the same, and on
        some extinct mammals of the caves of Anguilla, W. I., and other localities.
        Proc. Amer. Philos. Soc., vol. 11, pp. 171–192, pls. 3–5.

COPE, EDWARD DRINKER—Continued
1870. On some new and little known Myriapoda from the Southern Alleghanies. Trans. Amer. Ent. Soc., vol. 3, pp. 65–67.
1872. On the Wyandotte Cave and its fauna. Amer. Nat., vol. 6, pp. 406–422.

CURTIS, JOHN
1845. Observations on the natural history and economy of the insects called wire-worms, affecting the turnips, corn-crops, &c.; also of their parents the elaters or beetles, called skip-jacks, click-beetles, &c. Journ. Roy. Agr. Soc. England, vol. 5, art. 11, pp. 180–237, pls. I, J, figs. 1–55.

DADAY, EUGENIO
1890. Myriopoda extranea Musaei nationalis Hungarici. Term. Füz., vol. 12 (1889), pp. 115–156, pls. 4, 5.
1891. Myriopoda extranea collectionis zoologicae Universitatis Heidelbergensis. Term. Füz., vol. 14, pp. 135–154, pl. 7.

DRURY, DRU
1770–82. Illustrations of natural history; wherein are exhibited . . . figures of exotic insects, according to their different genera . . . , vols. 1–3, pls. 151. London.

FABRICIUS, JOHANN CHRISTIAN
1781. Species insectorum exhibentes eorum differentias specificas . . . etc., 2 vols. Hamburg and Cologne.

FANZAGO, F.
1875. Alcune nuove specie di miriapodi. Atti Acad. Sci. Veneto-Trentino-Istriana, vol. 4, pp. 149–152.

GERVAIS, PAUL
1836. Nouvelles espèces de myriapodes. L'Institut, sect. 1, vol. 4, No. 190, pp. 435–436.
1836. Nouvelles espèces de myriapodes. Bull. Soc. Philom. Paris, ser. 5, vol. 1 (Extraits des Procès-verbaux des Séances), pp. 71–72.
1844. Etudes pour servir à l'histoire naturelle des myriapodes. Am. Sci. Nat. ser. 3, vol. 2, pp. 51–80.
1847. Myriapodes, in Walckenaer and Gervais, Histoire naturelle des insectes. Aptères, vol. 4, pp. 1–333, 577–595, with atlas, pls. 37–45. Paris.

GIRARD, CHARLES
1853. Myriapods, in Marcy, Report on exploration of the Red River of Louisiana . . . in 1852, Appendix F, pp. 243–246, pls. 1.

GOLDFUSS, GEORG AUGUST
1820. Handbuch der zoologie, vol. 1.

GRAY, JOHN EDWARD
1832. Myriapods, in Griffith, The animal kingdom arranged in conformity with its organization by the Baron Cuvier, vol. 15 (Class Insecta, vol. 2), p. 787, pl. 135, fig. 1.
1842. In T. Rymer Jones, Myriapoda, in R. B. Todd, Cyclopedia of anatomy and physiology, vol. 3, pp. 544–560, figs. 304–326.
1844. List of the specimens of Myriapoda in the collection of the British Museum. London.

GUNTHROP, HORACE
1913. Annotated list of the Diplopoda and Chilopoda, with a key to the Myriapoda of Kansas. Kansas Univ. Sci. Bull., vol. 7, No. 6, pp. 161–183, figs. 1–6.

HARGER, OSCAR
1872. Descriptions of new North American myriapods. Amer. Journ. Sci. Arts, ser. 3, vol. 4, pp. 117–121, pls. 2.

HEFNER, R. A.
  1929. Studies of parajulid diplopods. I. The development of the external sexual structures of *Parajulus impressus* Say (8). Journ. Morph. Physiol., vol. 48, pp. 153–172, pls. 1–4, figs. 1–25.
HELLER, CAMIL
  1858. Beiträge zur österreichischen Grotten-Fauna. Sitz.-ber. Akad. Wiss., Wien, vol. 26 (1857), pp. 313–326, figs. 1–14.
HOFFMAN, RICHARD LAWRENCE
  1947. The status of the milliped *Lasiolathus virginicus*, with notes on *Scytonotus granulatus*. Proc. Biol. Soc. Washington, vol. 60, pp. 139–140.
  1948. Two new genera of xystodesmid millipeds from eastern United States. Proc. Biol. Soc. Washington, vol. 61, pp. 93–96, figs. 1–3.
  1948. Three new eastern millipeds of the family Xystodesmidae. Journ. Washington Acad. Sci., vol. 38, No. 10, pp. 346–350, figs. 1–6.
  1949. The identity of *Apheloria coriacea* (Diplopoda: Xystodesmidae). Amer. Mus. Novitates, No. 1405, pp. 1–6, figs. 1–4.
  1949. Three new species of Diplopoda from Virginia. Proc. Biol. Soc. Washington, vol. 62, pp. 81–88, figs. 1–6.
  1949. A new milliped of the genus *Toltecolus* from the United States (Anocheta: Atopetholidae). Chicago Acad. Sci. Nat. Hist. Misc., No. 46, pp. 1–3, fig. 1.
  1949. Nine new xystodesmid millipeds from Virginia and West Virginia, with records of established species. Proc. U. S. Nat. Mus., vol. 99, No. 3244, pp. 371–389, pls. 26, 27, figs. 1–18.
  1950. A preliminary list of the cleidogonid millipeds, with descriptions of a new genus from Guatemala and a new species from Virginia. Journ. Washington Acad. Sci., vol. 40, No. 3, pp. 87–92, figs. 1–6.
  1950. Records and descriptions of diplopods from the southern Appalachians. Journ. Elisha Mitchell Sci. Soc., vol. 66, No. 1, pp. 11–33, figs. 1–32.
  1950. Notes on some Virginia millipeds of the family Polydesmidae. Virginia Journ. Sci., new ser., vol. 1, No. 3, pp. 219–225, figs. 1–4.
  1950. American polydesmoid millipeds of the genus *Sigmoria*. Amer. Mus. Novitates, No. 1462, pp. 1–7.
  1950. The status of the milliped *Chelodesmus marxi* Cook and of the family name Chelodesmidae. Proc. Biol. Soc. Washington, vol. 63, pp. 185–188, pl. 13.
  1951. The name of the common eastern spiroboloid milliped. Florida Ent., vol. 34, No. 1, pp. 15–16.
  1951. Subspecies of the milliped *Apheloria trimaculata* (Wood). (Polydesmida: Xystodesmidae). Chicago Acad. Sci. Nat. Hist. Misc., No. 81, pp. 1–6, fig. 1.
  1951. A new genus of Central American milliped (family Euryuridae), with notes on the American genera. Proc. U. S. Nat. Mus., vol. 102, pp. 235–243, fig. 84.
  1952. The identity of the milliped genus *Fontaria* Gray (Polydesmida: Xystodesmidae). Ent. News, vol. 63, No. 3, pp. 72–74, fig. 1.
  1953. Studies on spiroboloid millipeds. I. The genus *Eurhinocricus* Brolemann. Proc. Biol. Soc. Washington, vol. 66. pp. 179–183, pl. 10, figs. 1–8.
  1954. Further studies on American millipeds of the family Euryuridae (Polydesmida) Journ. Washington Acad. Sci., vol. 44, pp. 49–58, figs. 1–4.
HOFFMAN, RICHARD L., AND CRABILL, RALPH E.
  1953. C. S. Rafinesque as the real father of American myriapodology. Florida Ent., vol. 36, No. 2, pp. 73–82.

HUMBERT, ALOIS, AND SAUSSURE, HENRI
    1869. Description de divers myriapodes du Musée de Vienna. Verh. Zool.-Bot.
          Ges. Wien, vol. 19, pp. 669–692.
    1870. Myriapoda Nova Americana: Description de divers Myriapodes nouveaux du
          musée de Vienne. Rev. Mag. Zool., ser. 2, vol. 22, pp. 172–177.

JACKSON, A. R.
    1915. On some arachnids and myriapods observed in 1914. Lancashire and
          Cheshire Nat., vol. 7, pp. 433–437.

JACOT, ARTHUR PAUL
    1938. Four new arthropods from New England. Amer. Midl. Nat., vol. 20, pp.
          571–574, figs. 1–3.

JAWLOWSKI, HIERONIM
    1939. Contribution to the knowledge of the Diplopoda of Nova Scotia and New-
          foundland. Fragmenta Faunistica Mus. Zool. Polonici, vol. 4, No. 8, pp.
          149–158, figs. 1.

JOHNSON, BERT M.
    1954. A new species of milliped, genus *Dixidesmus*, from Michigan. Chicago Acad.
          Sci. Nat. Hist. Misc., No. 137, pp. 1–5, fig. 1.

KARSCH, FERDINAND
    1881. Zum studium der Myriapoda Polydesmia. Arch. Naturg., vol. 47, pp. 36–49,
          pl. 3.
    1881. Einige neue diplopode Myriopoden des Berliner Museums. Mitth. Mün-
          chener Ent. Ver., vol. 4, pp. 140–144.
    1881. Neue Juliden des Berlinen-Museums, als Prodromus einer Juliden Mono-
          graphie. Zeitschr. Naturw., vol. 54 (ser. 3, vol. 6), pp. 1–79.

KENYON, FREDERICK C.
    1893. A preliminary list of the Myriapoda of Nebraska, with descriptions of new
          species. Publ. Nebraska Sci., vol. 3, pp. 14–18.

KINCAID, TREVOR
    1898. A new species of *Polyxenus*. Ent. News, vol. 9, pp. 192–193.

KINGSLEY, JOHN STERLING
    1888. The classification of the Myriapoda. Amer. Nat., vol. 22, pp. 1118–1121.

KOCH, CARL LUDWIG
    1835–1844. Deutschlands Crustaceen, Myriapoden und Arachniden. Ein Beitrag
          żur Deutschen Fauna von C. L. Koch . . . , *in* Herrich-Schäffer, Deutsch-
          lands Insecten, Hefte 136, 137, 142, 162, 190.
    1847. System der Myriapoden, *in* Herrich-Schäffer, Kritische Revision der Insecten-
          fauna Deutschlands, vol. 3.
    1863. Die Myriapoden. Getreu nach der Natur abgebildet undr beschrieben, . . . ,
          vol. 1, pp. 1–134, pls. 1–60, figs. 1–123; vol. 2, pp. 1–112, pls. 61–119, figs.
          124–234. Halle.

LATREILLE, PIERRE ANDRÉ
    1802. Histoire naturelle . . . des crustacés et des insectes, . . . , vol. 3, pp. 1–467.
    1804. Histoire naturelle . . . des crustacés et des insectes, . . . , vol. 7, p. 82.
    1817. Myriapodes, *in* Georges Cuvier, Le règne animal distribué d'après son
          organisation, . . . , vol. 3.
    1829. Myriapodes, *in* Georges Cuvier, Le règne animal distribué d'après son
          organisation, . . . , vol. 4, nouvelle édition.

LATZEL, ROBERT
    1884. Die Myriopoden der Osterreichisch-Ungarischen Monarchie . . . , vol. 2,
          Die Symphylen, Pauropoden und Diplopoden, pp. i–xi+1–414, pls. 1–16,
          figs. 1–210. Wien.

LATZEL, ROBERT—Continued

1884.   Suive de diagnoses d'espèces et de variétés nouvelles. Bull. Soc. Sci. Nat.
         Rouen, ser. 2, Ann. 19 (1883), pp. 251–266.

1884.   Diagnoses d'espèces et de variétés nouvelles. Bull. Soc. Sci. Nat. Rouen,
         ser. 2, Ann. 19 (1883), pp. 267–272, pl. 1, figs. 1–7.

1888.   Diagnoses d'espèces nouvelles. Bull. Soc. Hist. Nat. Toulouse, Proc. Verb.,
         pp. LXXXV–LXXXVI.

1895.   Myriopoden aus der Umgebung Hamburgs. Mitt. Naturh. Mus. Hamburg,
         vol. 12 (1894), pp. 99–109, figs. 1, 2.

LEACH, WILLIAM ELFORD

1815.   A tabular view of the external characters of four classes of animals,
         which Linné arranged under Insecta . . . . Trans. Linn. Soc. London,
         vol. 11, pp. 306–400.

1817.   The characters of the genera of the class Myriapoda, with descriptions of
         some species. Zoological Miscellany, London, vol. 3, pp. 31–45, pls.
         132–140.

LINNAEUS, CARL

1758.   Systema naturae . . . , ed. 10, vol. 1, pp. 1–824.

1761.   Fauna svecica, sistens animalia sveciae regni . . . , ed. 2, pp. 1–578, pls. 2.

LOHMANDER, HANS

1925.   Sveriges diplopoder. Göteborgs Vetensk. Samh. Handl., ser. 4, vol. 30, No. 2,
         pp. 1–115, figs.

LOOMIS, HAROLD FREDERICK

1933.   Egg-laying habits and larval stages of a milliped, *Arctobolus marginatus*
         (Say) Cook, native at Washington, D. C. Journ. Washington Acad. Sci.,
         vol. 23, No. 2, pp. 100–109, fig. 1.

1934.   Millipeds of the West Indies and Guiana collected by the Allison V. Armour
         Expedition in 1932. Smithsonian Misc. Coll., vol. 89, No. 14, pp. 1–69,
         figs. 1–33, pls. 1–4.

1936.   New millipeds of the American family Striariidae. Journ. Washington
         Acad. Sci., vol. 26, pp. 404–409, fig. 1.

1936.   Three new millipeds of the order Colobognatha from Tennessee, Texas, and
         Lower California, with records of previously known species. Proc. U. S.
         Nat. Mus., vol. 83, No. 2989, pp. 361–368, fig. 32.

1937.   Crested millipeds of the family Lysiopetalidae in North America, with de-
         scriptions of new genera and species. Proc. U. S. Nat. Mus., vol. 84, No.
         3006, pp. 97–135, figs. 16–18, pls. 3, 4.

1938.   The cambaloid millipeds of the United States, including a family new to the
         fauna and new genera and species. Proc. U. S. Nat. Mus., vol. 86, No. 3043,
         pp. 27–66, figs. 10–21, pl. 2

1939.   The millipeds collected in Appalachian caves by Mr. Kenneth Dearolf.
         Bull. Mus. Comp. Zool., vol. 86, No. 4, pp. 165–193, figs. 1–14.

1943.   New cave and epigean millipeds of the United States, with notes on some
         established species. Bull. Mus. Comp. Zool., vol. 92, No. 7, pp. 371–410,
         text figs. 1–18, pl. 1.

1943.   A new genus of Virginia millipeds related to *Scytonotus* and a new species
         from Florida. Journ. Washington Acad. Sci., vol. 33, No. 10, pp. 318–320,
         figs. 1, 2.

1944.   Millipeds principally collected by Professor V. E. Shelford in the eastern
         and southeastern United States. Psyche, vol. 51, Nos. 3–4, pp. 166–177,
         figs. 1–6.

1949.   New millipeds of the spiroboloid genus *Watichelus* from the Pacific Coast.
         Journ. Washington Acad. Sci., vol. 39, No. 7, pp. 241–244, figs. 1–10.

LOOMIS, HAROLD FREDERICK—Continued
  1950. Synonymy of some native American and introduced millipeds. Journ. Washington Acad. Sci., vol. 40, No. 5, pp. 164–166, fig. 1.
  1953. New millipeds of the western States and Lower California. Journ. Washington Acad. Sci., vol. 43, No. 12, pp. 417–422, figs. 1–20.
LOOMIS, HAROLD F., AND HOFFMAN, RICHARD L.
  1948. Synonymy of various diplopods. Proc. Biol. Soc. Washington, vol. 61, pp. 51–54.
LOOMIS, HAROLD F., AND DAVENPORT, DEMOREST
  1951. A luminescent new xystodesmid milliped from California. Journ. Washington Acad. Sci., vol. 41, pp. 270–272, fig. 1.
MCNEILL, JEROME
  1887. List of the myriapods found in Escambia County, Florida, with descriptions of six new species. Proc. U. S. Nat. Mus., vol. 10, pp. 323–327, pl. 11, figs. 1–7.
  1887. Descriptions of twelve new species of Myriapoda, chiefly from Indiana. Proc. U. S. Nat Mus., vol. 10, pp. 328–334, pl. 12, figs. 1–9.
  1888. A list, with brief descriptions, of all the species, including one new to science, of Myriapoda of Franklin County, Indiana. Bull. Brookville (Indiana) Soc. Nat. Hist., No. 3, pp. 1–20.
MAUCK, A. V.
  1901. On the swarming and variation in a myriapod (*Fontaria virginiensis*). Amer. Nat., vol. 35, pp. 477–478.
MEINERT, FRANZ
  1868. Danmarks Chilognather. Naturh. Tidsskr., ser. 3, vol. 5, pp. 1–32.
MENGE, FRANZ ANTON
  1851. Myriapoden der Umgebend von Danzig. Neueste Schrift. Naturf. Ges. Danzig, vol. 4, Heft 4, pp. 1–22, pls. 2.
MILEY, HUGH H.
  1927. Development of the male gonopods and life history of a polydesmid millipede. Ohio Journ. Sci., vol. 27, pp. 25–41, pls. 1, 2, figs. 1–9.
MORSE, MAX
  1902. Myriapods from Vinton, Ohio. Ohio Nat., vol. 2, p. 187.
  1903. Unusual abundance of a myriapod, *Parajulus pennsylvanicus* (Brandt). Science, new ser., vol. 18, pp. 59–60.
MURRAY, ANDREW
  1877. Economic entomology. Science handbook of the South Kensington Museum, 433 pp. London.
NĚMEC, BOHUMIL
  1895. O nových českých Diplopodech. Sitz.-ber. Böhmischen Ges. Wiss., pt. 2, No. 38, pp. 1–8, figs. 1–13.
NEWPORT, GEORGE
  1842. On some new genera of the Class Myriapoda. Proc. Zool. Soc. London, vol. 10, pp. 177–181.
  1843. Description of a new British *Julus*. Ann. Mag. Nat. Hist., vol. 11, p. 316.
  1844. A list of the species of Myriapoda in the collection of the British Museum. Ann. Mag. Nat. Hist. (ser. 1), vol. 13, pp. 263–270.
  1845. Monograph of the class Myriapoda, order Chilopoda; with observations on the general arrangement of the Articulata. Trans. Linn. Soc. London, vol. 19, pp. 265–302, pl. 33, figs. 1–38.
PACKARD, ALPHEUS SPRING, JR.
  1870. New or rare Neuroptera, Thysanura, and Myriapoda. Proc. Boston Soc. Nat. Hist., vol. 13, pp. 405–413.
  1871. The Mammoth Cave and its inhabitants. Amer. Nat., vol. 5, pp. 739–761.

PACKARD, ALPHEUS SPRING, JR.—Continued
1874. Report on the myriopods collected by Lieut. W. L. Carpenter, in 1873, in Colorado. Ann. Rep. U. S. Geol. Geogr. Surv. Terr. (Hayden), for 1873, p. 607.
1877. On a new cave fauna in Utah. Bull. U. S. Geol. Geogr. Surv. Terr. (Hayden), vol. 3, No. 1, art. 10, pp. 157–169, figs. 5–10.
1881. Fauna of the Luray and Newmarket caves, Virginia. Amer. Nat., vol. 15, pp. 231–232.
1883. A new Polydesmus with eyes. Amer. Nat., vol. 17, p. 428.
1883. A revision of the Lysiopetalidae, a family of Chilognath Myriopoda, with a notice of the genus Cambala. Proc. Amer. Philos. Soc., vol. 21, pp. 177–197.
1883. Repugnatorial pores in the Lysiopetalidae. Amer. Nat., vol. 17, p. 555.
1883. On the morphology of the Myriopoda. Proc. Amer. Philos. Soc., vol. 21, pp. 197–209.
PALISOT DE BEAUVOIS, AMBROSE MARIE FRANÇOIS JOSEPH
1805. Insectes recuellis en Afrique et en Amèrique, dans les royaumes d'Oware et de Benin, à Saint-Dominique et dans les États-Unis, pendant . . . 1786–1797. Aptères, pp. i–xvi+1–276, pls. 1–90.
PALMÉN, ERNST
1952. Survey of the diplopoda of Newfoundland. Ann. Zool. Soc. 'Vanamo,' vol. 15, No. 1, pp. 1–31, figs. 1–22.
PETERS, WILHELM CARL HARTWIG
1864. Übersicht der im Königl, zoologischen Museum befindlich Myriapoden aus der Familie der polydesmi, so wie Beschreibungen einer neuen Gattung, Trachyiulus, der Juli, und neuer Arten der Gattung Siphonophora. Monatsb. Preuss. Akad. Wiss. Berlin, 1864, pp. 529–551, 617–627.
PIERCE, W. DWIGHT
1940. A rare myriapod from Anacapa Island, compared with two Texas species. Bull. Southern California Acad. Sci., vol. 39, part 2, pp. 158–171, figs. 1–19.
POCOCK, REGINALD INNES
1887. On the classification of the Diplopoda. Ann. Mag. Nat. Hist., ser. 5, vol. 20, art. 35, pp. 283–295.
1894. Contributions to our knowledge of the arthropod fauna of the West Indies. Part III. Diplopoda and Malacopoda, with a supplement on the Arachnida of the class Pedipalpi. Journ. Linn. Soc. London, Zool., vol. 24 (No. 157), pp. 473–544, pls. 37–40.
1894. Chilopoda, Symphyla, and Diplopoda from the Malay Archipelago, in Weber, Zoologische Ergebnisse einer Reise in Niederländisch Ost-Indien, vol. 3, pp. 307–404, pls. 19–22.
1900. On two English millipedes (Iulus londinensis Leach and Iulus teutonicus, sp. n.). Ann. Mag. Nat. Hist., ser. 7, vol. 6, pp. 206–207.
1903–1910 Diplopoda, in Biologia Centrali-Americana, Zoologia, Chilopoda and Diplopoda, pp. 41–217, pls. 4–15.
VON PORAT [ALSO AS PORATH], CARL OSCAR
1866. Bidrag till Kännedom om Sveriges Myriapoder, Ordning Diplopoda. (Inaug. Dissert.). Stockholm.
1872. Myriopoda Africae australis, in Museo Regio Holmiensi asservata, recensuit. Pars. 2. Diplopoda. Öfvers Vet.-Akad. Förh., Stockholm, vol. 29, No. 5, pp. 3–45, pl. 4, figs. 1–8.
1889. Nya bidrag till Skandinaviska halföns myriopodologi. Ent. Tidskr., vol. 10, pp. 65–80.
PROVANCHER, LEON
1873. Myriapodes. Nat. Canadien, vol. 5, pp. 410–419.

RAFINESQUE, CONSTANTINE SAMUEL

1820. Annals of nature, or annual synopsis of new genera and species of animals and plants discovered in North America. First Annual Number for 1820, pp. 1–20.

RYDER, JOHN ADAM

1881. List of the North American species of myriapods belonging to the family of the Lysiopetalidae, with a description of a blind form from Luray Cave, Virginia. Proc. U. S. Nat. Mus., vol. 3, No. 181, pp. 524–529, figs. 1–3.

SAGER, ABRAM

1856 Description of three Myriapoda. Proc. Acad. Nat. Sci. Philadelphia, vol. 8, p. 109.

SAUSSURE, HENRI DE

1859. Note sur la familie des polydesmides, principalement au point de vue des espèces américaines. Linnea Ent., vol. 13, pp. 318–327.

1859. Diagnoses de divers Myriapodes nouveaux. Linnea Ent., vol. 13, pp. 328–332.

1860. Essai d'une faune des Myriapodes du Mexique, avec la description de quelques espèces des autres parties de l'Amérique. Mém. Soc. Phys. Hist. Nat. Genève, vol. 15, pt. 2, pp. 259–393, pls. 1–7, figs. 1–52.

SAUSSURE, HENRI DE, AND HUMBERT, ALOIS

1872. Études sur les myriapodes, in Mission scientifique au Mexique et dans l'Amérique Centrale, recherches zoologiques, pt. 6, sect. 2, pp. 1–211, pls. 1–6. Paris.

SAY, THOMAS

1821. Description of the myriapodae of the United States. Journ. Acad. Nat. Sci. Philadelphia, vol. 2, pp. 102–114.

SCHUBART, OTTO

1934. Tausendfüssler oder Myriapoda I: Diplopoda, in Dahl, Die Tierwelt Deutschlands und der angrenzenden Meeresteile nach ihren Merkmalen und nach ihrer Lebensweise, Teil 28, pp. i–vii+1–318, figs. 1–480. Jena.

1945. Os proterospermophora do Distrito Federal (Myriapoda Diplopoda). Arq. Mus. Nac. Brasil, vol. 38, pp. 1–156, figs. 1–138.

1946. Uma segunda especie do genero Cylindroiulus [Diplopoda] encontrada no Brasil. Comun. Zool. Mus. Hist. Nat. Montevideo, vol. 2, No. 29, pp. 1–5, figs. 1–3.

1946. Cambalopsis nordquisti Attems da Asia oriental, habitante do Distrito Federal do Brasil (Diplopoda, Cambalopsidae). Rev. Brasileira Biol., vol. 6, No. 3, pp. 395–406.

1951. Contribuição para a fauna do estado de São Paulo II. Os Rhinocricidae (Ophisthospermorphora, Diplopoda). Anais Acad. Brasileira Ciénc., vol. 23, No. 2, pp. 221–275, figs. 1–40.

SILVESTRI, FILIPPO

1894. Chilipodi e diplopodi della Papuasia, per Filippo Silvestri. Ann. Mus. Civ. Stor. Nat. Genova vol., 34 (ser. 2, vol. 14), pp. 619–659.

1894. I chilopodi ed i diplopodi di Sumatra e della isole Nias, Engano e Mentavei. Ann. Mus. Civ. Stor. Nat. Genova, vol. 34 (ser. 2, vol. 14), pp. 707–760, figs. 1–14.

1896. I Diplopodi. Parte I, Sistematica. Ann. Mus. Civ. Stor. Nat. Genova, vol. 36 (ser. 2, vol. 16), pp. 121–254, figs. 1–26.

1896. Una escursione in Tunisia (Symphyla, Chilopoda, Diplopoda). Nat. Siciliano, vol. 1, new ser., pp. 143–161, pl. 7.

1897. Viaggio del Dott. Alfredo Borelli nel Chaco Boliviano e nella Repubblica Argentina. IV. Chilopodi e Diplopodi. Bull. Mus. Zool. Anat. Comp. Univ. Torino, vol. 12, No. 283, pp. 1–11.

SILVESTRI, FILIPPO—Continued

1897. Systema Diplopodum. Ann. Mus. Civ. Stor. Nat. Genova, vol. 38 (ser. 2, vol. 18), pp. 644–651.

1898. Viaggio del Dott. E. Festa nella Repubblica dell' Ecuador. XI. Diplopodi. Boll. Mus. Zool. Anat. Comp. Univ. Torino, vol. 13, No. 324, pp. 1–11, figs. 1–29.

1909. Descrizioni preliminari di vari Artropodi, specialmente d'America. Atti Accad. Lincei Rendic., Classe Sci. Fis. Mat. Nat., ser. 5, vol. 18, pp. 229–233.

1910. Descrizioni preliminari di novi generi di Diplopodi. I. Polydesmoidea. Zool. Anz., vol. 35, pp. 357–364.

1929. Descrizione di un nuovo Diplopodo della famiglia Glomeridae della California. Boll. Lab Zool. Portici, vol. 22, pp. 198–203, figs. 2.

SINCLAIR, FREDERICK GRANVILLE

1895. Myriopoda, in Harmer and Shipley, The Cambridge natural history, vol. 5, pp. 27–80.

STUXBERG, A.

1885. Generic position of Polydesmus ocellatus (Craspedosoma). Amer. Nat., vol. 19, pp. 400, 401.

UNDERWOOD, LUCIEN MARCUS

1885. The North American Myriapoda. Ent. Amer., vol. 1, pp. 141–151.

1893. A review of the literature of the North American Myriapoda, in Bollman, The Myriapoda of North America. U. S. Nat. Mus. Bull. 46, pp. 9–17.

VERHOEFF, KARL WILHELM

1891. Ein Beitrag zur mitteleuropäischen Diplopoden-Fauna. Berliner Ent. Zeitschr., vol. 36, Heft 1, pp. 115–166, pls. 5–8, figs. 1–49.

1893. Vorläufige Mittheilung über neue Schaltstadium-Beobachtungen bei Juliden, eine neue Gruppierung der alten Gattung Julus und einige neue und seltene Diplopoden aus Tirol. Zool. Anz., vol. 16, pp. 479–482.

1894. Beiträge zur Anatomie und Systematik der Juliden. Verh. Zool.-Bot. Ges. Wien, vol. 44, pp. 137–162.

1894. Beiträge zur Diplopoden-Fauna Tirols. Verh. Zool.-Bot. Ges. Wien, vol. 44, pp. 9–34.

1896. Diplopoden Rheinpreussens und Beiträge zur Biologie und vergleichenden Faunistik europäischer Diplopoden, Vorläufer zu einer rheinischen Diplopodenfauna. Verh. Naturh. Vereins Rheinlands, Westfalens, und Osnabrück, vol. 53, 1896, pp. 186–280, 336.

1898. Ueber Diplopoden aus Bosnien, Herzogowina und Dalmatien. Arch. Naturg., vol. 64, Teil 4, Julidae, pp. 119–160, figs. 1–7, pls. 5, 6, figs. 1–34; Teil 5, Glomeridae and Polyzoniidae (Schluss), pp. 161–176, figs. 1, 2, pl. 7, figs. 1–22.

1900. Beiträge zur Kenntniss paläarktischer Myriopoden. X. Aufsatz. Zur vergleichenden Morphologie, Phylogenie, Gruppen- and Artsystematik der Lysiopetaliden. Zool. Jahrb., Abt. Syst., vol. 13, pp. 36–70, figs. 1–3, pls. 5–9.

1909. Superfamilien der Diplopoda-Opisthospermorpha. Zool. Anz., vol. 34, pp. 542–543.

1909. Neues System der Diplopoda-Ascospermorphora. Zool. Anz., vol. 34, pp. 566–572.

1909. Zur Kenntnis der Glomeriden. Zool. Anz., vol. 35, pp. 101–124, figs. 1–22.

1911–1914. Die Diplopoden Deutschlands . . . , pp. xiii+640, text figs. 1–460, pls. 1–25.

1913. Die Ordnungen der Proterandria und zur Kenntnis der Cambaliden. Zool. Anz., vol. 43, pp. 49–65, figs. 1–3.

VERHOEFF, KARL WILHELM—Continued

1924. Über Myriapoden von Juan Fernandez und der Osterinsel, *in* Skottsberg, The natural history of Juan Fernandez and Easter Island, vol. 3, pp. 405–418, figs. 1–18.

1926. Chilognathen-Beiträge. Zool. Anz., vol. 68, Heft 1/2, pp. 57–71, figs. 1–11, Heft 3/4, pp. 109–127, figs. 12–22.

1926–1932. Diplopoda, *in* H. G. Bronn, Klassen und Ordnungen des Tier-Reichs, wissenschaftlich dargestellt in Wort und Bild, Band 5, Abt. 2, Buch 2, Lief. 1–13, pp. 1–2084, figs. 1–1048.

1932. Diplopoden-Beiträge. Zool. Jahrb., Abt. Syst., vol. 62, pp. 469–524, pls. 4–6, figs. 1–50.

1938. *Californiulus* n. g. und *Paeromopellus* n. g. Vertreter einer neuen Familie der Symphyognatha-Arthrophora. Zool. Anz., vol. 122, Nos. 5–6, pp. 113–127, figs. 1–9.

1938. Über einige amerikanische Myriapoden. Zool. Anz., vol. 122, Nos. 11–12, pp. 273–284, figs. 1–5.

1939. Zur Kenntnis ostasiatischer Diplopoden. III., Zool. Anz., vol. 127, pp. 113–125, figs. 1–9.

1941. Versuch eines Siphonophoriden-Systems und geographisch-phylogenetische Beurteilung der Gonopoden. Zool. Anz., vol. 134, pp. 212–224, figs. 1–8.

1943. Ueber einige Diplopoden aus Minas Gerais (Brasilien). Arq. Mus. Nac. Brasil, vol. 37, pp. 247–288, figs. 1–37.

1944. Some Californian Chilognatha. Bull. Southern California Acad. Sci., vol. 43, part 2, pp. 53–70, pls. 12–13, figs. 1–14.

WALSH, BENJAMIN DANN

1866. *Iulus multistriatus*, n. sp. Practical Entomologist, vol. 2, pp. 34, 35, 70.

1869. Thousand-legged worms. Amer. Ent., vol. 2, p. 59.

WILLIAMS, ELIOT C., JR., AND WARD, DANIEL B.

1950. An unusual aggregation of the milliped *Zinaria butleri* (McNeill). Proc. Indiana Acad. Sci., vol. 60, pp. 329–331.

WILLIAMS, STEPHEN R., AND HEFNER, ROBERT A.

1928. The millipedes and centipedes of Ohio. Bull. Ohio Biol. Surv., No. 18, vol. 4, No. 3 (Ohio State Univ. Bull., vol. 33, No. 7), pp. 93–146, figs. 1–26.

WOOD, HORATIO C.

1864. Descriptions of new species of North American Polydesmidae. Proc. Acad. Nat. Sci. Philadelphia (vol. 16), pp. 6–10.

1864. Descriptions of new species of North American Julidae. Proc. Acad. Nat. Sci. Philadelphia (vol. 16), pp. 10–16.

1864. Descriptions of new genera and species of North American Myriapoda. Proc. Acad. Nat. Sci. Philadelphia (vol. 16), pp. 186–187.

1865. The Myriapoda of North America. Trans. Amer. Philos. Soc., new ser., vol. 13 (1869), pt. 2, art. 7, pp. 137–248, figs. 1–61, pls. 1–3.

1867. Descriptions of new species of Texan Myriapoda. Proc. Acad. Nat. Sci. Philadelphia (vol. 19), pp. 42–44.

1867. Notes on a collection of California Myriapoda, with descriptions of new eastern species. Proc. Acad. Nat. Sci. Philadelphia (vol. 19), pp. 127–130.

Index